PECK'S BAD BOY
AND HIS PA

[COMPLETE EDITION]

BY

GEORGE W. PECK

WITH 100 ILLUSTRATIONS BY TRUE WILLIAMS

AND A NEW INTRODUCTION BY

E. F. BLEILER

DOVER PUBLICATIONS, INC., NEW YORK

This Dover edition, first published in 1958, is an unabridged and unaltered republication of the complete edition of *Peck's Bad Boy and His Pa,* Volumes I and II, as published by Stanton and Van Vliet Co., Chicago, in 1912. The introduction by E. F. Bleiler was specially written for this Dover edition.

Standard Book Number: 486-20497-9
Library of Congress Catalog Card Number: 58-14376

Manufactured in the United States of America
Dover Publications, Inc.
180 Varick Street
New York, N. Y. 10014

INTRODUCTION TO DOVER EDITION

Peck's Bad Boy and His Pa first appeared in book form some 75 years ago, in 1883. Its author was George Wilbur Peck, a Wisconsin printer and newspaper owner, who eventually served two terms as Governor of Wisconsin.

Peck was born in Henderson, New York, in 1840, but was taken as a child to Wisconsin, where he spent most of his later life. His earlier years seem to have been a succession of small printing jobs and failing business enterprises, until he entered the Union Army in 1863. After his release he worked in New York on a newspaper in the Pomeroy chain for a time, then bought a newspaper in Lacrosse, Wisconsin from Pomeroy and returned to Wisconsin. It was not until the early 1880's, however, that he achieved any success; by this time his paper, *Peck's Sun,* had been moved to Milwaukee. His paper was a weekly, more a collection of editorial humor than a newspaper in the modern sense, and in it, in 1882, first appeared the nasty pranks which Hennery the Bad Boy played upon his drunken father.

The Bad Boy stories were immensely successful, and in a matter of months Peck found himself with a booming nation-wide circulation. In 1883 the Chicago publishers Belford, Clarke & Co. published the first series of Bad Boy stories, and in the same year issued the second series. Both books remained in print, though with different publishers, until at least 1925.

Peck's political career seems to have kept pace with his publishing history, and the Bad Boy bore him to the state capitol. Peck had previously dabbled in small politics, and had been city treasurer of Ripon and Chief of Police at Lacrosse. But by the end of the 1880's, thanks to the Bad Boy, he was one of the best-known men in the state, and ripe for political advancement.

An issue, too, was waiting. The Republican legislature, in one of the periodic outbursts of Know-Nothingism which have beset Wisconsin, had passed a bill prohibiting the use of foreign languages in schools. This was the Bennett Bill, which was aimed at the parochial schools, for the Lutherans taught in German, and the Roman Catholics taught in Latin.

Peck quipped loudly for tolerance in his newspaper, won the Democratic primaries handily, and in 1890 was elected Mayor of Milwaukee by the widest margin in the history of the city. In November of the same year he took the governorship of Wisconsin by a similar landslide. The Lutherans, it is said, marched to the polls in squads to elect him. He was reelected in 1892, but in a third try, in 1894, he was defeated. In 1904 he was entered for the governorship again, apparently to stop LaFollette, but was badly defeated, and he retired from politics. He seems to have been a correct, amiable, efficient governor, one of the few entertainers elected to American office who have worked out well. He died in 1916.

Peck's books are built mostly out of material from his newspaper. They include: *The Adventures of One Terence McGrant* [1871]; *Peck's Sunshine* [1882]; *Peck's Bad Boy and His Pa* [1883]; *Peck's Bad Boy and His Pa, Part II, The Grocery Man and Peck's Bad Boy* [1883]; *Mirth for the Millions* [1883, republished as *Peck's Fun*]; *Peck's Boss Book* [1884]; *Peck's Irish Friend Phelan Geoghan* [1887]; *Peck's Uncle Ike and the Red-headed Boy* [1899]; *Sunbeams and Humor* [1900]; *Peck's Bad Boy and the Circus* [1906]; *Peck's Bad Boy with the Cowboys* [1907].

ii

Peck's Bad Boy and His Pa was among the great best sellers of the late 19th century. There is no count of the number of copies that were sold, since it was published by small houses that have long since gone out of business, but it went through at least five legitimate editions, and circulated widely in paperback form. In newspaper versions alone it circulated in more than 80,000 copies.

Obviously, the pranks of the Bad Boy appealed to the

public palate, even though an occasional critic like O. G. Adams could denounce them as a mass of deplorable coarseness and vulgarity. Not that Adams was wholly wrong: Peck was willing to pay a price for vitality, and that price was gentility. The Bad Boy is often coarse, but he is also often vigorous, ingenious, and imaginative. *Peck's Bad Boy and His Pa* remains to this day the type specimen of the prank book, and its name has passed into a phrase. Everyone knows what a Peck's Bad Boy is.

According to modern standards *Peck's Bad Boy and His Pa* is a cruel book, for there is a strong element of pain in its situations. But it must be urged in the book's defence that it is not cruel because G. W. Peck was a cruel man, but because he lived in an era when practical jokes were almost a cult. It was written for a generation that liked its humor strong, imaginative, and painful — for the other person.

In the late 19th century, it would sometimes seem, old men and young men watched for weaknesses, contrived, and then sat back and laughed at the discomfort they had caused. What would we think today if Millikan or Urey were to bombard William Faulkner with ultrasonics, or if on a state visit Queen Elizabeth were to serve Adenauer with a roast dog? We would probably be horrified. But our ancestors thought differently. Thomas Edison was delighted when Mark Twain was lured upon a vibration device that caused violent diarrhoea; H. L. Mencken's father, a highly respectable factory owner — who owned a copy of *Peck's Bad Boy* — roared as he forged a Dun and Bradstreet report to discredit an elderly lumber merchant; and the Prince of Wales is said to have served the Kaiser of Germany a boarhound roasted as a buck.

All of Peck's humor was in one way or another topical, and the Bad Boy is no exception. Yet one reason for the Bad Boy's success may be sought in the clarity with which it sets forth the basic premise of the practical joker: that the "guy" is inferior to you, and deserves everything that he is stupid enough to take. And the Bad Boy's Pa takes a great deal: his flesh is blackened by firecrackers; his hat is lined with limburger cheese; his handkerchief, when he is attending a rabidly puritanical church service, is found to be soaked in rum and stuffed with playing cards; he is persuaded he is going mad when he sees green and blue poodles used as advertisements by a dye works; he is sold, apparently, to resurrectionists when he is in a drunken stupor; and is hit on the head by a "comet" manufactured of stove pipe and phosphorus.

Peck was obviously writing to suit the tastes of his time, and for his own pocketbook, not for posterity. And as a result his work constitutes one of the better culture gauges for his time. He mirrors the hidden feelings of his time and place much better than many more serious and more self-conscious books. There is little in *Peck's Bad Boy* about who rules whom, or who fought wars with whom, or who exploited whom — but there is a great deal about what Peck's contemporaries considered holy, and what they laughted at. And perhaps, for a historian, these two matters are just as important as more serious speculation.

Not that Peck does not mirror his external situation, too. The Bad Boy lives in Milwaukee, and Chicago can be visited in a few hours — during which it is entirely correct for the Bad Boy to convince the trainmen that his father is kidnaping him. Cities are bursting up on the shores of Lake Michigan, and new peoples are moving into the Middle West. Riotous Irishmen, divided into Fenians and Orangemen, are all ready to belabor Pa — or so people believed. Germanic and Slavic immigrants are settling in certain districts, and are lumped together as "Dutchmen." Anarchists are bearded gentry who carry spherical bombs shaped like modern street flares. John L. Sullivan is starting his famous tour of 1883, and will box Maori Slade in Racine — and a church tenor can convince a stupid preacher that Sullivan is a travelling evangelist. The forces of the new science are being felt in the electric lights of the Chicago Exhibition, and only plumbers and gasfitters have the money to buy strawberries out of season.

Peck's mirroring of social forces, however, is equally important. He wrote in a transition area, in the time-space between the Western past and the culture of the East, between decaying frontier evangelism and the new

secular life of the 20th century, between Victorian sta-
bility and modern change. He stood far enough from the
past to be critical and ironic, yet close enough to find
material important enough to wreck — for his thought
was basically destructive. He poked fun at the most
sacred institutions of the older folkways, and made a success of it. There was the Family — Pa is a drunken, pot-
bellied boob, and his son is a scoundrel; the Church —
the elders are all canting hypocrites, too ready to console
Peck's wife with brotherly pats; and Commerce — the
grocery man, a pillar of the church and the fraternal
organizations, is an out-and-out sharper.

Pa's relations with his church constitute an important
subcurrent in the ideas of *Peck's Bad Boy*. In a small
town in the Middle West, as Weber has observed, church
membership carried with it great social obligations, and
was a guarantee of responsibility. One had to meet high
standards to be a full member. Pa, in theory, recognizes
this moral supremacy of the local church, and admits that
his pious neighbors have the right to judge him for drinking and gambling. Again and again he submits himself
to their discipline — but, in each case, before the final
abasement, he manages to rebel and to remain an incor-
rigible but free individual.

Possibly Peck's readers restricted themselves upon
reading the adventures of the Bad Boy to the particular
rather than the general; perhaps they saw the grocery
man as an individual rather than as representative of an
institution. Perhaps they saw Pa, who talked of his hero-
ism in the Civil War, and really was a sutler who sold
poisonous whiskey at catastrophic prices, as a small type
rather than a general type. And perhaps they were right.
We cannot tell now what motivated either G. W. Peck or
his readers, but one undercurrent in their minds seems
to have been a rebellion, whether witting or unwitting,
against the goody-goody sentimentalism that was ramp-
ant. Horatio Alger and *Little Lord Fauntleroy*, it must be
remembered, box Peck in on either side in time. There is
some reason to believe that the Bad Boy is as much a
mirror image of priggishness as a prankster in his own
right; in one or two episodes of the second series he

reforms and almost breaks the spell of his revolting badness.

It is tempting to think that *Peck's Bad Boy and His Pa* influenced its times, and both suggested mischief to young boys and provided them with excuses. It is not impossible, for the Bad Boy has obviously left his mark upon literature. It would be difficult to imagine the Penrod books of Booth Tarkington without Hennery, the Bad Boy, and the early 20th century comic strip is obviously based upon Peck's work in structure, subject matter, and psychology. Peck had worked out the magical world where preadolescent boys are aided by all the forces of nature against their fathers. In this world the goat and the wildcat and the firecracker are symbols of punishment; glue forms an instantaneous bond between chairs and flesh; gout and greased stairs are hilarious; near-sighted elders mistake garden hose for macaroni and vest linings for pancakes; hornets, ants, and cursing parrots do their duties; boys can be disguised as bandits, dottards, or beautiful young women; and every incident demonstrates the inferiority of the parent and exposes him to daily humiliation. It is too bad, really, that Freud hadn't read *Peck's Bad Boy and His Pa* as well as *Oedipus Rex*.

There are many passages in *Peck's Bad Boy and His Pa* that you'll read with raised eyebrows: some, probably, that you'll read with a frown, for they tread upon anatomies that are painful to us now. And you may feel superior at times, for George Wilbur Peck did not deal in subtleties: a skunk in a coalbin had far more life and humor for him than a hundred pages of Henry James. But you will see what made your grandfathers laugh, and you will discover that much the same things make you laugh, too. G. W. Peck wrote honestly, vigorously, with a clear style and a vivid fantastic imagination. Besides being of historical importance, *Peck's Bad Boy and His Pa* is considerable fun.

New York, 1958

E. F. Bleiler

CONTENTS

CHAPTER I
THE BOY WITH A LAME BACK

CHAPTER II
THE BOY AT WORK AGAIN

CHAPTER III
THE BAD BOY GIVES HIS PA AWAY

CHAPTER IV
THE BAD BOY'S FOURTH OF JULY

CHAPTER V

THE BAD BOY'S MA COMES HOME   PAGE

CHAPTER VI

HIS PA IS A DARN COWARD

CHAPTER VII

HIS PA GETS A BITE

CHAPTER VIII

HE IS TOO HEALTHY

CHAPTER IX

HIS PA HAS GOT 'EM AGAIN

CHAPTER X

HIS PA HAS GOT RELIGION

PAGE

CHAPTER XI

HIS PA TAKES A TRICK

CHAPTER XII

HIS PA GETS PULLED

CHAPTER XIII

HIS PA GOES TO THE EXPOSITION

CHAPTER XIV

HIS PA CATCHES ON

CHAPTER XV

HIS PA AT THE REUNION

CHAPTER XVI

THE BAD BOY IN LOVE

CHAPTER XVII

HIS PA FIGHTS HORNETS

CHAPTER XVIII

HIS PA GOES HUNTING

CHAPTER XIX

HIS PA IS "NISHIATED"

CHAPTER XX

HIS GIRL GOES BACK ON HIM

PAGE

CHAPTER XXI

HE AND HIS PA IN CHICAGO

CHAPTER XXII

HIS PA IS DISCOURAGED

CHAPTER XXIII

HE BECOMES A DRUGGIST

CHAPTER XXIV

HE QUITS THE DRUG BUSINESS

CHAPTER XXX
HIS PA DISSECTED   PAGE

CHAPTER XXXI
HIS PA JOINS A TEMPERANCE SOCIETY

CHAPTER XXXII
HIS PA'S MARVELOUS ESCAPE

CHAPTER XXXIII
HIS PA JOKES HIM

CHAPTER XXXIV
HIS PA GETS MAD

CONTENTS

VOL. II

CHAPTER V
HIS PA AND DYNAMITE

CHAPTER VI
HIS PA AN ORANGEMAN

CHAPTER VII
HIS MA DECEIVED HIM

CHAPTER VIII
THE BABY AND THE GOAT

CHAPTER IX
A FUNERAL PROCESSION

CHAPTER X

THE OLD MAN MAKES A SPEECH

PAGE

CHAPTER XI

GARDENING UNDER DIFFICULTIES

CHAPTER XII

THE OLD MAN SHOOTS THE MINISTER

CHAPTER XIII

THE BAD BOY A THOROUGHBRED

CHAPTER XIV

ENTERTAINING Y. M. C. A. DELEGATES

CHAPTER XX

FOURTH OF JULY MISADVENTURES <small>PAGE</small>

Trouble in the Pistol Pocket—The Grocery Man's Cat—The Bad Boy a Ministering Angel—Asleep on the Fourth of July—Goes with His Girl to the Soldiers' Home—Terrible Fourth of July Misadventures—The Girl who Went Out Comes Back a Burnt Offering... 301

CHAPTER XXI

WORKING ON SUNDAY

Turning a Grindstone is Healthy—"Not Any Grindstone for Hennery!"—This Hypocrisy is Played Out—Another Job on the Old Man—How the Days of the Week ·Got Mixed—The Numerous Funerals—The Minister Appears—The Bad Boy Goes over the Back Fence................................. 308

CHAPTER XXII

THE OLD MAN AWFULLY BLOATED

The Old Man Begins Drinking Again—Thinks Betting is Harmless—Had to Walk Home from Chicago—The Spectacles Changed—A Small Suit of Clothes—The Old Man Awfully Bloated—"Hennery, Your Pa is a Mighty Sick Man"—The Swelling Suddenly Goes Down............................. 314

CHAPTER XXIII

THE GROCERY MAN AND THE GHOST

Ghosts Don't Steal Wormy Figs—A Grand Rehearsal—The Minister Murders Hamlet—The Watermelon Knife—The Old Man Wanted to Rehearse the Drunken Scene in Rip Van Winkle—No Hugging Allowed—Hamlet Wouldn't Have Two Ghosts—"How Would You Like to be an Idiot?".................... 320

CHAPTER XXIV

THE CRUEL WOMAN AND THE LUCKLESS DOG

The Bad Boy with a Dog and a Black Eye—Where Did You Steal Him?—Angels Don't Break Dogs' Legs—A Woman Who Breaks Dogs' Legs Has no Show with St. Peter—Another Burglar Scare—The Grocery Delivery Man Scared......... 325

LIST OF ILLUSTRATIONS

xxiii

A CARD FROM THE AUTHOR

OFFICE OF "PECK'S SUN."
Milwaukee.

GENTS—If you have made up your minds that the world will cease to move unless these "Bad Boy" articles are given to the public in book form, why go ahead, and peace to your ashes. The "Bad Boy" is not a "myth," though there may be some stretches of imagination in the articles. The counterpart of this boy is located in every city, village and country hamlet throughout the land. He is wide awake, full of vinegar and is ready to crawl under the canvas of a circus or repeat a hundred verses of the New Testament in Sunday School. He knows where every melon patch in the neighborhood is located, and at what hours the dog is chained up. He will tie an oyster can to a dog's tail to give the dog exercise, or will fight at the drop of the hat to protect the smaller boy or a school girl. He gets in his work everywhere there is a fair prospect of fun, and his heart is easily touched by an appeal in the right way, though his coat-tail is oftener touched with a boot than his heart is by kindness. But he shuffles through life until the time comes for him to make a mark in the world, and then he buckles on the harness and goes to the front, and becomes successful, and then those who said he would bring up in State Prison, remember that he always *was* a mighty smart lad, and they never tire of telling of some of his deviltry when he was a boy, though they thought he was pretty tough at the time. This book is respectfully dedicated to boys, to the men who have been boys themselves, to the girls who like the boys, and to the mothers, bless them, who like both the boys and the girls.

Very respectfully,

GEO. W. PECK.

PECK'S BAD BOY

AND HIS PA

CHAPTER I

THE BOY WITH A LAME BACK

The boy couldn't sit down—A practical joke on the Old Man—A letter from "Daisy"—Guarding the four corners—The Old Man is unusually generous—Ma asks awkward questions—The boy talked to with a bed-slat—No encouragement for a boy.

A YOUNG fellow who is pretty smart on general principles, and who is always in good humor, went into a store the other morning limping and seemed to be broken up generally. The proprietor asked him if he wouldn't sit down, and he said he couldn't very well, as his back was lame. He seemed discouraged, and the proprietor asked him what was the matter. "Well," says he, as he put his hand on his pistol pocket and groaned: "There is no encouragement for a boy to have any fun nowadays. If a boy tries to play an innocent joke he gets kicked all over the house." The store keeper asked him what had happened to disturb his hilarity. He said he had played a joke on his father and he had been limping ever since.

"You see, I thought the old man was a little spry. You know he is no spring chicken yourself; and though his eyes are not what they used to be, yet he can see a pretty girl further than I can. The other day I wrote a note in a fine hand and addressed it to him, asking him to meet me on the

23

corner of Wisconsin and Milwaukee streets, at 7:30 on Saturday evening, and signed the name of 'Daisy' to it. At supper time Pa he was all shaved up and had his hair plastered over the bald spot, and he got on some clean cuffs, and said he was going to the Consistory to initiate some candidates from the country, and he might not be in till late. He didn't eat much supper, and hurried off with my umbrella. I winked at Ma, but didn't say anything. At 7:30 I went

THE GROCERYMAN.

down town and he was standing there by the postoffice corner, in a dark place. I went by him and said, 'Hello, Pa, what are you doing there?' He said he was waiting for a man. I went down street and pretty soon I went up on the other corner by Chapman's and he was standing there. You see, he didn't know what corner 'Daisy' was going to be on, and he had to cover all four corners. I saluted him and asked him if he hadn't found his man yet, and he said no, the man was a little late. It is a mean boy that won't speak to his Pa when he sees him standing on a corner. I went up street and saw Pa cross over by the drug store in a sort of a hurry, and I could see a girl going by with a waterproof on, but she skited right along and Pa looked kind of solemn, the way he does when I ask him for new clothes. I turned and came back and he was standing in the doorway, and I said, 'Pa, you will catch cold if you stand around waiting for a man. You go down to the Consistory and let me lay for the man.' Pa said, 'never you mind, you go about your business and I will attend to the man.'

"Well, when a boy's Pa tells him to never you mind, and looks spunky, my experience is that a boy wants to go right away from there, and I went down street. I thought I would cross over, go up the other side, and see how long he would stay. There was a girl or two going up ahead of me, and I see a man hurrying across from the drug store to Van Pelt's corner. It was Pa, and as the girls went along and never looked around Pa looked mad and stepped into the doorway.

PA LOOKED MAD AND STEPPED INTO THE DOORWAY.

It was about eight o'clock then, and Pa was tired, and I felt sorry for him and I went up to him and asked him for half a dollar to go to the Academy. I never knew him to shell out so freely and so quick. He gave me a dollar, and I told him I would go and get it changed and bring him back the half dollar, but he said I needn't mind the change. It is awful mean of a boy that has always been treated well to play it on his Pa that way, and I felt ashamed. As I turned the corner and saw him standing there shivering, waiting for the man, my conscience troubled me, and I told a policeman to go and tell Pa that 'Daisy' had been suddenly taken with worms, and would not be there that evening. I peeked around the corner and Pa and the policeman went off to get a drink. I was glad they did, cause Pa needed it, after standing around so long. Well, when I went home the joke was so good I told Ma about it, and she was mad. I guess she was mad at me for treating Pa that way. I heard Pa come home about eleven o'clock, and Ma was real kind to him. She told him to warm his feet, cause they were just like chunks of ice. Then she asked him how many they initiated in the Consistory, and he said six, and then she asked him if they initiated 'Daisy' in the Consistory, and pretty soon I heard Pa snoring. In the morning he took me into the basement, and gave me the hardest talking to that I ever had, with a bed slat. He said that he knew that I wrote that note all the time, and he thought he would pretend that he was looking for 'Daisy,' just to fool me. It don't look reasonable that a man would catch epizootic and rheumatism just to fool his boy, does it? What did he give me the dollar for? Ma and Pa don't seem to call each other pet any more, and as for me, they both look at me as though I was a hard citizen. I am going to Missouri to take Jesse James' place. There is no encouragement for a boy here. Well, good morning. If Pa comes in here asking for me tell him that you saw an express wagon going to the morgue with the remains of a pretty boy who acted as though he died from concussion of a bed slat on the pistol pocket. That will make Pa feel sorry. O, he has got the awfulest cold, though."

And the boy limped out to separate a couple of dogs that were fighting.

CHAPTER II

OF course all boys are not full of tricks, but the best of
them are. That is, those who are readiest to play innocent
jokes, and who are continually looking for chances to make
Rome howl, are the most apt to turn out to be first-class
business men. There is a boy in the Seventh Ward who is
so full of fun that sometimes it makes him ache. He is the
same boy who not long since wrote a note to his father and
signed the name "Daisy" to it, and got the old man to stand
on a corner for two hours waiting for the girl. After that
scrape the old man told the boy that he had no objection to
innocent jokes, such as would not bring reproach upon him,
and as long as the boy confined himself to jokes that would
simply cause pleasant laughter, and not cause the finger of
scorn to be pointed at a parent, he would be the last one to
kick. So the boy has been for the three weeks trying to
think of some innocent joke to play on his father. The old
man is getting a little near sighted, and his teeth are not as
good as they used to be, but the old man will not admit it.
Nothing that anybody can say can make him own up that
his eyesight is failing, or that his teeth are poor, and he
would bet a hundred dollars that he could see as far as ever.
The boy knew the failing, and made up his mind to demon-
strate to the old man that he was rapidly getting off his base.
The old person is very fond of macaroni, and eats it about
three times a week. The other day the boy was in a drug
store and noticed in a show case a lot of small rubber hose,

about the size of sticks of macaroni, such as is used on nursing bottles, and other rubber utensils. It was white and nice, and the boy's mind was made up at once. He bought a yard of it, and took it home. When the macaroni was cooked and ready to be served, he hired the table girl to help him play it on the old man. They took a pair of shears and cut the rubber hose in pieces about the same length as the pieces of boiled macaroni, and put them in a saucer with a little macaroni over the rubber pipes, and placed the dish at the old man's plate. Well, we suppose if ten thousand peo-

HE WAS MAD AND GLAD.

ple could have had reserved seats and seen the old man struggle with the India rubber macaroni, and have seen the boy's struggle to keep from laughing, they would have had more fun than they would at a circus. First the old delegate attempted to cut the macaroni into small pieces, and failing, he remarked that it was not cooked enough. The boy said his macaroni was cooked too tender, and that his father's teeth were so poor that he would have to eat soup entirely pretty soon. The old man said, "Never you mind my teeth, young man," and decided that he would not complain of anything again. He took up a couple of pieces of rubber and one piece of macaroni on a fork and put them in his mouth. The macaroni dissolved easy enough, and went down perfectly easy, but the fiat macaroni was too much for him. He chewed on it for a minute or two, and talked about the weather in order that none of the family should see that he was in trouble, and when he found the macaroni would not down, he called their attention to something out of the window and took the rubber slyly from his mouth, and laid it under the edge of his plate. He was more than half convinced that his teeth were played out, but went on eating something else for awhile, and finally he thought he would just chance the macaroni once more for luck, and he mowed away another fork full in his mouth. It was the same old story. He chewed like a seminary girl chewing gum, and his eyes stuck out and his face became red, and his wife looked at him as though afraid he was going to die of apoplexy, and finally the servant girl burst out laughing, and went out of the room with her apron stuffed in her mouth, and the boy felt as though it was unhealthy to tarry too long at the table, and he went out.

Left alone with his wife the old man took the rubber macaroni from his mouth and laid it on his plate, and he and his wife held an inquest over it. The wife tried to spear it with a fork, but couldn't make any impression on it, and then she saw it was rubber hose, and told the old man. He was mad and glad, at the same time; glad because he had found his teeth were not to blame, and mad because the grocer had sold him boarding house macaroni. Then the girl came in and was put on the confessional, and told all, and presently there was a sound of revelry by night, in the wood shed, and the still, small voice was saying, "O, Pa, don't! you said you didn't care for innocent jokes. Oh!" And then the old man, between the strokes of the piece of clap-board would say, "Feed your father a hose cart next, won't ye? Be firing car springs and clothes wringers down me next, eh? Put some gravy on a rubber overcoat, probably, and serve it to me for salad. Try a piece of overshoe,

with a bone in it, for my beefsteak, likely. Give your poor
old father a slice of rubber bib in place of tripe to-morrow,
I expect. Boil me a rubber water bag for apple dumplings,
pretty soon, if I don't look out. There! You go and split
the kindling wood." 'Twas ever thus. A boy can't have
any fun now days.

CHAPTER III

THE BAD BOY GIVES HIS PA AWAY.

Pa is a hard citizen—Drinking sozodont—Making up the spare bed—
The midnight war-dance—An appointment by the coal bin.

THE bad boy's mother was out of town for a week, and
when she came home she found every thing topsy turvy.
The beds were all mussed up, and there was not a thing hung
up anywhere. She called the bad boy and asked him what
in the deuce had been going on, and he made it pleasant for
his Pa about as follows:

"Well, Ma, I know I will get killed, but I shall die like a
man. When Pa met you at the depot he looked too innocent for any use, but he's a hard citizen, and don't you forget
it. He hasn't been home a single night till after eleven
o'clock, and he was tired every night, and he had somebody
come home with him."

"O, heavens, Hennery," said the mother, with a sigh,
"are you sure about this?"

"Sure!" says the bad boy, "I was on to the whole racket.
The first night they came home awful tickled, and I guess
they drank some of your Sozodont, cause they seemed to
foam at the mouth. Pa wanted to put his friend in the spare
bed, but there were no sheets on it, and he went to rummaging around in the drawers for sheets. He got out all the towels
and table-cloths, and made up the bed with table-cloths, the
first night, and in the morning the visitor kicked because
there was a big coffee stain on the table-cloth sheet. You
know that table-cloth you spilled the coffee on last spring,
when Pa scared you by having his whiskers cut off. O, they
raised thunder around the room. Pa took your night-shirt,
you know the one with the lace work all down the front, and

put a pillow in it, and set it on a chair, and then took a
burned match and marked eyes and nose on the pillow, and
put your bonnet on it, and then they had a war dance. Pa
hurt the bald spot on his head by hitting it against the gas
shandelier, and then he said dammit. Then they throwed
pillows at each other. Pa's friend didn't have any night
shirt, and Pa gave his friend one of your'n, and the friend

PA MARKED EYES AND NOSE ON THE PILLOW.

took that old hoop-skirt in the closet, the one Pa always
steps on when he goes in the closet after a towel and hurts
his bare foot, you know, and put it under the night shirt, and
they walked around arm in arm. O, it made me tired to see
a man Pa's age act so like a darned fool."

"Hennery," says the mother, with a deep meaning in her
voice, "I want to ask you one question. Did your Pa's
friend *wear a dress?*"

"O, yes," said the bad boy, coolly, not noticing the pale

face of his Ma, "the friend put on that old blue dress of yours, with the pistol pocket in front, you know, and pinned a red cloth on for a train, and they danced the can-can."

Just at this point Pa came home to dinner, and the bad boy said, "Pa, I was just telling Ma what a nice time you had the first night she went away, with the pillow, and—"

"Hennery!" says the old gentleman severely, "you are a confounded fool."

"Izick," said the wife more severely, "Why did you bring a female home with you that night? Have you got no—"

"O, Ma," says the bad boy, "it was not a woman. It was young Mr. Brown, Pa's clerk at the store, you know."

"O!" said Ma, with a smile and a sigh.

"Hennery," said the stern parent, "I want to see you there by the coal bin for a minute or two. You are the gaul durndest fool I ever see. What you want to learn the first thing you do is to keep your mouth shut," and then they went on with the frugal meal, while Hennery seemed to feel as though something was coming.

CHAPTER IV

THE BAD BOY'S FOURTH OF JULY

Pa is a Pointer not a Setter—Special arrangements for the Fourth of July—A grand supply of fire works—The explosion—The air full of Pa and dog and rockets—The new Hell—A Scene that beggars description.

"How long do you think it will be before your father will be able to come down to the office?" asked the druggist of the bad boy as he was buying some arnica and court plaster.

"O, the doc. says he could come down now if he would, on some street where there were no horses to scare," said the boy as he bought some gum, "but he says he ain't in no hurry to come down till his hair grows out, and he gets some new clothes made. Say, do you wet this court plaster and stick it on?"

The druggist told him how the court plaster worked, and then asked him if his Pa couldn't ride down town.

"Ride down? well, I guess nix. He would have to set down if he rode down town, and Pa is no setter this trip, he is a pointer. That's where the pin wheel struck him."

"Well how did it happen?" asked the druggist as he wrapped a yellow paper over the bottle of arnica, and twisted the ends, and then helped the boy stick the strip of court plaster on his nose.

"Nobody knows how it happened but Pa, and when I come near to ask him about it he feels around his nightshirt where his pistol pocket would be if it was pants he had on, and tells me to leave his sight forever, and I leave too quick. You see he is afraid I will get hurt every Fourth of July, and he told me if I wouldn't fire a fire-cracker all day, he would let me get four dollars' worth of nice fire-works

35

and he would fire them off for me in the evening in the back yard. I promised, and he gave me the money and I bought a dandy lot of fire-works, and don't you forget it. I had a lot of rockets and Roman candles, and six-pin wheels, and a lot of nigger chasers, and some of these cannon fire-crackers, and torpedoes, and a box of parlor matches. I took them home and put the package in our big stuffed chair and put a newspaper over them.

Pa always takes a nap in that stuffed chair after dinner, and he went into the sitting room and I heard him driving our poodle dog out of that chair, and heard him ask the dog what he was a-chewing, and just then the explosion took place, and we all rushed in there. I tell you what I honestly think. I think that dog was chewing that box of parlor matches. This kind that pops so when you step on them. Pa was just going to set down when the whole air was filled with dog, and Pa, and rockets, and everything. When I got in there Pa had a sofa pillow trying to put the dog out. In the meantime Pa's linen pants were afire. I grabbed a pail of this indigo water that they had been rinsing clothes with and throwed it on Pa, or there wouldn't have been a place on him bigger'n a six-pence that wasn't burnt, and then he threw a camp chair at me and told me to go to Gehenna. Ma says that's the new hell they have got up in the revised edition of the Bible for bad boys. When Pa's pants were out his coat-tail blazed up and a Roman candle was firing blue and red balls at his legs, and a rocket got in to his white vest. The scene beggared description, like that Racine fire. A nigger chaser got after Ma and treed her on top of the sofa, and another one took after a girl that Ma invited to dinner, and burnt one of her stockings so she had to wear one of Ma's stockings, a good deal too big for her, home. After things got a little quiet, and we opened the doors and windows to let out the smoke and smell of burnt dog hair and Pa's whiskers, the big fire crackers began to go off, and a policeman came to the door and asked what was the matter, and Pa told him to go along with me

A NIGGER CHASER GOT AFTER MA AND
TREED HER ON TOP OF THE SOFA.

to Gehenna, but I don't want to go with a policeman. It would give me dead away. Well, there was nobody hurt much but the dog and Pa. I felt awful sorry for the dog. He hasn't got hair enough to cover hisself. Pa didn't have much hair anyway, except by the ears, but he thought a good deal of his whiskers,cause they wasn't very gray. Say, couldn't you send this anarchy up to the house? If I go up there Pa will say I am the damest fool on record. This is the last Fourth of July you catch me celebrating. I am going to work in a glue factory, where nobody will ever come to see me."

And the boy went out to pick up some squib fire crackers that had failed to explode, in front of the drug store.

CHAPTER V

"WHEN is your Ma coming back?" asked the grocery man, of the bad boy, as he found him standing on the sidewalk when the grocery was opened in the morning, taking some pieces of brick out of his coat tail pockets.

"O she got back at midnight, last night," said the boy as he eat a few blue berries out of a case. "That's what makes me up so early. Pa has been kicking at these pieces of brick with his bare feet, and when I came away he had his toes in his hand and was trying to go back up-stairs on one foot. Pa haint got no sense."

"I am afraid you are a terror," said the grocery man, as he looked at the innocent face of the boy. "You are always making your parents some trouble, and it is a wonder to me they don't send you to some reform school. What deviltry were you up to last night to get kicked this morning?"

"No deviltry, just a little fun. You see, Ma went to Chicago to stay a week, and she got tired, and telegraphed she would be home last night, and Pa was down town and I forgot to give him the dispatch, and after he went to bed, me and a chum of mine thought we would have a Fourth of July.

"You see, my chum has got a sister about as big as Ma, and we hooked some of her clothes and after Pa got to snoring we put them in Pa's room. O, you'd a laffed. We put a pair of number one slippers with blue stockings, down in front of the rocking chair, beside Pa's boots, and a red corset on a chair, and my chum's sister's best black silk

39

dress on another chair, and a hat with a white feather on, on the bureau, and some frizzes on the gas bracket, and every-

thing we could find that belonged to a girl in my chum's sister's room. O, we got a red parasol too and left it right in the middle of the floor. Well, when I looked at the layout, and heard Pa snoring, I thought I should die. You see, Ma knows Pa is a darn good feller, but she is easily excited. My chum slept with me that night, and when we heard the door-bell ring, I stuffed a pillow in my mouth. There was nobody to meet Ma at the depot, and she hired a hack and came right up. Nobody heard the bell

THEN I SLIPPED UP-STAIRS AND LOOKED OVER THE BANISTERS.

but me, and I had to go down and let Ma in. She was pretty hot, now you bet, at not being met at the depot.

"Where's your father?" said she, as she began to go up stairs.

"I told her I guessed Pa had gone to sleep by this time, but I heard a good deal of noise in the room about an hour ago, and may be he was taking a bath. Then I slipped up stairs and looked over the banisters. Ma said something about heavens and earth, and 'where is the huzzy,' and a lot of things I couldn't hear, and Pa said 'damfino' and 'its no such thing,' and the door slammed and they talked for two hours. I s'pose they finally laid it to me, as they always do, 'cause Pa called me very early this morning, and when I came down stairs he came out in the hall and his face was redder'n a beet, and he tried to stab me with his big toe-nail, and if it hadn't been for these pieces of brick he would have hurt my feelings. I see they had my chum's sister's clothes all pinned up in a newspaper; and I s'pose when I go back I shall have to carry them home, and then she will be down on me. I'll tell you what, I have got a good notion to take some shoemakers' wax and stick my chum on my back and travel with a circus as a double-headed boy from Borneo. A fellow could have more fun, and not get kicked all the time."

And the boy sampled some strawberries in a case in front of the store and went down the street whistling for his chum, who was looking out of an alley to see if the coast was clear.

CHAPTER VI

HIS PA IS A DARN COWARD

His Pa has been a major—How he would deal with burglars—His
bravery put to the test—The ice revolver—His Pa begins to pray—
Tells where the change is—"Please, Mr. Burglar, spare a poor
man's life!"—Ma wakes up—The bad boy and his chum run—
Fish-pole sauce—Ma would make a good chief of police.

"I suppose you think my Pa is a brave man," said the
boy to the grocer, as he was trying a new can opener on a
tin biscuit box in the grocery, while the grocer was putting
up some canned goods for the boy, who said the goods were
for the folks to use at a picnic, but which was to be taken
out camping by the boy and his chum.

"O, I suppose he is a brave man," said the grocer as he
charged the goods to the boy's father. "Your Pa is called
a major, and you know at the time of the re-union he wore
a veteran badge, and talked to the boys about how they
suffered during the war."

"Suffered nothing," remarked the boy, with a sneer;
"unless they suffered from the peach brandy and leather
pies Pa sold them. Pa was a suttler, that's the kind of a
veteran he was, and he is a coward."

"What makes you think your Pa is a coward?" asked
the grocer, as he saw the boy slipping some sweet crackers
into his pistol pocket.

"Well, my chum and me tried him last night, and he is
so sick this morning that he can't get up. You see, since
the burglars got into Magie's, Pa has been telling what he
would do if the burglars got into our house. He said he
would jump out of bed and knock one senseless with his
fist, and throw the other over the banister. I told my chum
Pa was a coward, and we fixed up like burglars, with masks

42

on, and I had Pa's long hunting boots on, and we pulled
caps down over our eyes, and looked fit to frighten a policeman. I took Pa's meerchaum pipe case and tied a little
piece of ice over the end the stem goes in, and after Pa and
Ma was asleep we went into the room, and I put the cold
muzzle of the ice revolver to Pa's temple, and when he woke
up I told him if he moved a muscle or said a word I would

THEN I STOOD OFF AND TOLD HIM TO HOLD UP HIS HANDS.

spatter the wall and the counterpane with his brains. He
closed his eyes and began to pray. Then I stood off and
told him to hold up his hands, and tell me where the valuables
was. He held up his hands, and sat up in bed, and sweat
and trembled, and told us the change was in his left hand
pants pocket, and that Ma's money purse was in the bureau
drawer in the cuff box, and my chum went and got them.
Pa shook so the bed fairly squeaked and I told him I was
a good notion to shoot a few holes in him just for fun,

and he cried and said, 'Please Mr. Burglar, take all I have got, but spare a poor old man's life who never did any harm!' Then I told him to lay down on his stomach and pull the clothes over his head, and stick his feet over the foot board, and he did it, and I took a shawl strap and was strapping his feet together, and he was scared, I tell you. It would have been all right if Ma hadn't woke up. Pa trembled so Ma woke up and thought he had the ager, and my chum turned up the light to see how much there was in Ma's purse, and Ma seen me, and asked me what I was doing and I told her I was a burglar, robbing the house. I didn't know whether Ma tumbled to the racket or not, but she threw a pillow at me, and said 'get out of here or I'll take you across my knee,' and she got up and we run. She followed us to my room, and took Pa's jointed fish pole and mauled us both until I don't want any more burglaring, and my chum says he will never speak to me again. I didn't think Ma had so much sand. She is as brave as a lion, but Pa is a regular squaw. Pa sent for me to come to his room this morning, but I ain't well, and am going out to Pewaukee to camp out till the burglar scare is over. If Pa comes around here talking about war times, and how he faced the enemy on many a well fought field you ask him if he ever threw any burglars down a banister. He is a fraud, Pa is, but Ma would make a good chief of police, and don't you let it escape you."

And the boy took his canned ham and lobster, and tucking some crackers inside the bosom of his blue flannel shirt, started for Pewaukee, while the grocer looked at him as though he were a hard citizen.

CHAPTER VII

HIS PA GETS A BITE

His Pa gets too much water—The doctors disagree—How to spoil boys—His Pa goes to Pewaukee in search of his son—Anxious to fish—"Stop 'er, I've got a whale!"—Overboard—His Pa is saved—Goes to cut a switch—A dollar for his pants.

"So the doctor thinks your Pa has ruptured a blood vessel, eh?" says the street car driver to the bad boy, as the youngster was playing sweet on him to get a free ride down town.

"Well, they don't know. The doctor at Pewaukee said Pa had dropsy, until he found the water that they wrung out of his pants was lake water, and there was a doctor on the cars belonging to the Insane Asylum, when we put Pa on the train, who said from the looks of his face, sort of red and blue, it was apoplexy, but a horse doctor that was down at the depot when we put Pa in the carriage to take him home, said he was off his feed, and had been taking too much water when he was hot, and got foundered. O, you can't tell anything about doctors. No two of 'em guesses alike," answered the boy, as he turned the brake for the driver to stop the car for a sister of charity, and then punched the mule with a fish pole, when the driver was looking back, to see if he couldn't jerk her off the back step.

"Well, how did your Pa happen to fall out of the boat? Didn't he know the lake was wet?"

"He had a suspicion that it was damp, when his back struck the water, I think. I'll tell you how it was. When my chum and I run away to Pewaukee, Ma thought we had gone off to be piruts, and she told Pa it was a duty he owed to society to go and get us to come back, and be good. She told him if he would treat me as an equal, and laugh

45

and joke with me, I wouldn't be so bad. She said kicking
and pounding spoiled more boys than all the Sunday schools.
So Pa came out to our camp, about two miles up the lake
from Pewaukee, and he was just as good natured as though
we had never had any trouble at all. We let him stay all
night with us, and gave him a napkin with a red border to
sleep on under a tree, cause there was not blankets enough
to go around, and in the morning I let him have one of the
soda crackers I had in my shirt bosom and he wanted to
go fishing with us. He said he would show us how to fish.
So he got a piece of pork rind at a farm house for bait,
and he put it on a hook, and we got in an old boat, and my
chum rowed and Pa and I trolled. In swinging the boat
around Pa's line got under the boat, and come right up near
me. I don't know what possessed me, but I took hold of Pa's
line and gave it a 'yank,' and Pa jumped so quick his hat
went off in the lake. 'Stop 'er,' says Pa, 'I've got a whale.'
It's mean in a man to call his chubby faced little boy a
whale, but the whale yanked again and Pa began to pull
him in. I hung on, and let the line out a little at a time,
just zackly like a fish, and he pulled, and sweat, and the
bald spot on his head was getting sun burnt, and the line
cut my hand, so I wound it around the oar-lock, and Pa
pulled hard enough to tip the boat over. He thought he had
a forty pound musculunger, and he stood up in the boat and
pulled on that oar-lock as hard as he could. I ought not to
have done it, but I loosened the line from the oar-lock, and
when it slacked up Pa went right out over the side of the
boat, and struck on his pants, and split a hole in the water
as big as a wash tub. His head went down under water
and his boot heels hung over the boat. 'What you doin'?
Diving after the fish?' says I as Pa's head came up and he
blowed out the water. I thought Pa belonged to the church,
but he said 'youdamidyut.' I guess he was talking to the
fish. Well, sir, my chum took hold of my Pa's foot and the
collar of his coat, and held him in the stern of the boat,
and I paddled the boat to the shore, and Pa crawled out and

shook himself. I never had no ijee a man's pants could hold
so much water. It was just like when they pull the thing
on a street sprinkler. Then Pa took off his pants and my
chum and me took hold of the legs and Pa took hold of the
summer kitchen and we wrung the water out. Pa wan't so
sociable after that, and he went back into the woods with his
knife, with nothing on but a linen duster and a neck-tie,
while his pants were drying on a tree, to cut a switch, and
we hollered to him that a party of picnicers from Lake Side
were coming ashore right where his pants were, to pic-nic,
and Pa he run into the woods. He was afraid there would

THEN PA CRAWLED OUT AND SHOOK HIMSELF.

be some wimmen in the pic-nic that he knowed, and he
coaxed us to come in the woods where he was, and he said
he would give us a dollar apiece and not be mad any more
if we would bring him his pants. We got his pants, and you
ought to see how they was wrinkled when he put them on.
They looked as though they had been ironed with waffle
irons. We went to the depot and came home on the freight
train, and Pa sneezed all the way in the caboose, and I don't
think he has ruptured any blood vessel. Well, I get off here
at Mitchell's bank," and the boy turned the break and jumped
off without paying his fare.

CHAPTER VIII

HE IS TOO HEALTHY

An empty Champagne bottle and a black eye—He is arrested—Oconomowoc for health—His Pa is an old masher—Danced till the cows
came home—The girl from the Sunny South—The bad boy is sent
home.

"THERE, I knew you would get into trouble," said the
grocery man to the bad boy, as a policeman came along
leading him by the ear, the boy having an empty champagne
bottle in one hand, and a black eye. "What has he been
doing Mr. Policeman?" asked the grocery man, as the policeman halted with the boy in front of the store.

"Well, I was going by a house up here when this kid
opened the door with a quart bottle of champagne, and he
cut the wire and fired the cork at another boy, and the champagne went all over the sidewalk, and some of it went on
me, and I knew there was something wrong, cause champagne is too expensive to waste that way, and he said he was
running the shebang and if I would bring him here you
would say he was all right. If you say so I will let him go."

The grocery man said he had better let the boy go, as
his parents would not like to have their little pet locked up.
So the policeman let go his ear, and he throwed the empty
bottle on a coal wagon, and after the policeman had brushed
the champagne off his coat, and smelled of his fingers, and
started off, the grocery man turned to the boy, who was peeling a cucumber, and said:

"Now, what kind of a circus have you been having, and
what do you mean by destroying wine that way? And where
are your folks?"

"Well, I'll tell you. Ma has got the hay fever and
has gone to Lake Superior to see if she can't stop sneezing,

and Saturday Pa said he and me would go out to Oconomowoc and stay over Sunday, and try and recuperate our
health.   Pa said it would be a good joke for me not to call
him Pa, but to act as though I was his younger brother, and
we would have a real nice time.   I knowed what he wanted.
He is an old masher, that's what's the matter with him, and
he was going to play himself for a bachelor.   O, thunder, I
got on to his racket in a minute.   He was introduced to

"IF YOU SAY SO I'LL LET HIM GO," SAID THE POLICEMAN.

some of the girls and Saturday evening he danced till the
cows come home.   At home he is awful 'fraid of rheumatiz,
and he never sweats, or sits in a draft; but the water just
poured off'n him, and he stood in the door and let a girl fan
him till I was afraid he would freeze, and just as he was telling a girl from Tennessee, who was joking him about being
an old bach, that he was not sure as he would always hold
out a woman hater if he was to be thrown into contact with
the charming ladies of the Sunny South, I pulled his coat
and said, 'Pa how do you spose Ma's hay fever is to-night?

I'll bet she is just sneezing the top of her head off.' Wall, sir, you just oughten see that girl and Pa. Pa looked at me as if I was a total stranger, and told the porter if that freckled face boot-black belonged around the house he had better be fired out of the ball-room, and the girl said 'the disgustin' thing,' and just before they fired me I told Pa he had better look out or he would sweat through his liver-pad.

"I went to bed and Pa staid up till the lights were put out. He was mad when he came to bed, but he didn't lick me, cause the people in the next room would hear him, but the next morning he talked to me. He said I might go back home Sunday night, and he would stay a day or two. He sat around on the verandah all the afternoon, talking with the girls, and when he would see me coming along he would look cross. He took a girl out boat riding, and when I asked him if I couldn't go along, he said he was afraid I would get drowned, and he said if I went home there was nothing there too good for me, and so my chum and me got to firing bottles of champane, and he hit me in the eye with a cork, and I drove him out doors and was going to shell his earth works, when the policeman collared me. Say, what's good for a black eye?"

The grocery man told him his Pa would cure it when he got home. "What do you think your Pa's object was in passing himself off for a single man at Oconomowoc?" asked the grocery man, as he charged up the cucumber to the boy's father.

"That's what beats me. Aside from Ma's hay fever she is one of the healthiest women in town. O, I suppose he does it for his health, the way they all do when they go to a summer resort, but it leaves a boy an orphan, don't it, to have such kitteny parents."

CHAPTER IX

His Pa is drinking hard—He has become a terror—A jumping dog—
The Old Man is shamefully assaulted—"This is a hellish climate,
my boy!"—His Pa swears off—His Ma still sneezing at Lake
Superior.

"IF the dogs in our neighborhood hold out I guess I can
do something that all the temperance societies in this town
have failed to do," says the bad boy to the grocery man, as
he cut off a piece of cheese and took a handful of crackers
out of a box.

"Well for Heaven's sake, what have you been doing now,
you little reprobate?" asked the grocery man, as he went to
the desk and charged the boy's father with a pound and four
ounces of cheese and two pounds of crackers. "If you was
my boy and played any of your tricks on me I would maul
the everlasting life out of you. Your father is a cussed fool
that he don't send you to the reform school. The hired girl
was over this morning and says your father is sick, and I
should think he would be. What you done? Poisoned him
I suppose."

"No, I didn't poison him; I just scared the liver out of
him, that's all."

"How was it?" asked the groceryman, as he charged up
a pound of prunes to the boy's father.

"Well, I'll tell you, but if you ever tell Pa I won't trade
here any more. You see, Pa belongs to all the secret societies, and when there is a grand lodge or anything here, he
drinks awfully. There was something last week, some sort
of a leather apron affair, or a sash over the shoulder, and
every night he was out till the next day, and his breath
smelled all the time like in front of a vinegar store, where

they·keep yeast. Ever since Ma took her hay fever with
her up to Lake Superior, Pa has been a terror, and I thought
something ought to be done. Since that variegated dog
trick was played on him he has been pretty sober till Ma
went away, and I happened to think of a dog a boy in the
Third Ward has got, that will do tricks. He will jump
up and take a man's hat off, and bring a handkerchief, and
all that. So I got the boy to come up on our street, and
Monday night, about dark, I got in the house and told the
boy when Pa came along to make the dog take his hat,

THE DOG GAVE ONE BARK AND WENT FOR PA'S DUSTER.

and to pin a handkerchief to Pa's coat tail and make the dog
take that, and then for him and the dog to light out for
home. Well, you'd a died. Pa came up the street as dig-
nified and important as though he had gone through bank-
ruptcy, and tried to walk straight, and just as he got near
the door the boy pointed to Pa's hat and said, 'Fetch it.'
The dog is a big Newfoundland, but he is a jumper, and
don't you forget it. Pa is short and thick, and when the
dog struck him on the shoulder and took his hat Pa almost
fell over, and then he said, 'Get out,' and he kicked and backed
up toward the step, and then turned around and the boy

pointed to the handkerchief and said, 'fetch it,' and the dog gave one bark and went for it, and got hold of it and part of Pa's duster, and Pa tried to climb up the steps on his hands and feet, and the dog pulled the other way, and it is an old last year's duster anyway, and the whole back breadth come out, and when I opened the door there Pa stood with the front of his coat and the sleeves on, but the back was gone, and I took hold of his arm, and he said, 'Get out,' and was going to kick me, thinking I was a dog, and I told him I was his own little boy, and asked him if anything was the matter. 'M (hic) atter enough. New F (hic) land dog chawing me last hour'n a half. Why didn't you come and k (hic) ill 'em?' I told Pa there was no dog at all, and he must be careful of his health or I wouldn't have no Pa at all. He looked at me and asked me, as he felt for the place where the back of his linen duster was, what had become of his coat tail and hat if there was no dog, and I told him he had probably caught his coat on that barbed wire fence down street, and he said he saw the dog and a boy just as plain as could be, and for me to help him up stairs and go for the doctor. I got him in the bed, and he said, 'this is a hellish climate, my boy,' and I went for the doctor. Pa said he wanted to be cauterised, so he wouldn't go mad. I told the doc. the joke, and he said he would keep it up, and he gave Pa some powders, and told him if he drank any more before Christmas he was a dead man. Pa says it has learned him a lesson and they can never get any more pizen down him, but don't you give me away, will you, cause he would go and complain to the police about the dog, and they would shoot it. Ma will be back as soon as she gets through sneezing, and I will tell her, and she will give me a chromo, cause she don't like to have Pa drink only between meals. Well, good day. There's an Italian got a bear that performs in the street, and I am going to find where he is showing, and feed the bear a cayenne pepper lozenger, and see him clean out the Polack settlement. Good bye." And the boy went to look for the bear.

CHAPTER X

HIS PA HAS GOT RELIGION

The bad boy goes to Sunday school—Promises reformation— The Old Man on trial for six months—What Ma thinks—Ants in Pa's liver-pad—The Old Man in church—Religion is one thing—Ants another.

WELL, that beats the devil," said the grocery man, as he stood in front of his grocery and saw the bad boy coming along on the way home from Sunday school, with a clean shirt on, and a testament and some dime novels under his arm. "What has got into you, and what has come over your Pa? I see he has braced up, and looks pale and solemn. You haven't converted him, have you?"

"No, Pa has not got religion enough to hurt yet, but he has got the symptoms. He has joined the church on probation, and is trying to be good so he can get in the church for keeps. He said it was hell living the way he did, and he has got me to promise to go to Sunday school. He said if I didn't he would maul me so my skin wouldn't hold water. You see, Ma said Pa had got to be on trial for six months before he could get in the church, and if he could get along without swearing and doing anything bad, he was all right, and we must try him and see if we could cause him to swear. She said she thought a person, when they was on probation, ought to be a martyr, and try and overcome all temptations to do evil, and if Pa could go through six months of our home life, and not cuss the hinges off the door, he was sure of a glorious immortality beyond the grave. She said it wouldn't be wrong for me to continue to play innocent jokes on Pa, and if he took it all right he was a Christian, but if he got a hot box, and flew around mad, he was better out of church than in it. There he comes now," said the boy as he got behind a sign, "and he is pretty hot for a

Christian. He is looking for me. You had ought to have seen him in church this morning. You see, I commenced the exercises at home after breakfast by putting a piece of ice in each of Pa's boots, and when he pulled on the boots he yelled that his feet were all on fire, and we told him that it was nothing but symptoms of gout, so he left the ice in his boots to melt, and he said all the morning that he felt as though he had sweat his boots full. But that was not the worst. You know, Pa he wears a liver-pad. Well, on Saturday my chum and me was out on the lake shore and we found a nest of ants, these little red ants, and I got a pop bottle half full of the ants and took them home. I didn't know what I would do with the ants, but ants are always handy to have in the house. This morning, when Pa was dressing for church, I saw his liver-pad on a chair, and noticed a hole in it, and I thought what a good place it would be for the ants. I don't know what possessed me, but I took the liver-pad into my room, and opened the bottle, and put the hole over the mouth of the bottle and I guess the ants thought there was something to eat in the liver-pad, cause they all went into it, and they crawled around in the bran and condition powders inside of it, and I took it back to Pa, and he put it on under his shirt, and dressed himself, and we went to church. Pa squirmed a little when the minister was praying, and I guess some of the ants had come to view the landscape o'er. When we got up to sing the hymn Pa kept kicking, as though he was nervous, and he felt down his neck and looked sort of wild, the way he did when he had the jim-jams. When we sat down Pa couldn't keep still, and I like to dide when I saw some of the ants come out of his shirt bosom and go racing around his white vest. Pa tried to look pious and resigned, but he couldn't keep his legs still, and he sweat mor'n a pail full. When the minister preached about 'the worm that never dieth,' Pa reached into his vest and scratched his ribs, and he looked as though he would give ten dollars if the minister would get through. Ma she looked at Pa as though she would bite his head off, but Pa he just squirmed, and acted as though his soul was on fire. Say, does it bite, or just crawl around? Well, when the minister said amen, and prayed the second round, and then said a brother who was a missionary to the heathen would like to make a few remarks about the work of the missionaries in Bengal, and take up a collection, Pa told Ma they would have to excuse *him*, and he lit out for home, slapping himself on the legs and on the arms and on the back, and he acted crazy. Ma and me went

THE LIVER PAD WAS ON THE FLOOR AND PA STAMPING ON IT.

home, after the heathen got through, and found Pa in his bed room, with part of his clothes off, and the liver-pad was on the floor, and Pa was stamping on it with his boots, and talking offul.

"'What is the matter,' says Ma. 'Don't your religion agree with you?'

"'Religion be dashed,' says Pa, as he kicked the liver-pad. 'I would give ten dollars to know how a pint of red ants got into my liver-pad. Religion is one thing, and a million ants walking all over a man, playing tag, is another.

I didn't know the liver-pad was loaded. How in Gehenna did they get in there?' and Pa scowled at Ma as though he would kill her.

" 'Don't swear, dear,' says Ma, as she threw down her hymn book, and took off her bonnet. 'You should be patient. Remember Job was patient and he was afflicted with sore boils.'

"I don't care," says Pa, as he chased the ants out of his drawers, 'Job never had ants in his liver-pad. If he had he would have swore the shingles off a barn. Here you,' says Pa, speaking to me, 'you head off them ants running under the budeau. If the truth was known I believe you would be responsible for this outrage.' And Pa looked at me kind of hard.

" 'O, Pa,' says I, with tears in my eyes. 'Do you think your little Sunday school boy would catch ants in a pop bottle on the lake shore, and bring them home, and put them in the hole of your liver-pad, just before you put it on to go to church? You are too bad.' And I shed some tears. I can shed tears now any time I want to, but it didn't do any good this time. Pa knew it was me, and while he was looking for the shawl strap I went to Sunday school, and now I guess he is after me, and I will go and take a walk down to Bay View."

The boy moved off as his Pa turned a corner, and the grocery man said, "Well, that boy beats all I ever saw. If he was mine I would give him away."

CHAPTER XI

HIS PA TAKES A TRICK

Jamaica rum and cards—The bad boy possessed of a devil—The kind deacon—At prayer meeting—The Old Man tells his experience—The flying cards—The prayer meeting suddenly closed.

"WHAT is it I hear about your Pa being turned out of prayer meeting Wednesday night?" asker the grocer of the bad boy, as he came over after some canteloupes for breakfast, and plugged a couple to see if they were ripe.

"He wasn't turned out of prayer meeting at all. The people all went away and Pa and me was the last ones out of the church. But Pa was mad, and don't you forget it."

"Well, what seemed to be the trouble? Has your Pa become a backslider?"

"O, no, his flag is still there. But something seems to go wrong. You see, when we got ready to go to prayer meeting last night, Pa told me to go up stairs and get him a handkerchief, and to drop a little perfumery on it, and put it in the tail pocket of his black coat. I did it, but I guess I got hold of the wrong bottle of fumery. There was a label on the fumery bottle that said 'Jamaica Rum,' and I thought it was the same as Bay Rum, and I put on a whole lot. Just afore I put the handkerchief in Pa's pocket, I noticed a pack of cards on the stand, that Pa used to play hi-lo-jack with Ma evenings when he was so sick he couldn't go down town, before he got 'ligion, and I wrapped the handkercher around the pack of cards and put them in his pocket. I don't know what made me do it, and Pa don't, either, I guess 'cause he told Ma this morning I was possessed of a devil. I never owned no devil, but I had a pair of pet goats onct, and they played hell all around, Pa said. That's what the

59

devil does, ain't it? Well, I must go home with these melons, or they won't keep."

"But hold on," says the grocery man as he gave the boy
a few raisins with worms in, that he couldn't sell, to keep
him, "what about the prayer meeting?"

"O, I like to forgot. Well, Pa and me went to prayer
meeting, and Ma came along afterwards with a deakin that
is mashed on her, I guess, 'cause he says she is to be pitted
for havin' to go through life yoked to such an old prize ox
as Pa. I heard him tell Ma that, when he was helping her
put on her rubber waterprivilege to go home in the rain the
night of the sociable, and she looked at him just as she does
at me when she wants me to go down to the hair foundry
after her switch, and said, 'O, you dear brother,' and all the
way home he kept her waterprivilege on by putting his arm
on the small of her back. Ma asked Pa if he didn't think
the deakin was real kind, and Pa said, 'yez, dam kind,' but
that was afore he got 'ligion. We sat in a pew, at the
prayer meeting, next to Ma and the deakin, and there was
lots of pious folks all around there. After the preacher had
gone to bat, and an old lady had her innings, a praying, and
the singers had gone out on first base, Pa was on deck, and
the preacher said they would like to hear from the recent
convert, who was trying to walk in the straight and narrow
way, but who found it so hard, owing to the many crosses he
had to bear. Pa knowed it was him that had to go to bat,
and he got up and said he felt it was good to be there. He
said he didn't feel that he was a full sized Christian yet, but
he was getting in his work the best he could. He said at
times everything looked dark to him, and he feared he should
falter by the wayside, but by a firm resolve he kept his eye
sot on the future, and if he was tempted to do wrong he said,
'Get thee behind me, Satan,' and stuck in his toe-nails for a
pull for the right. He said he was thankful to the brothers
and sisters, particularly the sisters, for all they had done to
make his burden light, and hoped to meet them all in—.
When Pa got as far as that he sort of broke down. I spose

he was going to say heaven, though after a few minutes
they all thought he wanted to meet them in a saloon. When
his eyes began to leak, Pa put his hand in his tail pocket for
his handkerchief, and got hold of it, and gave it a jerk, and

HE HOPED TO MEET THEM ALL IN——.

out came the handkercher, and the cards. Well, if he had
shuffled them, and Ma had cut them, and he had dealt six
hands, they couldn't have been dealt any better. They flew
into everybody's lap. The deakin that was with Ma got the
jack of spades and three aces and a deuce, and Ma got some
nine spots and a king of hearts, and Ma nearly fainted, cause

she didn't get a better hand, I spose. The preacher got a
pair of deuces, and a queen of hearts, and he looked up at
Pa as though it was a misdeal, and a old woman who sat
across the isle, she only got two cards, but that was enough.
Pa didn't see what he had done at first, cause he had the
handkerchief over his eyes, but when he smelt the rum on it,
he took it away, and when he saw everybody discarding, and
he thought he had struck a poker game, and he looked
around as though he was mad cause they didn't deal him a
hand. The minister adjourned the prayer meeting and
whispered to Pa, and everybody went out holding their
noses on account of Pa's fumery, and when Pa came home he
asked Ma what he should do to be saved. Ma said she didn't
know. The deakin told her Pa seemed wedded to his idols.
Pa said the deakin better run his own idols, and Pa would
run his. I don't know how it is going to turn out, but Pa
says he is going to stick to the church."

CHAPTER XII

HIS PA GETS PULLED

The Old Man studies the Bible—Daniel in the lion's den—The mule and the mule's father—Murder in the Third Ward—The Old Man Arrested—The Old Man fans the dust out of his son's pants.

"WHAT was you and your Ma down at the police station for so late last night?" asked the grocery man of the bad boy, as he kicked a dog away from a basket of peaches standing on the sidewalk. "Your Ma seemed to be much affected."

"That's a family secret. But if you will give me some of those rotten peaches I will tell you, if you won't ever ask Pa how he came to be pulled by the police."

The grocery man told him to help himself out of the basket that the dog had been smelling of, and he filled his pockets, and the bosom of his flannel shirt, and his hat, and said:

"Well, you know Pa is studying up on the Bible, and he is trying to get me interested, and he wants me to ask him questions, but if I ask him any questions that he can't answer he gets mad. When I asked him about Daniel in the den of lions, and if he didn't think Dan was traveling with a show, and had the lions chloroformed, he said I was a scoffer, and would go to Gehenna. Now I don't want to go to Gehenna just for wanting to get posted in the show business of old times, do you? When Pa said Dan was saved from the jaws of the lions because he prayed three times every day, and had faith, I told him that was just what the duffer that goes into the lions' den in Coup's circus did because I saw him in the dressing room, when me and my chum got in for carrying water for the elephant, and he was exhorting with a girl in tights who was going to ride two horses. Pa said I was mistaken, cause they never prayed in circus, 'cept the lemonade butchers. I guess I know when I hear a man pray. Coup's Daniel talked just like a deacon at class meeting, and told the girl to go to the place where the minister says we will all go if we don't do different. Pa says it is wicked to speak of Daniel in the same breath that you speak of a circus, so I am wicked I spose. Well, I couldn't help it and when he wanted me to ask him questions about Elijah going up in a chariot of fire, I asked him if he believed a chariot like the ones in the circus, with eight horses, could carry a man right up to the clouds, and Pa said of course it could. Then I asked him what they did with the horses after they got up there, or if the chariot kept running back and forth like a bust to a pic-nic, and whether they had stalls for the horses and harness-makers to repair harnesses, and wagon-makers, 'cause a chariot is liable to run off a wheel, if it strikes a cloud in turning a corner. Pa said I made him tired. He said I had no more conception of the beauties of scripture than a mule, and then I told Pa he couldn't expect a mule to know much unless the mule's father had brought him up right, and where a mule's father had been a regular old bummer till he got the jim jams, and only got religion to keep out of the inebriate asylum, that the little mule was entitled to more charity for his shortcomings than the mule's Papa. That seemed to make Pa mad, and he said the scripture lessons would be continued some other time, and I might go out and play, and if I wasn't in before nine o'clock he would come after me and warm my jacket. Well, I was out playing, and me and my chum heard of the murder in the Third Ward, and went down there to see the dead and wounded, and it was after ten o'clock, and Pa was searching for me, and I saw Pa go into an alley, in his shirt sleeves and no hat on, and the police were looking for the murderer, and I told the policeman there was a suspicious looking man in the alley, and the policeman went in there and jumped on his back, and held him down, and the patrol

wagon came, and they loaded Pa in, and he gnashed his
teeth, and said they would pay dearly for this, and they held
his hands and told him not to talk, as he would commit himself, and they tore off his suspender buttons, and I went home
and told Ma the police had pulled Pa for being in a suspicious
place, and she said she had always been afraid he would
come to some bad end, and we went down to the station and

HE WAS EXHORTING A GIRL IN TIGHTS.

the police let Pa go on promise that he wouldn't do so again,
and we went home and Pa fanned the dust out of my pants.
But he did it in a pious manner and I can't complain. He
was trying to explain to Ma how it was that he was pulled,
when I came away, and I guess he will make out to square
himself. Say, don't these peaches seem to have a darn queer
taste? Well, good bye, I am going down to the morgue
to have some fun."

CHAPTER XIII

HIS PA GOES TO THE EXPOSITION

The bad boy acts as guide—The circus story—The Old Man wants to sit down—Tries to eat pancakes—Drinks some mineral water—The Old Man falls in love with a wax woman—A policeman interferes —The lights go out—The grocery man don't want a clerk.

"Well, everything seems to be quiet over to your house this week," says the grocery man to the bad boy as the youth was putting his thumb into some peaches through the mosquito netting over the baskets, to see if they were soft enough to steal, "I suppose you have let up on the old man, haven't you?"

"O, no. We keep it right up. The minister of the church that Pa has joined says while Pa is on probation it is perfectly proper for us to do everything to try him, and make him fall from grace. The minister says if Pa comes out of his six months' probation without falling by the way-side he has got the elements to make the boss christian, and Ma and me are doing all we can."

"What was the doctor at your house for this morning?" asked the grocery man. "Is your Ma sick?"

"No, Ma is worth two in the bush. It's Pa that ain't well. He is having some trouble with his digestion. You see he went to the exposition with me as guide, and that is enough to ruin any man's digestion. Pa is near-sighted, and said he wanted me to go along and show him things. Well, I never had so much fun since Pa fell out of the boat. First we went in by the fountain, and Pa had never been in the exposition building before. Last year he was in Yourip and he was astonished at the magnitude of everything. First I made him jump clear across the aisle there, where the stuffed tigers are, by the fur place. I told him the keeper

66

was just coming along with some meat to feed the animals, and when they smelled the meat, they just chawed things. He run against a show-case, and then wanted to go away.

He said he traveled with a circus when he was young, and nobody knew the dangers of fooling around wild animals better than he did. He said once he fought with seven tigers and two Nubian lions for five hours, with Mabee's old show. I asked him if that was afore he got religion, and he said, 'Never you mind.' He is an old liar, even if he is converted. Ma says he never was with a circus, and she has known him ever since he wore short dresses. Wall, you would a dide to see Pa there by the furniture place, where they have got beautiful beds and chairs. There was one blue chair under a glass case, all velvet, and a sign was over it, telling people to keep their hands off. Pa asked me what the sign was, and I told him it said ladies and gentlemen are requested to sit in the chairs and try them. Pa climbed over the railing and was just going to sit down on the glass show-case over the chair, when one of the walk-around fellows, with imitation police hats, took him by the collar and yanked him back over the railing, and was going to kick Pa's pants. Pa was mad to have his coat collar pulled up over his head, and have the set of his coat spoiled, and was going to sass the man, when I told Pa the man was a lunatic from the asylum, that was on exhibition, and Pa wanted to go away from there. He said he didn't know what they wanted to exhibit lunatics for. We went up stairs to the pancake bazar, where they broil pancakes out of self rising flour, and put butter and sugar on them and give them away. Pa said he could eat more pancakes than any man out of jail, and wanted me to get him some. I took a couple of pancakes and tore out a piece of the lining of my coat and put it between the pancakes and handed them to Pa, with a paper around the pancakes. Pa didn't notice the paper nor the cloth, and it would have made you laff to see him chew on them. I told him I guessed he didn't have as good teeth as he used to, and he said, 'Never you mind the teeth,' and he

kept on until he swallowed the whole business, and he
said he guessed he didn't want any more.   He is so sensitive about his teeth that he would eat a leather apron if
anybody told him he couldn't.   When the Doctor said Pa's
digestion was bad, I told him if he could let Pa swallow a
seamstress or a sewing machine, to sew up the cloth, he
would get well, and the doc. says I am going to be the death
of Pa some day. But I thought I should split when Pa wanted
a drink of water.   I asked him if he would druther have mineral water, and he said he guessed it would take the strong-
est kind of mineral water to wash down them pancakes, so
I took him to where the fire extinguishers are, and got him
to take the nozzle of the extinguisher in his mouth, and I
turned the faucet.   I don't think he got more than a quart
of the stuff out of the saleratus machine down him, but he
rared right up and said he be condamed if he believed that
water was ever intended to drink, and he felt as though he
should bust, and just then the man who kicks the big organ
struck up and the building shook, and I guess Pa thought he
had busted.   The most fun was when we came along to
where the wax woman is.   They have got a wax woman
dressed up to kill, and she looks just as natural as if she
could breathe.   She had a handkerchief in her hand, and as
we came along I told Pa there was a lady that seemed to
know him.   Pa is on the mash himself, and he looked at her
and smiled and said good evening and asked me who she
was.

"I told him it looked to me like the girl that sings in the
choir at our church, and Pa said course it is, and he went
right in where she was and said 'Pretty good show, isn't it?'
and put out his hand to shake hands with her, but the woman
who tends the stand came along and thought Pa was drunk
and said, 'Old gentleman, I guess you had better get out
of here.   This is for ladies only.'

"Pa said he didn't care nothing for her ladies only, all he
wanted was to converse with an acquaintance, and then
one of the policemen came along and told Pa he had better

go down to the saloon where he belonged. Pa excused himself to the wax woman, and said he would see her later, and told the policeman if he would come out to the sidewalk he would knock leven kinds of stuffing out of him. The policeman told him that would be all right, and I led Pa away. He was offul mad. But it was the best fun when the lights went out. You see this electric light machine slipped a cog or lost its cud and all of a sudden the lights went out

THIS IS FOR LADIES ONLY.

and it was as dark as a squaw's pocket. Pa wanted to know what made it so dark, and I told him it was not dark. He said, 'Boy, don't you fool me.' You see I thought it would be fun to make Pa believe he was struck blind, so I told him his eyes must be wrong. He said, 'Do you mean to say you can see?' and I told him everything was as plain as day, and I pointed out the different things, and explained them and walked Pa along, and acted just as though I could see, and Pa said it had come at last. He had felt for years as though he would some day lose his eyesight and now it had come and he said he laid it all to the condamned mineral water. After a little they lit some of the gas burners, and Pa said he could see a little, and wanted to go home, and I took him home. When we got out of the building he began to see things, and said his eyes were coming around all right. Pa is the easiest man to fool ever I saw."

"Well, I should think he would kill you," said the grocery man. "Don't he ever catch on, and find out you have deceived him?"

"O, sometimes. But about nine times in ten I can get away with him. Say, don't you want to hire me for a clerk?"

The grocery man said that he had rather have a spotted hyena, and the boy stole a melon and went away.

CHAPTER XIV

"WHERE have you been for a week back?" asked the grocery man of the bad boy, as the boy pulled the tail board out of the delivery wagon accidentally and let a couple of bushels of potatoes roll out into the gutter. "I haven't seen you around here, and you look pale. You haven't been sick, have you?"

"No, I have not been sick. Pa locked me up in the bath room for two days and two nights, and didn't give me nothing to eat but bread and water. Since he has got religious he seems to be harder than ever on me. Say, do you think religion softens a man's heart, or does it give him a caked breast? I 'spect Pa will burn me at the stake next."

The grocery man said that when a man had truly been converted his heart was softened, and he was always looking for a chance to do good and be kind to the poor, but if he only had this galvanized religion, this roll plate piety, or whitewashed reformation, he was liable to be a harder citizen than before. "What made your Pa lock you up in the bathroom on bread and water?" he asked.

"Well, says the boy, as he eat a couple of salt pickles out of a jar on the sidewalk, "Pa is not converted enough to hurt him, and I knowed it, and I thought it would be a good joke to try him and see if he was so confounded good, so I got my chum to dress up in a suit of his sister's summer

71

clothes. Well, you wouldn't believe my chum would look
so much like a girl. He would fool the oldest inhabitant,
You know how fat he is. He had to sell his bicycle to a slim
fellow that clerks in a store, cause he didn't want it any more.
His neck is just as fat and there are dimples in it, and with a
dress low in the neck, and long at the trail he looks as tall as
my Ma. He busted one of his sisters slipper's getting them
on, and her stockings were a good deal too big for him, but
he tucked his drawers down in them and tied a suspender
around his leg above the knee, and they stayed on all right.
Well, he looked killin', I should prevaricate, with his sister's
muslin dress on, starched as stiff as a shirt, and her recep-
tion hat with a white feather as big as a Newfoundland dog's
tail. Pa said he had to go down town to see some of the
old soldiers of his regiment, and I loafed along behind. My
chum met Pa on the corner and asked him where the Lake
Shore Park was. 'She' said she was a stranger from
Chicago, that her husband had deserted her and she didn't
know but she would jump into the lake. Pa looked into
my chum's eye and sized her up, and said it would be
a shame to commit suicide, and asked if she didn't want
to take a walk. My chum said he should titter, and he
took Pa's arm and they walked up to the lake and back.
Well, you may talk about joining the church on probation all you please, but they get their arm around a girl all
the same. Pa hugged my chum till he says he thought Pa
would break his sister's corset all to pieces, and he squeezed
my chum's hand till the ring cut right into his finger and he
has to wear a piece of court plaster on it. They started for
the Court House park, as I told my chum to do, and I went
and got Ma. It was about time for the soldiers to go to
the exposition for the evening bizness, and I told Ma we
could go down and see them go by. Ma just throwed a
shawl over her head and we started down through the park.
When we got near Pa and my chum I told Ma it was a
shame for so many people to be sitting around lally-gagging
right before folks, and she said it was disgustin', and then

I pointed to my chum who had his head on Pa's bosom, and Pa was patting my chum on the cheek, while he held his other arm around his waist. They was on the iron seat, and

we came right up be-
hind them and when
Ma saw Pa's bald
head I thought she
would bust. She knew
his head as quick as
she sot eyes on it. My
chum asked Pa if he
was married, and he
said he was a wid-
ower. He said his
wife died fourteen
years ago, of liver
complaint. Well, Ma
shook like a leaf, and
I could hear her new
teeth rattle just like
chewing strawberries
with sand in them.
Then my chum put his
arms around Pa's neck
and said, 'If you love
me kiss me in the
mouth.' Pa was just
leaning down to kiss
my chum when Ma
couldn't stand it any
longer, and she went

"MA COULDN'T STAND IT ANY LONGER."

right around in front of them, and she grabbed my chum
by the hair and it all came off, hat and all, and my chum
jumped up and Ma scratched him in the face, and my
chum tried to get his hand in his pants pockets to get his
handkerchief to wipe off the blood on his nose, and Ma she
turned to Pa and he turned pale, and then she was going

for my chum again when he said, 'O let up on a feller,' and
he see she was mad and he grabbed the hat and hair off the
gravel walk and took the skirt of his sister's dress in his hand
and lifted out for home on a gallop, and Ma took Pa by the
elbow and said, 'You are a nice old party ain't you? I am
dead, am I? Died of liver complaint fourteen years ago,
did I? You will find an animated corpse on your hands.
Around kissing spry women out in the night, sir.' When
they started home Pa seemed to be as weak as a cat, and
couldn't say a word, and I asked him if I could go to the
exposition, and they said I could. I don't know what happened after they got home, but Pa was setting up for me
when I got back and he wanted to know what I brought
Ma down there for, and how I knew he was there.

"I thought it would help Pa out of the scrape and so I told
him it was not a girl he was hugging at all, but it was my
chum, and he laughed at first, and told Ma it was not a girl
but Ma said she knew a darn sight better. She guessed she
could tell a girl.

"Then Pa was mad and he said I was at the bottom of the
whole bizness, and he locked me up, and said I was enough
to paralyze a saint. I told him through the key-hole that a
saint that had any sense ought to tell a boy from a girl, and
then he throwed a chair at me through the transom. The
worst of the whole thing is my chum is mad at me cause
Ma scratched him, and he says that lets him out. He don't
go into any more schemes with me. Well, I must be going.
Pa is going to have my measure taken for a raw hide, he
says, and I have got to stay at home from the sparring match
and learn my Sunday school lesson."

CHAPTER XV

The old man in military splendor—Tells how he mowed down the
rebels—"I and Grant"—What is a sutler?—Ten dollars for pickles!
—"Let us hang him!"—The old man on a run—He stands up to
supper—The bad boy is to die at sunset.

"I saw your Pa wearing a red, white, and blue badge,
and a round red badge, and several other badges, last week,
during the re-union," said the grocery man to the bad boy,
as the youth asked for a piece of codfish skin to settle coffee
with. "He looked like a hero, with his old black hat, with
a gold cord around it."

"Yes, he wore all the badges he could get, the first day,
but after he blundered into a place where there were a lot of
fellows from his own regiment, he took off the badges, and
he wasn't very numerous around the boys the rest of the
week. But he was lightning on the sham battle," says the
boy.

"What was the matter? Didn't the soldiers treat him
well? Didn't they seem to yearn for his society?" asked
the grocery man, as the boy was making a lunch on some
sweet crackers in a tin canister.

"Well, they were not very much mashed on Pa. You
see, Pa never gets tired telling us about how he fit in the
army. For several years I didn't know what a sutler was,
and when Pa would tell about taking a musket that a dead
soldier had dropped, and going into the thickest of the fight,
and fairly mowing down the rebels in swaths, the way they
cut hay, I thought he was the greatest man that ever was.
Until I was eleven years old I thought Pa killed men enough
to fill the Forest Home cemetery. I thought a sutler was
something higher than a general, and Pa used to talk about

'I and Grant,' and what Sheridan told him, and how Sherman marched with him to the sea, and all that kind of rot, until I wondered why they didn't have pictures of Pa on a white horse, with epaulets on, and a sword. One day at school I told a boy that my Pa killed more men than Grant, and the boy said he didn't doubt it, but he killed them with commissary whisky. The boy said his Pa was in the same regiment that my Pa was a sutler of, and his Pa said my Pa charged him five dollars for a canteen of pepper sauce and alcohol and called it whisky. Then I began to inquire into it, and found out that a sutler was a sort of liquid peanut stand, and that his rank in the army was about the same as a chestnut roaster on the sidewalk here at home. It made me sick, and I never

THE SOLDIER STARTED AFTER PA WITH SABER DRAWN.

had the same respect for Pa after that. But Pa don't care. He thinks he is a hero, and tried to get a pension on account of losing a piece of his thumb, but when the officers found he was wounded by the explosion of a can of baked beans they couldn't give it to him. Pa was down town when the veterans were here, and I was with him, and I saw a lot of old soldiers looking at Pa, and I told him they acted as though they knew him, and he put on his glasses, and said to one of them, 'How are you Bill?' The soldier looked at Pa and called the other soldiers, and one said, 'That's the old duffer that sold me the bottle of brandy peaches at Chickamauga for three dollars, and they eat a hole through my stummick.' Another said, 'He's the cuss that took ten dollars out of my pay for pickles that were put up in *aqua fortis*. Look at the corps badges he has on.' Another said, 'The old whelp! He charged me fifty cents a pound for onions when I had the scurvy at Atlanta.' Another said, 'He beat me out of my wages playing draw poker with a cold deck, and the aces up his sleeve. Let us hang him.' By this time Pa's nerves got unstrung and began to hurt him, and he said he wanted to go home, and when we got around the corner he tore off his badges and threw them in the sewer, and said it was all a man's life was worth to be a veteran nowadays. He didn't go down town again till next day, and when he heard a band playing he would go around a block. But at the sham battle where there were no veterans hardly, he was all right with the militia boys, and told them how he did when he was in the army. I thought it would be fun to see Pa run, and so when one of the cavalry fellows lost his cap in the charge, and was looking for it, I told the dragoon that the pussy old man over by the fence had stolen his cap. That was Pa. Then I told Pa that the soldier on the horse said he was a rebel, and he was going to kill him. The soldier started after Pa with his sabre drawn, and Pa started to run, and it was funny, you bet. The soldier galloped his horse, and yelled, and Pa put in his best licks, and run up to the track to where there was a board off the fence, and tried to get through, but he got stuck, and the soldier put the point of his sabre on Pa's pants and pushed, and Pa got through the fence and I guess he ran all the way home. At supper time Pa would not come to the table, but stood up and ate off the sideboard, and Ma said Pa's shirt was all bloody, and Pa said mor'n fifty of them cavalry men charged on him, and he held them at bay as long as he could, and then retired in good order. This morning a boy told him that I set the cavalry men onto him, and he made me wear two mouse straps on my ears all the forenoon, and he says he will kill me at sunset. I ain't going to be there at sunset, and don't you remember about it. Well, good bye. I have got to go down to the morgue and see them bring in the man that was found on the lake shore, and see if the morgue keeper is drunk this time."

CHAPTER XVI

THE BAD BOY IN LOVE

Are you a Christian?—No getting to Heaven on small potatoes!—The
bad boy has to chew cobs—Ma says its good for a boy to be in
love—Love weakens the bad boy—How much does it cost to get
married?—Mad dog!—Never eat ice cream.

"ARE you a Christian?" asked the bad boy of the grocery
man, as that gentleman was placing vegetables out in front
of the grocery one morning.

"Well, I hope so," answered the grocery man, "I try to
do what is right, and hope to wear the golden crown when
the time comes to close my books."

"Then how is it that you put out a box of great big sweet
potatoes, and when we order some, and they come to the
table, they are little bits of things, not bigger than a radish?
Do you expect to get to heaven on such small potatoes, when
you use big ones for a sign?" asked the boy, as he took out
a silk handkerchief and brushed a speck of dust off his nicely
blacked shoes.

The grocery man blushed and said he did not mean to
take any such advantage of his customers. He said it must
have been a mistake of the boy that delivers groceries.

"Then you must hire the boy to make mistakes, for it has
been so every time we have had sweet potatoes for five
years," said the boy. "And about green corn. You have
a few ears stripped down to show how nice and plump it is,
and if we order a dozen ears there are only two that have
got any corn on at all, and Pa and Ma gets them, and the
rest of us have to chew cobs. Do you hope to wear a crown
of glory on that kind of corn?"

"O, such things will happen," said the grocery man with
a laugh. "But don't let's talk about heaven. Let's talk

about the other place. How's things over to your house? And say, what's the matter with you? You are all dressed up, and have got a clean shirt on, and your shoes blacked, and I notice your pants are not raveled out so at the bottoms of the legs behind. You are not in love are you?"

"Well, I should smile," said the boy, as he looked in a small mirror on the counter, covered with fly specks. "A girl got mashed on me, and Ma says it is good for a boy who hasn't got no sister, to be in love with a girl, and so I kind of tumbled to myself and she don't go nowhere without I go with her. I take her to dancing school, and everywhere, and she loves me like a house afire. Say, was you ever in love? Makes a fellow feel queer, don't it? Well sir, the first time I went home with her I put my arm around her, and honest it scared me. It was just like when you take hold of the handles of an electric battery, and you can't let go till the man turns the knob. Honest, I was just as weak as a cat. I thought she had needles in her belt and was going to take my arm away, but it was just like it was glued on. I asked her if she felt that way too, she said she used to, but it was nothing when you got used to it. That made me mad. But she is older than me and knows more about it. When I was going to leave her at the gate, she kissed me, and that was worse than putting my arm around her. By gosh, I trembled all over, just like I had chills, but I was as warm as toast. She wouldn't let go for as much as a minute, and I was tired as though I had been carrying coal up stairs. I didn't want to go home at all, but she said it would be the best way for me to go home, and come again the next day, and the next morning I went to her house before any of them were up, and her Pa came out to let the cat in, and I asked him what time his girl got up, and he laffed at me and said that I had got it bad and that I better go home and not be picked till I got ripe. Say, how much does it cost to get married?"

"Well, I should say you had got it bad," said the grocery man, as he set out a basket of beets. "Your getting in love will be a great thing for your Pa. You won't have any time to play any more jokes on him."

"O, I guess we can find time to keep Pa from being lonesome. Have you seen him this morning? You ought to have seen him last night. You see, my chum's Pa has got a setter dog stuffed. It is one that died two years ago and he thought a great deal of it, and he had it stuffed for an ornament. Well, my chum and me took the dog and put it on our front steps, and took some cotton and fastened it to the dog's mouth so it looked just like froth, and we got behind the door and waited for Pa to come home from the theater. When Pa started to come up the steps I growled and Pa looked at the dog and said, 'Mad dog, by crimis,' and he started down the sidewalk, and my chum barked just like a dog, and I 'Ki-yi'd' and growled like a dog that gets licked,

PA WANTED HER TO SIT IN HIS LAP.

and you ought to see Pa run. He went around in the alley and was going to get in the basement window, and my chum had a revolver with some blank cartridges, and he went down in the basement and when Pa was trying to open the window my chum began to fire towards Pa. Pa hollered that it was only him, and not a burglar, but after my chum fired four shots Pa run and climbed over the fence, and then we took the dog home and I stayed with my chum all night, and this morning Ma said Pa didn't get home till four o'clock and then a policeman came with him, and Pa talked about mad dogs and being taken for a burglar and nearly killed, and she said she was afraid Pa had took to drinking again, and she asked me if I heard any firing of guns, and I said no, and then she put a wet towel on Pa's head."

"You ought to be ashamed," said the grocery man. "How does your Pa like your being in love with the girl? Does he seem to encourage you in it?"

"Oh Yes, she was up to our house to borrow some tea, and Pa patted her on the cheek and hugged her and said she was a dear little daisy, and wanted her to sit in his lap, but when I wanted him to let me have fifty cents to buy her some ice cream he said that was all nonsense. He said: 'Look ot your Ma. Eating ice cream when she was a girl was what injured her health for life." I asked Ma about it, and she said Pa never laid out ten cents for ice cream or any luxury for her in all the five years he was sparking her. She says he took her to a circus once but he got free tickets for carrying water for the elephant. She says Pa was tighter than the bark to a tree. I tell you it's going to be different with me. If there is anything that girl wants she is going to have it if I have to sell Ma's copper boiler to get the money. What is the use of having wealth if you hoard it up and don't enjoy it? This family will be run on different principles after this, you bet. Say, how much are those yellow wooden pocket combs in the show case? I've a good notion to buy them for her. How would one of them round mirrors, with a zinc cover, do for a present for a girl? There's nothing too good for her."

CHAPTER XVII

HIS PA FIGHTS HORNETS

The Old Man looks bad—The woods of Wauwatosa—The Old Man takes a nap—"Helen damnation"—"Hell is out for noon"—The liver medicine—Its wonderful effects—The bad boy is drunk! Give me a lemon!—A sight of the comet!—The hired girl's religion.

"Go away from here now," said the grocery man to the bad boy, as he came into the store and was going to draw some cider out of a barrel into a pint measure that had flies in it. "Get right out of this place, and don't let me see you around here until the health officer says your Pa has got over the small-pox. I saw him this morning and his face is all covered with postules, and they will have him in the pest house before night. You git," and he picked up a butter tryer and went for the boy, who took refuge behind a barrel of onions, and held up his hands as though Jesse James had drawn a bead on him.

"O, you go and chase yourself. That is not small-pox Pa has got. He had a fight with a nest of hornets," said the boy.

"Hornets! Well, I'll be cussed," remarked the grocery man, as he put up the butter tryer, and handed the boy a slice of rotten muskmelon. "How in the world did he get into a nest of hornets? I hope you did not have anything to do with it."

The boy buried his face in the melon, until he looked as though a yellow gash had been cut from his mouth to his ears, and after swallowing the melon, he said, "Well, Pa says I was responsible, and he says that settles it, and I can go my way and he will go his. He said he was willing to overlook everything I had done to make his life unbearable, but steering him into a nest of hornets, and then getting drunk, was too much, and I can go."

"What, you haven't been drunk," says the grocery man. "Great heavens, that will kill your poor old father."

"O, I guess it won't kill him very much. He has been getting drunk for twenty years, and he says he is healthier to-day than he ever was, since his liver got to working again. You see, Monday was a regular Indian summer day, and Pa said he would take me and my chum out in the woods to gather hickory nuts, if we would be good. I said I would and my chum said he would, and we got a couple of bags and went away out to Wauwatosa, in the woods. We clubbed the trees and got more nuts than anybody, and had a lunch, and Pa was just enjoying his religion first rate. While Pa was taking a nap under a tree, my chum and me looked around and found a hornets' nest on the lower limb of the tree we were sitting under, and my chum said it would be a good joke to get a pole and run it into the hornet's nest and then run. Honest, I didn't think about Pa being under the tree, and I went into the field and got a hop pole, and put the small end of it into the nest, and gouged the nest a couple of times, and when the boss hornet came out of the hole, and looked sassy, and then looked back in the hole and whistled to the other hornets to come out and have a circus and they began to come out, my chum and me run and climbed over a fence, and got behind a pile of hop poles that was stacked up. I guess the hornets saw my Pa just as quick as they got out of the nest, cause pretty soon we heard Pa call to 'Helen Damnation,' or some woman we didn't know, and then he took his coat, that he had been using for a pillow, and whipped around, and he slapped hisself on the shoulders, and then he picked up the lunch basket and pounded around like he was crazy, and bime-by he started on a run toward town, holding his pants up, cause his suspenders was hanging down on his hips, and I never see a man run so, and fan himself with a basket. We could hear him yell, 'Come on boys. Hell is out for noon' and he went over a hill, and we didn't see him any more. We waited till near dark because we was afraid to go after the bags of nuts till the hornets had gone to bed, and then we came home. The bags were awful heavy, and I think it was real mean in Pa to go off and leave us, and not help carry the bags."

THAT IS NOT THE SMALL POX HE HAS GOT.

"I swan," says the grocery man, "You are too mean to live. But what about your getting drunk?"

"O, I was going to tell you. Pa had a bottle of liver medicine in his coat pocket, and when he was whipping his hornets the bottle dropped out, and I picked it up to carry it home to him. My chum wanted to smell of the liver medi-

cine, so he took out the cork and it smelled just like in front
of a liquor store on East Water street, and my chum said his
liver was bad, too, and he took a swaller, and he said he
should think it was enough to cut a feller's liver up in slices,
but it was good, and then I had a peculiar feeling in my
liver, and my chum said his liver felt better after he took
a swaller, and so I took a swaller, and it was the offulest
liver remedy I ever tasted. It scorched my throat just like
the diphtheria, but it beats the diphtheria, or sore throat,
all to pieces, and my chum and me laughed we was so tickled. Did you ever take liver medicine? You know how it
makes you feel as if your liver had got on top of your lights,
and like you wanted to jump and holler. Well, sir, honest
that liver medicine made me dance a jig on the viaduct
bridge, and an old soldier from the soldier's home came
along and asked us what was the matter, and we told him
about our livers, and the liver medicine, and showed him the
bottle, and he said he sposed he had the worst liver in the
world, and said the doctors at the home couldn't cure him.
It's a mean boy that won't help an old veteran cure his liver,
so I told him to try Pa's liver remedy and he took a regular
cow swaller, and said, 'Here's to your livers, boys.' He
must have a liver bigger nor a cow's, and I guess it is better
now."

"Then my liver begun to feel curious again, and my chum
said his liver, was getting torpid some more, and we both
of us took another dose, and started home and we got generous, and gave our nuts all away to some boys. Say, does
liver medicine make a feller give away all he has got?
We kept taking medicine every five blocks, and we locked
arms and went down a back street and sung 'O it is a
glorious thing to be a pirut king,' and when we got home
my head felt bigger nor a washtub and I thought p'raps
my liver had gone to my head, and Pa came to the door
with his face tied up in towels, and some yellow stuff on
the towels that smelled like anarchy, and I slapped him
on the shoulder and shouted, 'Hello, Gov., how's your

liver?' and gave him the bottle, and it was empty, and he asked me if we had been drinking that medicine and he said he was ruined, and I told him he could get some more down to the saloon, and he took hold of my collar and I lammed him in the ear, and he bounced me up stairs, and then I turned pale, and had cramps, and I didn't remember any more till I woke up and the doctor was with me, and Pa and Ma looked scared, and the doc. had a tin thing like you

HERE'S TO YOUR LIVER. BOYS.

draw water out of a country cistern, only smaller, and Ma said if it hadn't been for the stomach pump she wouldn't have had any little boy, and I looked at the knobs on Pa's face and I laffed and asked Pa if he got into the hornets, too. Then the doc. laffed, and Ma cried, and Pa swore, and I groaned, and got sick again, and then they let me go to sleep again, and this morning I had the offulest headache, and Pa's face looks like he had fallen on a picket fence. When I got out I went to my chum's house to see if they had got him pumped out, and his Ma drove me out with a broom, and she says I will ruin every boy in the neighborhood. Pa says I was drunk and kicked him in the groin when he fired me up stairs, and I asked him how I could be drunk just taking medicine for my liver, and he said 'Go to the devil,' and I came over here. Say, give me a lemon to settle my stomach."

"But, look-a-here," says the grocery man, as he gave the boy a little dried up lemon, about as big as a prune, and told him he was a terror, "what is the matter with your eye winkers and your hair? They seem to be burned off."

"O, thunder, didn't Pa tell you about the comet exploding and burning us all? That was the worst thing since the flood, when Noar run the excursion boat from Kalamazoo to Mount Ararat. You see we had been reading about the comet, which is visible at four o'clock in the morning, and I heard Pa tell the hired girl to wake him and Ma up when she got up to set the pancakes and go to early mass so they could see the comet. The hired girl is a Cathlick, and she don't make no fuss about it, but she has got more good, square religion than a dozen like Pa. It makes a good deal of difference how religion affects different people, don't it? Now Pa's religion makes him wild, and he wants to kick my pants and pull my hair, but the hired girl's religion makes her want to hug me, if I am abused; and she puts anarchy on my bruises, and gives me pie. Pa wouldn't get up at four o'clock in the morning to go to early mass, unless he could take a fish pole along and some angle worms. The hired girl prays when nobody sees her but God, but Pa wants to get a church full of sisterin', and pray loud, as though he was an auctioneer selling tin razors. Say, it beats all what a difference liver medicine has on two people, too. Now that hickory nut day, when me and my chum got full of Pa's liver medicine, I felt so good natured I gave my hickory nuts away to the children, and wanted to give my coat and pants to a poor tramp, but my chum, who ain't no bigger'n me, got on his ear and wanted to kick the socks off a little girl who was going home from school. It's queer, ain't it? Well, about the comet. When I heard Pa tell the hired girl to wake him and Ma up, I told her to wake me up about half an hour before she waked Pa up, and then I got my chum to stay with me, and we made a comet to play on Pa. You see my room is right over Pa's room, and

I got two lengths of stove pipe and covered them all over with phosphorus, so they looked just as bright as a comet. Then we got two Roman candles and a big sky rocket, and we were going to touch off the Roman candles and the sky rocket just as Pa and Ma got to looking at the comet. I didn't know that a sky rocket would kick back, did you?

Well, you'd a dide to see that comet. We tied a piece of white rubber garden hose to the stove pipe for a tail and went to bed, and when the girl woke us up we laid for Pa and Ma. Pretty soon we heard Pa's window open, and I looked out, and Pa and Ma had their heads and half their bodies out of the window. They had their night shirts on and looked just like the picture of Millerites waiting for the world to come to an end. Pa looked up and seed the stove pipe and he said:

" 'Hanner, for God's sake look up there. That is the damest comet I ever see. It is as bright as day. See the tail of it. Now that is worth getting up to see.'

"Just then my chum lit the two Roman candles and I touched off the rocket, and that's where my eye winkers went. The rocket busted and the joints of the stove pipe and they fell down on Pa, but Ma got her head inside before the comet struck, and wasn't hurt, but one length of the stove pipe struck Pa endways on the neck and almost cut a biscuit out of him, and the fire and sparks just poured down in his hair, and burned his night shirt. Pa was scart. He thought the world was coming to an end, and the window came down on his back and he began to sing, 'Earth's but a desert drear, Heaven is my home.' I see he was caught in the window, and I went down stairs to put out the fire on his night shirt and put up the window to let him in, and he said: 'My boy, your Ma and I are going to Heaven, but I fear you will go to the bad place.' and I told him I would take my chances, and he better put on his pants if he was going anywhere where there would be liable to be ladies present and when he got his head in Ma told him the world was not coming to an end, but somebody had been setting off fireworks, and she said she guessed it was their dear little boy, and when I saw Pa feeling under the bed for a bed slat I got upstairs pretty previous now, and don't you forget it, and Ma put cold cream on where the sparks burn't Pa's shirt, and Pa said another day wouldn't pass over his head before he had me in the Reform School.

Well, if I go to the Reform School somebody's got to pay attention, you can bet your liver. A boy can't have any fun these days without everybody thinks he is an heathen. What hurt did it do to play comet? It's a mean father that won't stand a little scorching in the interest of science."

The boy went out, scratching the place where his eye winkers were, and then the grocery man knew what it was that caused the fire engines to be out around at four o'clock in the morning looking for a fire.

CHAPTER XVIII

HIS PA GOES HUNTING

Mutilated jaw—The old man has taken to swearing again—Out west duck shooting—His coat-tail shot off—Shoots at a wild goose—The gun kicks!—Throws a chair at his son—The astonished she Deacon.

"WHAT has your Pa got his jaw tied up for, and what makes his right eye so black and blue?" asked the grocery man of the bad boy, as the boy came to bring some butter back that was strong enough to work on the street. "You haven't hurt your poor old Pa, have you?"

"O, his jaw is all right now. You ought to have seen him when the gun was engaged in kicking him," says the boy as he set the butter plate on the cheese box.

"Well, tell us about it. What had the gun against your Pa? I guess it was the son-of-a-gun that kicked him," said the grocery man, as he winked at a servant girl who came in with her apron over her head, after two cents worth of yeast.

"I'll tell you, if you will keep watch down street for Pa. He says he is damned if he will stand this foolishness any longer."

"What, does your father swear, while he is on probation?"

"Swear! Well, I should cackle. You ought to have heard him when he come to, and spit out the loose teeth. You see, since Pa quit drinking he is a little nervous, and the doctor said he ought to go out somewhere and get bizness off his mind, and hunt ducks, and row a boat, and get strength, and Pa said shooting ducks was just in his hand, and for me to go and borrow a gun, and I could go along and carry game. So I got a gun at the gun store, and some cartridges, and we went away out west on the cars, more

94

than fifty miles, and stayed two days. You ought to seen
Pa. He was just like a boy that was sick, and couldn't go to
school. When we got out by the lake he jumped up and
cracked his heels together, and yelled. I thought he was
crazy, but he was only cunning. First I scared him nearly to
death by firing off the gun behind him, as we were going
along the bank, and blowing off a piece of his coat-tail. I

THE GUN FLEW OUT OF HIS HANDS.

knew it wouldn't hurt him, but he turned pale and told me
to lay down that gun, and he picked it up and carried it the
rest of the way, and I was offul glad cause it was a heavy
gun. His coat-tail smelled like when you burn a rag to
make the air in the room stop smelling so, all the forenoon.
You know Pa is a little near sighted but he don't believe it,
so I got some of the wooden decoy ducks that the hunters
use, and put them in the lake, and you ought to see Pa get

down on his belly and crawl through the grass, to get up
close to them. He shot twenty times at the wooden ducks,
and wanted me to go in and fetch them out, but I told him
I was no retriever dog. Then Pa was mad, and said all he
brought me along for was to carry game, and I had come
near shooting his hind leg off, and now I wouldn't carry
ducks. While he was coaxing me to go in the cold water
without my pants on, I heard some wild geese squawking,
and then Pa heard them, and he was excited. He said 'You
lay down behind the muskrat house, and I will get a goose.'
I told him he couldn't kill a goose with that fine shot, and I
gave him a large cartridge the gun store man loaded for me,
with a handful of powder in, and I told Pa it was a goose
cartridge, and Pa put it in the gun. The geese came along,
about a mile high, squawking, and Pa aimed at a dark cloud
and fired. Well, I was offul scared, I thought I had killed
him. The gun just rared up and come down on his jaw,
shoulder and everywhere, and he went over a log and struck
on his shoulder, the gun flew out of his hands, and Pa he
laid there on his neck, with his feet over the log, and that
was the first time he didn't scold me since he got religion.
I felt offul sorry, and got some dirty water in my hat and
poured it down his neck, and laid him out, and pretty soon
he opened his eyes and asked if any of the passengers got
ashore alive. Then his eye swelled out so it looked like a
blue door-knob, and Pa felt of his jaw, and asked if the engineer and fireman jumped off, or if they went down with
the engine. He seemed dazed, and then he saw the gun,
and he said 'Take the dam thing away, it is going to kick me
again.' Then he got his senses and wanted to know if he
killed a goose, and I told him no, but he nearly broke one's
jaw, and then he said the gun kicked him when it went off,
and he laid down and the gun kept kicking him more than
twenty times, when he was trying to sleep. He went back
to the tavern where we were stopping and wouldn't touch
the gun, but made me lug it. He told the tavern keeper
that he fell over a wire fence, but I think he began to sus-

pect, after he spit the loose teeth out, that the gun was loaded for bear. I suppose he will kill me some day. Don't you think he will?"

"Any coroner's jury would let him off and call it justifiable, if he should kill you. You must be a lunatic. Has your Pa talked much about it since you got back?" asked the grocery man.

"Not much. You see he can't talk much without breaking his jaw. But he was able to throw a chair at me. You see I thought I would joke him a little, cause when anybody feels bad a joke kind of livens em up, so we were talking about Pa's liver and Ma said he seemed to be better since his liver had become more active, and I said, 'Pa, when you was a rolling over with the gun chasing you, and kicking you every round, your liver was active enough, cause it was on top half the time.' Then Pa throwed the chair at me. He says he believes I knew that cartridge was loaded. But you ought to seen the fun when an old she deacon of Pa's church called to collect some money to send to the heathens. Ma wasn't in, so Pa went to the parlor to stand her off, and when she see that Pa's face was tied up, and his eye was black, and his jaw cracked, she held up both hands and said, 'O, my dear brother you have been drunk again. You have backslid. You will have to go back and commence your probation all over again,' and Pa said, 'Damfido,' and the old she deacon screamed and went off without getting enough money to buy a deck of round cornered cards for the heathen. Say, what does 'damfido,' mean? Pa has some of the queerest expressions since he joined the church."

CHAPTER XIX

HIS PA IS "NISHIATED"

Are you a Mason?—No Harm to Play at Lodge—Why Goats are Kept in Stables—The bad boy Gets the Goat up Stairs—The Grand Bumper Degree—Kyan Pepper on the Goat's Beard—"Bring Forth the Royal Bumper"—The Goat on the Rampage.

"SAY, are you a Mason, or a nodfellow, or anything?" asked the bad boy of the grocery man, as he went to the cinnamon bag on the shelf and took out a long stick of cinnamon bark to chew.

"Why, yes, of course I am, but what set you to thinking of that?" asked the grocery man, as he went to the desk and charged the boy's father with half a pound of cinnamon.

"Well, do the goats bunt when you nishiate a fresh candidate?"

"No, of course not. The goats are cheap ones, that have no life, and we muzzle them, and put pillows over their heads, so they can't hurt anybody," says the grocery man, as he winked at a brother Odd Fellow who was seated on a sugar barrel, looking mysterious, "But why do you ask?"

"O, nothin, only I wish me and my chum had muzzled our goat with a pillow. Pa would have enjoyed his becoming a member of our lodge better. You see, Pa had been telling us how much good the Masons and Odd Fellows did, and said we ought to try and grow up good so we could jine the lodges when we got big, and I asked Pa if it would do any hurt for us to have a play lodge in my room, and purtend to nishiate, and Pa said it wouldn't do any hurt. He said it would improve our minds and learn us to be men. So my chum and me borried a goat that lives in a livery stable. Say, did you know they keep a goat in a livery stable so the horses won't get sick? They get used to the smell of the

98

goat, and after that nothing can make them sick but a glue factory. I wish my girl boarded in a livery stable, then she would get used to the smell. I went home with her from church Sunday night, and the smell of the goat on my clothes made her sick to her stummick, and she acted just like an excursion on the lake, and said if I didn't go and

bury myself and take the smell out of me she wouldn't never go with me again. She was just as pale as a ghost, and the prespiration on her lip was just zif she had been hit by a street sprinkler. You see my chum and me had to carry the goat up to my room when Pa and Ma was out riding, and he blatted so we had to tie a handkerchief around his nose, and his feet made such a noise on the floor that we put some baby's socks on his feet. Gosh, how frowy a goat smells,

don't it? I should think you Masons must have strong stum-
micks. Why don't you have a skunk or a mule for a trade
mark? Take a mule, and annoint it with limburg cheese and
you could nishiate and make a candidate smell just as bad
as with a gosh darn mildewed goat.

"Well, my chum and me practiced with that goat until
he could bunt the picture of a goat every time. We borried a buck beer sign from a saloon man and hung it on
the back of a chair, and the goat would hit it every time.
That night Pa wanted to know what we were doing up in my
room, and I told him we were playing lodge, and improving
our minds, and Pa said that was right, there was nothing that
did boys of our age half so much good as to imitate men,
and store by useful nollidge. Then my chum asked Pa if he
didn't want to come up and take the grand bumper degree,
and Pa laffed and said he didn't care if he did, just to encourage us boys in innocent pastime, that was so improving
to our intellex. We had shut the goat up in a closet in my
room, and he had got over blatting, so we took off the handkerchief, and he was eating some of my paper collars, and
skate straps. We went up stairs, and told Pa to come up
pretty soon and give three distinct raps, and when we asked
him who come there must say 'A pilgrim who wants to
join your ancient order and ride the goat.' Ma wanted to
come up too, but we told her if she come in it would break
up the lodge cause a woman couldn't keep a secret, and we
didn't have any side saddle for the goat. Say, if you never
tried it, the next time you nishiate a man in your Mason's
lodge you sprinkle a little kyan pepper on the goat's beard
just afore you turn him loose. You can get three times as
much fun to the square inch of goat. You wouldn't think it
was the same goat. Well, we got all fixed up and Pa rapped,
and we let him in and told him he must be blindfolded, and
he got on his knees a laffing and I tied a towel around his
eyes, and then I turned him around and made him get down
on his hands also, and then his back was right toward the
closet door, and I put the buck beer sign right against Pa's

clothes. He was laffing all the time, and said we boys were as full of fun as they made 'em and we told him it was a solemn occasion, and we wouldn't permit no levity, and if he didn't stop laffing we couldn't give him the grand bumper degree. Then everything was ready, and my chum had his hand on the closet door, and some kyan pepper in his other hand and I asked Pa in low bass tones if he felt as though he wanted to turn back, or if he had nerve enough to go ahead and take the degree. I warned him that it was full of dangers, as the goat was loaded for bear, and told him he yet had time to retrace his steps if he wanted to. He said he

THE GOAT WOULD HIT IT EVERY TIME.

wanted the whole buzness, and we could go ahead with the menagerie. Then I said to Pa that if he had decided to go ahead, and not blame us for the conquences, to repeat after me the following: 'Bring forth the Royal Bumper and let him Bump.'

"Pa repeated the words and my chum sprinkled the kyan pepper on the goat's mustache, and he sneezed once and looked sassy, and then he see the lager beer goat raring up, and he started for it, just like a cow catcher, and blatted. Pa is real fat, but he knew he got hit, and he grunted, and he said, 'Hell's-fire, what you boys doin'?' and then the goat gave him another degree, and Pa pulled off the towel and got up and started for the stairs, and so did the goat,

and Ma was at the bottom of the stairs listening, and when
I looked over the banisters Pa and Ma and the goat were all
in a heap, and Pa was yelling murder, and Ma was screaming fire, and the goat was blatting, and sneezing, and bunt-
ing, and the hired girl came into the hall and the goat took
after her and she crossed herself just as the goat struck her
and said, 'Howly mother protect me!' and went down stairs
the way we boys slide down hill, with both hands on herself,
and the goat rared up and blatted, and Pa and Ma went
into their room and shut the door, and then my chum and
me opened the front door and drove the goat out. The
minister, who comes to see Ma every three times a week,
was just ringing the bell, and the goat thought he wanted
to be nishiated too, and gave him one, for luck, and then
went down the sidewalk blatting, and sneezing, and the
minister came into the parlor and said he was stabbed,
and then Pa came out of his room with his suspenders hanging down, and he didn't know the minister was there, and
he said cuss words, and Ma cried and told Pa he would go
to hell sure, and Pa said he didn't care, he would kill that
kussid goat afore he went, and I told Pa the minister was
in the parlor, and he and Ma went down and said the
weather was propitious for a revival, and it seemed as
though an outpouring of the Spirit was about to be vouch-
safed to His people, and none of them sot down but Ma,
cause the goat didn't hit her, and while they were talking
religion, with their mouths, and kussin the goat inwardly,
my chum and me adjourned the lodge, and I went and stayed
with him all night, and I haven't been home since. But I
don't believe Pa will lick me, cause he said he would not hold
us responsible for the consequences. He ordered the goat
hisself, and we filled the order, don't you see? Well, I guess
I will go and sneak in the back way, and find out from the
hired girl how the land lays. She won't go back on me,
cause the goat was not loaded for hired girls. She just happened to get in at the wrong time. Good-bye, sir, Remember and give your goat kyan pepper in your lodge."

As the boy went away, and skipped over the back fence, the grocery man said to his brother Odd Fellow, "If that boy don't beat the devil then I never saw one that did. The old man ought to have him sent to a lunatic asylum."

CHAPTER XX

HIS GIRL GOES BACK ON HIM

The grocery man is afraid—But the bad boy is a wreck!—"My girl
has shook me!"—The bad boy's heart is broken—Still he enjoys a
bit of fun—Cod-liver oil on the pan-cakes—The hired girls made
victims—The bad boy vows vengeance on his girl and the telegraph messenger.

"Now you git right away from here," said the grocery
man to the bad boy, as he came in with a hungry look on
his face, and a wild light in his eye. "I am afraid of you.
I wouldn't be surprised to see you go off half cocked and
blow us all up. I think you are a devil. You may have a
billy goat, or a shot gun or a bottle of poison concealed
about you. Condemn you, the police ought to muzzle you.
You will kill somebody yet. Here, take a handful of prunes
and go off somewhere and enjoy yourself, and keep away
from here;" and the grocery man went on sorting potatoes,
and watching the haggard face of the boy. "What ails you
anyway?" he added, as the boy refused the prunes, and
seemed to be sick to the stomach.

"Oh, I am a wreck," said the boy, as he grated his teeth.
and looked wicked. "You see before you a shadow. I
have drank of the sweets of life, and now only the dregs
remain. I look back at the happiness of the past two weeks,
during which I have been permitted to gaze into the fond
blue eyes of my loved one, and carry her rubbers to school
for her to wear home when it rained, to hear the sweet
words that fell from her lips as she lovingly told me I
was a terror, and as I think it is all over, and that I shall
never again place my arm around her waist, I feel as if the
world had been kicked off its base and was whirling through

space, liable to be knocked into a cocked hat, and I don't care a darn. My girl has shook me."

"Sho! You don't say so," said the grocery man as he threw a rotten potato into a basket of good ones that were going to the orphan asylum. "Well, she showed sense. You would have blown her up, or broken her neck, or something. But don't feel bad. You will soon find another girl that will discount her, and you will forget this one."

"Never!" said the boy, as he nibbled at a piece of codfish that he had picked off. "I shall never allow my affections to become entwined about another piece of calico. It unmans me, sir. Henceforth I am a hater of the whole girl race. From this out I shall harbor revenge in my heart, and no girl can cross my path and live. I want to grow up to become a he school ma'am, or a he milliner, or something, where I can grind girls into the dust under the heel of a terrible despotism, and make them sue for mercy. To think that girl, on whom I have lavished my heart's best love and over thirty cents, in the past two weeks, could let the smell of a goat on my clothes come between us, and break off an acquaintance that seemed to be the forerunner of a happy future, and say, 'ta-ta' to me, and go off to dancing school with a telegraph messenger boy who wears a sleeping-car porter uniform, is too much, and my heart is broken. I will lay for that messenger some night, when he is delivering a message in our ward, and I will make him think lightning has struck the wire and run in on his bench. O, you don't know anything about the woe there is in this world. You never loved many people, did you?"

The grocery man admitted he never loved very hard, but he knew a little something about it from an aunt of his, who got mashed on a Chicago drummer. "But your father must be having a rest while your whole mind is occupied with your love affair," said he.

"Yes," said the boy, with a vacant look, "I take no interest in the pleasure of the chase any more, though I did have a little quiet fun this morning at the breakfast table. You see

I WILL LAY FOR THE MESSENGER BOY.

Pa is the contrariest man ever was. If I complain that anything at the table don't taste good, Pa says it is all right. This morning I took the syrup pitcher and emptied out the white syrup and put in some cod-liver oil that Ma is taking for her cough. I put some on my pancakes and pretended to taste it, and I told Pa the syrup was sour and not fit to eat. Pa was mad in a second, and he poured out some on his pancakes, and said I was getting too confounded particular. He said the syrup was good enough for him and he sopped his pancakes in it and fired some down his neck. He is a gaul d u r n e d hypocrite, that's what he is. I could by his face that the cod-liver oil was nearly killing him, but he said that syrup was all right, and if I didn't eat mine he would break my back, and by gosh, I had to eat it, and Pa said he guessed he hadn't got much appetite, and he would just drink a cup of coffee and eat a donut.

"I like to dide, and that is one thing, I think, that makes this disappointment in love harder to bear. But I felt sorry for Ma. Ma ain't got a very strong stummick, and when she got some of that cod-liver oil in her mouth she went right up stairs, sicker'n a horse, and Pa had to help her, and she had nooralgia all the morning. I eat pickles to take the taste out of my mouth, and then I laid for the hired girls. They eat too much syrup, anyway, and when they got on to that cod-liver oil, and swallowed a lot of it, one of them, a Irish girl, she got up from the table and put her hand on her corset, and said, 'Howly Jaysus,' and went out in the kitchen, as pale as Ma is when she has powder on her face, and the other girl who is Dutch, she swallowed a pancake and said, 'Mine Gott, vas de matter from me,' and she went out and leaned on the coal bin, then they talked Irish and Dutch, and got clubs, and started to look for me, and I

PA.

MA

"HOWLY—!"

"MEIN GOTT!"

thought I would come over here. The whole family is sick, but it not from love, like my illness, and they will get over it, while I shall fill an early grave, but not till I have made that girl and the telegraph messenger wish they were dead. Pa and I are going to Chicago next week, and I'll bet we'll have some fun. Pa says I need a change of air, and I think he is going to try and lose me. It's a cold day when I get left anywhere that I can't find my way back. Well, good-bye, old rotten potatoes."

CHAPTER XXI

HE AND HIS PA IN CHICAGO

Nothing like traveling to give tone—Laughing in the wrong place—
A diabolical plot—His Pa arrested as a kidnapper—The numbers
on the doors changed—The wrong room—"Nothin' the mazzer
with me, pet!"—The tell-tale hat.

"WHAT is this I hear about your Pa's being arrested in
Chicago?" said the grocery man to the bad boy, as he came
in with a can for kerosene and a jug for vinegar.

"Well, it was true, but the police let him go after they
hit him a few licks and took him to the station," said the
boy, as he got the vinegar into the kerosene can, and the
kerosene in the jug. "You see, Pa and me went down there
to stay over night, and have fun. Ma said she druther we
would be away than not when they were cleaning house,
and Pa thought it would do me good to travel, and sort of
get tone, and he thought maybe I'd be better, and not play
jokes, but I guess it is born in me. Do you know I actually
think of mean things to do when I am in the most solemn
places. They took me to a funeral once, and I got to
thinking what a stampede there would be if the corpse
would come to life and sit up in the coffin, and I snickered
right out, and Pa took me out doors and kicked my pants.
I don't think he orter kicked me for it, cause I didn't think
of it a purpose. Such things have occurred, and I have
read about them, and a poor boy ought to be allowed to
think, hadn't he?"

"Yes, but what about his being arrested? Never mind the
funeral," said the grocery man, as he took his knife and
picked some of the lead out of the weights on the scales.

"We went down on the cars, and Pa had a headache, because he had been out all night electioneering for the pro-

109

hibition ticket, and he was cross, and scolded me, and once
he pulled my ear 'cause I asked him if he knew the girl he
was winking at in a seat across the aisle.   I didn't enjoy myself much, and some men were talking about kidnapping
children, and it gave me an ijee, and just before I got to
Chicago I went after a drink of water at the other end of the
car, and I saw a man who looked as though he wouldn't
stand any fooling, and I whispered to him that the bald-
headed man I was sitting with was taking me away from my
home in Milwaukee, and I mistrusted he was going to make
a thief or a pickpocket of me.   I said 's-h-h-h,' and told him
not to say anything or the man would maul me.   Then I
went back to the seat and asked Pa to buy me a gold watch,
and he looked mad and cuffed me on the ear.   The man that
I whispered to got talking with some other men, and when
we got off the cars at Chicago a policeman came up to Pa
and took him by the neck and said, 'Mr. Kidnapper, I guess
we will run you in.'   Pa was mad and tried to jerk away, and
the cop choked him, and another cop came along and helped,
and the passengers crowded around and wanted to lynch Pa,
and Pa wanted to know what they meant, and they asked
him where he stole the kid, and he said I was his kid, and
asked me if I wasn't, and I looked scared, as though I was
afraid to say no, and I said 'Y-e-s S-e-r, I guess so.'   Then
the police said the poor boy was scart, and they would take
us both to the station, and they made Pa walk spry, and
when he held back they jerked him along.   He was offul
mad and said he would make somebody smart for this, and I
hoped it wouldn't be me.   At the station they charged Pa
with kidnapping a boy from Milwaukee, and he said it was
a lie, and I was his boy, and I said of course I was, and the
boss asked who told the cops Pa was a kidnapper, and they
said 'damfino,' and then the boss told Pa he could go, but
not to let it occur again, and Pa and me went away.   I looked
so sorry for Pa that he never tumbled to me, that I was to
blame.   We walked around town all day, and went to the
stores, and at night Pa was offul tired, and he put me to bed

in the tavern and he went out to walk around and get rested.
I was not tired, and I walked all around the hotel. I thought
Pa had gone to a theater, and that made me mad, and I
thought I would play a joke on him. Our room was 210 and
the next was 212, and an old maid with a Scotch terrier
occupied 212. I saw her twice and she called me names,
cause she thought I wanted to steal her dog. That made me
mad at her, and so I took my jack **knife** and drew the tacks

WHEN PA HELD BACK, THEY JERKED HIM ALONG.

out of the tin thing that the numbers were painted on, and
put the old maid's number on our door and our number on
her door, and then I went to bed. I tried to keep awake so
as to help Pa if he had any difficulty, but I guess I got asleep,
but woke up when the dog barked. If the dog had not woke
me up, the woman's scream would, and if that hadn't, Pa
would. You see, Pa came home from the theatre about
'leven, and he had been drinking. He says everybody drinks
when they go to Chicago, even the minister. Pa looked at
the numbers on the doors all along the hall till he found 210
and walked right in and pulled off his coat and threw it on

the lounge where the dog was. The old maid was asleep, but the dog barked, and Pa said, 'That cussed boy has bought a dog,' and he kicked the dog, and then the old maid said, 'What is the matter, pet?'

"Pa laffed and said, 'Nothin' the mazzer with *me,* pet,' and then you ought to have heard the yelling. The old maid covered her head and kicked and yelled, and the dog snarled and bit Pa on the pants, and Pa had his vest off and his suspenders unbuttoned, and he got scared and took his coat and vest and went out in the hall, and I opened our door and told Pa he was in the wrong room, and he said he guessed he knowed it, and he came in our room and I locked the door, and then the bell boy, and the porter, and the clerk came up to see what ailed the old maid, and she said a burglar got in the room, and they found Pa's hat on the lounge, and they took it and told her to be quiet and they would find the burglar. Pa was so scared that he sweat like everything, and the bed was offul warm, and he pretended to go to sleep, but he was wondering how he could get his hat back. In the morning I told him it would be hard work to explain it to Ma how he happened to get into the wrong room, and he said it wasn't necessary to say anything about it to Ma.

"Then he gave me five dollars to go out and buy him a new hat, and he said I might keep the change if I would not mention it when I got home, and I got him one for ten shillings, and we took the eight o'clock train in the morning and came home, and I 'spose the Chicago detectives are trying to fit Pa's hat onto a burglar. Pa seemed offully relieved when we got across the state line into Wisconsin. But you'd a dide to see him come out of that old lady's room with his coat and vest on his arm, and his suspenders hanging down, looking scart. He dassent lick me any more or I'll tell Ma where Pa left his hat."

CHAPTER XXII

HIS PA IS DISCOURAGED

"I ain't no Joner!"—The story of the Ancient Prophet—The Sunday School Folks go back on the bad boy—Caged Cats—A Committee Meeting—A remarkable Cat-astrophe!—"That boy beats Hell!"—Basting the bad boy—The Hot-water-in-the-sponge trick.

"Say, you leave here mighty quick," said the grocery man to the bad boy, as he came in, with his arm in a sling, and backed up against the stove to get warm. "Everything has gone wrong since you got to coming here, and I think you are a regular Jonah. I find sand in my sugar, kerosene in the butter, the codfish is all picked off, and there is something wrong every time you come here. Now you leave."

"I ain't no Joner," said the boy as he wiped his nose on his coat sleeve, and reached into a barrel for a snow apple. "I never swallered no whale. Say, do you believe that story about Joner being in the whale's belly all night? I don't. The minister was telling about it at Sunday school last Sunday, and asked me what I thought Joner was doing while he was in there, and I told him I interpreted the story this way, that the whale was fixed up inside with upper and lower berths, like a sleeping car, and Joner had a lower berth and the porter made up the berth as soon as Joner came in with his satchel, and Joner pulled off his boots and gave them to the porter to black, and put his watch under his pillow and turned in. The boys in Sunday school all laffed, and the minister said I was a bigger fool than Pa was, and that was useless. If you go back on me now, I won't have a friend, except my chum and a dog and I swear, by my halidom that I never put no sand in your sugar, or kerosene in your butter. I admit the picking off of the codfish, but you can charge it to Pa, the same as you did the eggs that I

113

pushed my chum over into last summer, though I thought
you did wrong in charging Christmas prices for dog days'
eggs. When my chum's Ma scraped his pants she said there
was not an egg represented on there that was less than two
years old. The Sunday school folks have gone back on me,
since I put kyan pepper on the stove, when they were singing
'Little Drops of Water,' and they all had to go out doors and
air themselves. But I didn't mean to let the pepper drop on
the stove. I was just holding it over the stove to warm it,
when my chum hit the funny bone of my elbow. Pa says I
am a terror to cats. Every time Pa says anything, it gives
me a new idea. I tell you Pa has got a great brain, but
sometimes he don't have it with him. When he said I was
a terror to cats I thought what fun there is in cats, and me
and my chum went to stealing cats right off, and before night
we had eleven cats caged. We had one in a canary bird
cage, three in Pa's old hat boxes, three in Ma's band box,
four in valises, two in a trunk, and the rest in a closet up
stairs.

"That night Pa said he wanted me to stay home because
the committee that is going to get up a noyster supper in the
church was going to meet at our house, and they might
want to send me on errands. I asked him if my chum
couldn't stay too, cause he is the healthiest infant to run
after errands that ever was, and Pa said he could stay, but
we must remember that there musn't be no monkey business
going on. I told him there shouldn't be no monkey business
but I didn't promise nothing about cats. Well, sir, you'd
a dide. The committee was in the library by the back
stairs, and me and my chum got the cat boxes all together,
at the top of the stairs, and we took them all out and put
them in a clothes basket, and just as the minister was
speaking, and telling what a great good was done by these
oyster sociables, in bringing the young people together, and
taking their minds from the wickedness of the world, and
turning their thoughts into different channels, one of the old
tom cats in the basket gave a 'purmeow' that sounded like

the wail of a lost soul or a challenge to battle. I told my chum that we couldn't hold the bread-board over the clothes basket much longer, when two or three cats began to yowl. and the minister stopped talking, and Pa told Ma to open

A YELLOW CAT WITHOUT ANY TAIL WAS WALKING
OVER THE MINISTER.

the stair door and tell the hired girl to see what was the matter up there. She thought our cat had got shut up in the storm door, and she opened the stair door to yell to the girl, and then I pushed the clothes basket, cats and all down the back stairs. Well, sir, I suppose no committee for a noyster supper was ever more astonished. I heard Ma fall

over a willow rocking chair, and say, 'Scat,' and I heard Pa
say, 'Well, I'm dam'd,' and a girl that sings in the choir say,
'Heavens, I am stabbed,' then my chum and me run to the
front of the house and come down the front stairs looking
as innocent as could be, and we went into the library, and
I was just going to tell Pa if there was any errands he
wanted run, my chum and me was just aching to run them,
when a yellow cat without any tail was walking over the
minister, and Pa was throwing a hassock at two cats that
were clawing each other under the piano, and Ma was trying
to get her frizzes back on her head, and the choir girl was
standing on the lounge with her dress pulled up, trying
to scare cats with her striped stockings, and the minister
was holding his hands up, and I guess he was asking a
blessing on the cats, and my chum opened the front door
and all the cats went out. Pa and Ma looked at me, and
I said it wasn't me, and the minister wanted to know how
so much cat hair got on my coat and vest, and I said a cat
met me in the hall and kicked me, and Ma cried, and Pa
said, 'That boy beats hell,' and the minister said I would be
all right if he had been properly brought up, and then Ma
was mad, and the committee broke up. Well, to tell the
honest truth, Pa basted me, and yanked me around until
I had to have my arm in a sling, but what's the use of making
such a fuss about a few cats? Ma said she never wanted to
have any company again, cause I spoiled everything. But
I got even with Pa for basting me, this morning, and I
dassant go home. You see, Ma has got a great big bath
sponge as big as a chair cushion, and this morning I took
the sponge and filled it with warm water, and took the
feather cushion out of the chair Pa sits in at the table, and
put the sponge in its place, and covered it over with the
cushion cover, and when we all got set down to the table
Pa came in and set down on it to ask a blessing. He started
in by closing his eyes and placing his hands up in front of
him like a letter V, and then he began to ask that the food
we were about to partake of be blessed, and then he was

going on to ask that all of us be made to see the error of our ways, when he began to hitch around, and he opened one eye and looked at me and I looked as pious as a boy can look when he knows the pancakes are getting cold, and Pa he kind of sighed and said, 'Amen' sort of snappish, and he got up and told Ma he didn't feel well, and she would have to take his place and pass around the sassidge and potatoes, and he looked kind of scart and went out with his

PA OPENED ONE EYE AND LOOKED AT ME.

hands on his pistol pocket, as though he would like to shoot, and Ma she got up and went around and sat in Pa's chair. The sponge didn't hold more than half a pail full of water, and I didn't want to play no joke on Ma, cause the cats nearly broke her up, but she s.. down and was just going to help me, when she rung the bell and called the hired girl, and said she felt as though her nooralgia was coming on, and she would go to her room, and told the girl to sit down and help Hennery. The girl sat down and poured me out some coffee, and then she said, 'Howly Saint Patrick, but I blave those pancakes are burning,' and she went out in the kitchen. I drank my coffee, and then took the big sponge out of the chair and put the cushion in the place of it, and then I put the sponge in the bath room, and I went up to Pa and Ma's room, and asked them if I should go after the doctor, and Pa had changed his clothes and got on his Sunday pants, and he said, 'Never mind the doctor, I guess we will pull through,' and for me to get out and go to the devil, and I came over here. Say, there is no harm in a little warm water, is there? Well, I'd like to know what Pa and Ma and the hired girl thought. I am the only real healthy one there is in our family."

CHAPTER XXIII

HE BECOMES A DRUGGIST

"I have gone into business!"—A new rose geranium perfume—The
bad boy in a druggist's store—Practicing on his Pa—An explosion
—The seidletz powder—His Pa's frequent pains—Pounding India-
Rubber—Curing a wart.

"Whew! What is that smells so about this store? It
seems as though everything had turned frowy," said the
grocery man to his clerk, in the presence of the bad boy,
who was standing with his back to the stove, his coat tails
parted with his hands, and a cigarette in his mouth.

"May be it is me that smells frowy," said the boy as he
put his thumbs in the armholes of his vest, and spit at the
keyhole in the door. "I have gone into business."

"By thunder, I believe it is you," said the grocery man,
as he went up to the boy, snuffed a couple of times, and
then held his hands to his nose. "The board of health will
kerosene you, if they ever smell that smell, and send you
to the glue factory. What business you gone into to make
you smell so rank?"

"Well, you see Pa began to think it was time I learned
a trade, or a perfession, and he saw a sign in a drug store
window, 'Boy wanted,' and as he had a boy he didn't want,
he went to the druggist and got a job for me. This smell on
me will go off in a few weeks. You know I wanted to try
all the perfumery in the store, and after I had got about
forty different extracts on my clothes, another boy that
worked there he fixed up a bottle of benzine and assafety
and brimstone, and a whole lot of other horrid stuff, and
labeled it 'rose geranium,' and I guess I just wallered in it.
It *is* awful, aint it? It kerflummixed Ma when I went into
the dining-room the first night that I got home from the

store, and broke Pa all up. He said I reminded him of the
time when they had a litter of skunks under the barn. The
air seemed fixed around where I am, and everybody seems
to know who fixed it. A girl came in the store yesterday to
buy a satchet, and there wasn't anybody there but me, and
I didn't know what it was, and I took down everything in
the store pretty near before I found it, and then I wouldn't
have found it only the proprietor came in. The girl asked
the proprietor if there wasn't a good deal of sewer-gas in the
store, and he told me to go out and shake myself. I think
the girl was mad at me because I got a nursing bottle out of
the show case, with a rubber nozzle, and asked her if that
was what she wanted. Well, she told me a satchet was
something for the stummick, and I thought a nursing bottle
was the nearest thing to it."

"I should think you would drive all the customers away
from the store," said the grocery man, as he opened the door
to let the fresh air in.

"I don't know but I will, but I am hired for a month on
trial, and I shall stay. You see, I shan't practice on anybody but Pa for a spell. I made up my mind to that when I
gave a woman some salts instead of powdered borax, and
she came back mad. Pa seems to want to encourage me,
and is willing to take anything that I ask him to. He had a
sore throat and wanted something for it, and the boss drugger told me to put some tannin and chlorate of potash in a
mortar, and grind it, and I let Pa pound it with the mortar,
and while he was pounding I dropped in a couple of drops
of sulphuric acid, and it exploded and blowed Pa's hat clear
across the store, and Pa was whiter than a sheet. He said he
guessed his throat was all right, and he wouldn't come near
me again that day. The next day, Pa came in and I was laying for him. I took a white seidletz powder and a blue one,
and dissolved them in separate glasses, and when Pa came in
I asked him if he didn't want some lemonade, and he said he
did, and I gave him the sour one and he drank it. He said
it was too sour, and then I gave him the other glass, that

looked like water, to take the taste out of his mouth, and he
drank it. Well, sir, when those two powders got together
in Pa's stummick, and began to siz and steam, and foam, Pa

I ASKED HER IF THAT WAS WHAT SHE WANTED.

pretty near choked to death, and the suds came out of his
nostrils, and his eyes stuck out, and as soon as he could get
his breath he yelled 'Fire,' and said he was poisoned, and
called for a doctor, but I thought as long as we had a doctor
right in the family there was no use of hiring one, so I

got a stomach pump, and I would have had him baled out
in no time, only the proprietor came in and told me to go
and wash some bottles, and he gave Pa a drink of brandy,
and Pa said he felt better. Pa has learned where we keep
the liquor, and he comes in two or three times a day with
a pain in his stomach. They play awful mean tricks on a boy
in a drug store. The first day they put a chunk of something
sort of blue into a mortar, and told me to pulverize it, and
then make it up into two grain pills. Well, sir, I pounded
that chunk all the forenoon, and it never pulverized at all,
and the boss told me to hurry up, as the woman was waiting
for the pills, and I mauled it till I was nearly dead, and when
it was time to go to supper the boss came and looked in
mortar, and took out the chunk, and said, 'You darn fool,
you have been pounding all day on a chunk of India-rubber
instead of blue mass!' Well, how did I know? But I will
get even with them if I stay there long enough, and don't
you forget it. If you have a prescription you want filled
you can come down to the store and I will put it up for you
myself, and then you will be sure you get what you pay for."

"Yes," said the grocery man, as he cut off a piece of
limberg cheese and put it on the stove, to purify the air in the
room. "I should laugh to see myself taking any medicine
you put up. You will kill some one yet by giving them
poison instead of quinine. But what has your Pa got his
nose tied up for? He looks as though he had had a fight."

"O, that was from my treatment. He had a wart on his
nose. You know that wart. You remember how the minister told him if other people's business had a button-hole in it,
Pa could button the wart in the button-hole, as he always
had his nose there. Well, I told Pa I could cure that wart
with caustic, and he said he would give five dollars if I could
cure it, so I took a stick of caustic and burned the wart off,
but I guess I burned down into the nose a little, for it
swelled up as big as a lobster. Pa says he would rather
have a whole nest of warts than such a nose, but it will be
all right in a year or two."

CHAPTER XXIV

HE QUITS THE DRUG BUSINESS

He has dissolved with the drugger—The old lady and the gin—The bad
    boy ignominiously fired—How he dosed his Pa's brandy—The
    bad boy as "hawty as a dook"—He gets even with his girl—The
    bad boy wants a quiet place—The old man threatens the parson.

"What are you loafing around here for?" says the grocery man to the bad boy one day this week. "It is after nine o'clock, and I should think you would want to be down to the drug store. How do you know but there may be somebody dying for a dose of pills?"

"O, darn the drug store. I have got sick of that business, and I have dissolved with the drugger. I have resigned. The policy of the store did not meet with my approval, and I have stepped out and am waiting for them to come and tender me a better position at an increased salary," said the boy, as he threw a cigar stub into a barrel of prunes and lit a fresh one.

"Resigned, eh?" said the grocery man as he fished out the cigar stub and charged the boy's father with two pounds of prunes, "didn't you and the boss agree?"

"Not exactly; I gave an old lady some gin when she asked for camphor and water, and she made a show of herself. I thought I would fool her, but she knew mighty well what it was, and she drank about half a pint of gin, and got to tipping over bottles and kegs of paint, and when the drug man came in with his wife, the old lady threw her arms around his neck and called him her darling, and when he pushed her away, and told her she was drunk, she picked up a bottle of citrate of magnesia and pointed it at him, and the cork came out like a pistol, and he thought he was shot, and his wife fainted away, and the police came and took the old

gin refrigerator away, and the drug man told me to face the
door, and when I wasn't looking he kicked me four times,
and I landed in the street, and he said if I ever came in sight
of the store again he would kill me dead. That is the way
I resigned. I tell you, they will send for me again. They
never can run that store without me."

"I guess they will worry along without you," said the
grocery man. "How does your Pa take your being fired out?
I should think it would break him all up."

"O, I think Pa rather likes it. At first he thought he had
a soft snap with me in the drug store, cause he has got to
drinking again like a fish, and he has gone back on the
church entirely; but after I had put a few things in his
brandy he concluded it was cheaper to buy it, and he is now
patronizing a barrel house down by the river.

"One day I put some castile soap in a drink of brandy,
and Pa leaned over the back fence more than an hour, with
his finger down his throat. The man that collects the ashes
from the alley asked Pa if he had lost anything, and Pa said
he was only 'sugaring off.' I don't know what that is.
When Pa felt better he came in and wanted a little whiskey,
to take the taste out of his mouth, and I gave him some with
about a teaspoonful of pulverized alum in it. Well, sir, you'd
a dide. Pa's mouth and throat was so puckered up, that he
couldn't talk. I don't think the drug man will make any
thing by firing me out, because I shall turn all the trade that
I control to another store. Why sir, sometimes there were
eight and nine girls in the store all at wonct, on account of
my being there. They came to have me put extracts on their
handkerchiefs and to eat gum-drops; he will lose all that
trade now. My girl that went back on me for the telegraph
messenger boy, she came with the rest of the girls, but she
found that I could be as 'hawty as a dook.' I got even with
her, though. I pretended I wasn't mad, and when she wanted
me to put some perfumery on her handkerchief I said, 'All
right,' and I put on a little geranium and white rose, and then
I got some tincture of assafet and sprinkled it on her dress

and cloak when she went out. That is about the worst
smelling stuff that ever was, and I was glad when she went
out and met the telegraph boy on the corner. They went
off together, but he came back pretty soon, about the home-
sickest boy you ever saw, and he told my chum he would

THEN THE DRUG MAN TOLD ME TO FACE THE DOOR.

never go with that girl again because she smelled like
spoiled oysters or sewer gas. Her folks noticed it, and
made her go and wash her feet and soak herself, and her
brother told my chum it didn't do any good, she smelled
just like a glue factory, and my chum—the darn fool—
told her brother that it was me who perfumed her, and he

hit me in the eye with a frozen fish, down by the fish store, and that's what made my eye black; but I know how to cure a black eye. I have not been in the drug store eight days, and not know how to cure a black eye, and I guess I learned that girl not to go back on a boy cause he smelled like a goat."

"Well, what was it about your leaving the wrong medicine at houses? The policeman in this ward told me you come pretty near killing several people by leaving the wrong medicine."

"The way of it was this. There was about a dozen different kinds of medicine to leave at different places, and I was in a hurry to go to the roller skating rink, so I got my chum to help me, and we just took the numbers of the houses, and when we rung the bell we would hand out the first package we come to, and I understand there was a good deal of complaint. One old maid who ordered powder for her face, her ticket drew some worm lozengers, and she kicked awfully, and a widow who was going to be married, she ordered a celluloid comb and brush, and she got a nursing bottle with a rubber nozzle, and a toothing ring, and she made quite a fuss; but the woman who was weaning her baby and wanted the nursing bottle, she got the comb and brush and some blue pills, and she never made any fuss at all. It makes a good deal of difference I notice, whether a person gets a better thing than they ordered or not. But the drug business is too lively for me. I have got to have a quiet place, and I guess I will be a cash boy in a store. Pa says he thinks I was cut out for a bunko steerer, and I may look for that kind of a job. Pa he is a terror since he got to drinking again. He came home the other day, when the minister was calling on Ma, and just cause the minister was sitting on the sofa with Ma, and had his hand on her shoulder, where she said the pain was when the rheumatiz came on, Pa was mad and told the minister he would kick his liver clear around on the other side if he caught him there again, and Ma felt awful about it. After the minister had gone away, Ma told Pa he had got no feeling at all, and Pa said he had got enough feeling for one family, and he didn't want no sky-sharp to help him. He said he could cure all the rheumatiz there was around his house, and then he went down town and didn't get home till most breakfast time. Ma says she thinks I am responsible for Pa's falling into bad ways again, and now I am

PA WAS MAD JUST BECAUSE THE MINISTER HAD HIS HAND ON
HER SHOULDERS.

going to cure him. You watch me, and see if I don't have Pa in the church in less than a week, praying and singing, and going home with the choir singers, just as pious as ever. I am going to get a boy that writes a woman's hand, to write to Pa, and—but I must not give it away. But you just watch Pa, that's all. Well, I must go and saw some wood. It is coming down a good deal, from a drug clerk to sawing wood, but I will get on top yet, and don't you forget it."

CHAPTER XXV

HIS PA KILLS HIM

A genius at whistling—A fur-lined cloak a sure cure for consumption—
Another letter sent to the old man—He resolves on immediate
punishment—The bladder-buffer—The explosion—A tragic scene—
His Pa vows to reform.

"For heaven's sake dry up that whistling," said the grocery man to the bad boy, as he sat on a bag of peanuts,
whistling and filling his pockets. "There is no sense in
such whistling. What do you whistle for, anyway?"

"I am practicing my profession," said the boy, as he got
up and stretched himself, and cut off a slice of cheese, and
took a few crackers. "I have always been a good whistler,
and I have decided to turn my talent to account. I am going
to hire an office and put out a sign, 'Boy furnished to whistle
for lost dogs.' You see there are dogs lost every day, and
any man would give half a dollar to a boy to find his dog.
I can hire out to whistle for dogs, and can go around
whistling and enjoying myself, and make money. Don't
you think it a good scheme?" asked the boy of the grocery
man.

"Naw," said the grocery man, as he charged the cheese
to the boy's father, and picked up his cigar stub, which he
had left on the counter, and which the boy had rubbed on
the kerosene barrel. "No, sir, the whistle would scare any
dog that heard it. Say, what was your Pa running after the
doctor in his shirt sleeves for last Sunday morning? He
looked scared. Was your Ma sick again?"

"O, no, Ma is healthy enough, now she has got a new
fur-lined cloak. She played consumption on Pa and
coughed so she like to raise her lights and liver, and made
Pa believe that she couldn't live, and got the doctor to pre-

scribe a fur-lined circular, and Pa went and got one, and Ma has improved awfully. Her cough is all gone and she can walk ten miles. I was the one that was sick. You see, I wanted to get Pa into the church again, and get him to stop drinking, so I got a boy to write a letter to him in

PA SAID, "NOW HENNERY."

a female hand, and sign the name of a choir singer Pa was mashed on, and tell him she was yearning for him to come back to the church, and that the church seemed blank without his smiling face, and benevolent heart, and to please come back for her sake. Pa got the letter Saturday night

9

and he seemed tickled, but I guess he dieamed about it all
night, and Sunday morning he was mad, and he took me by
the ear and said I couldn't come no 'Daisy' business on
him the second time. He said he knew I wrote the letter,
and for me to go up to the store room and prepare for the
almightiest licking a boy ever had, and he went down stairs
and broke up an apple barrel and got a stave to whip me
with. Well I had to think mighty quick, but I was enough
for him. I got a dried bladder in my room, one that me
and my chum got to the slaughter house, and blowed it
partly up, so it would be sort of flat-like, and I put it down
inside of the back part of my pants, right about where Pa
hits when he punishes me. I knowed when the barrel stave
hit the bladder it would explode. Well, Pa he came up and
found me crying. I can cry just as easy as you can turn on
water at the faucet, and Pa took off his coat and looked
sorry. I was afraid he would give up whipping me when he
see me cry and I wanted the bladder experiment to go on,
so I looked kind of hard, as if I was defying him to do his
worst, and then he took me by the neck and laid me across
a trunk. I didn't dare struggle much for fear the bladder
would loose itself, and Pa said, 'Now Hennery, I am going
to break you of this dam foolishness, or I will break your
back,' and he spit on his hands and brought the barrel stave
down on my best pants.   Well, you'd a dide if you had
heard the explosion. It almost knocked me off the trunk.
It sounded like firing a fire-cracker away down cellar in a
barrel, and Pa looked scared, I rolled off the trunk, on the
floor, and put some flour on my face, to make me look pale,
and then I kind of kicked my legs like a fellow who is dying
on the stage after being stabbed with a piece of lath, and
groaned and said, 'Pa you have killed me, but I forgive
you,' and then rolled around, and frothed at the mouth, cause
I had a piece of soap in my mouth to make foam. Well,
Pa was broken up. He said, 'Great God, what have I done?
I have broken his spinal column. O, my poor boy do not
die!' I kept chewing the soap and foaming at the mouth,

and I drew up my legs and kicked and clutched my chair, and rolled my eyes, and then kicked Pa in the stummick as he bent over me, and knocked the breath out of him, and then my limbs began to get rigid, and I said, 'Too late, Pa, I die at the hand of an assassin. Go for a doctor.' Pa throwed his coat over me, and started down stairs on a run, 'I have murdered my brave boy,' and he told Ma to go upstairs and stay with me, cause I had fallen off a trunk and ruptured a blood vessel, and he went after a doctor. When he went out the front door, I sat up and lit a cigarette, and Ma came up and I told her all about how I fooled Pa, and if she would take on and cry, when Pa got back, I would get him to go to church again, and swear off drinking and she said she would.

"So when Pa and the doc. came back, Ma was sitting on a velocipede I used to ride, which was in the store-room, and she had her apron over her face, and she just more than bellowed. Pa he was pale and he told the doc. he was just playing with me with a little piece of board and he heard something crack, and he guessed my spine got broke falling off the trunk. The doctor wanted to feel where my spine was broke, but I opened my eyes and had a vacant kind of stare, like a woman who leads a dog by a string, and looked as though my mind was wandering, and I told the doctor there was no use setting my spine as it was broke in several places and I wouldn't let him feel of the dried bladder. I told Pa I was going to die and I wanted him to promise me two things on my dying bed. He cried and said he would, and I told him to promise me he would quit drinking, and attend church regular, and he said he would never drink another drop, and would go to church every Sunday. I made him get down on his knees beside me and swear it, and the doc. witnessed it, and Ma said she was so glad, and Ma called the doctor out in the hall and told him the joke, and the doc. came in and told Pa he was afraid Pa's presence would excite the patient, and for him to put on his coat and go out and walk around the block, or go to church, and Ma and he would remove me to another room, and do all that was possible to make my last hours pleasant. Pa he cried and said he would put on his plug hat and go to church, and he kissed me and got flour on his nose, and I came near laughing right out, to see the white flour on his red nose, when I thought how the people in church would laugh at Pa. But he went out feeling mighty bad, and then I got up and pulled the bladder out of my pants, and Ma and the doc. laughed awful. When Pa got back from church and asked for me, Ma said that I had gone down town. She said the doctor found my spine was only uncoupled and he coupled it together, and I was all right. Pa said it was 'Almighty strange, cause I heard the spine break, when I struck him with the barrel stave.' Pa was nervous all the afternoon, and Ma thinks he suspects that we played it on him. Say, you don't think there is any harm in playing it on an old man a little for a good cause, do you?"

The grocery man said he supposed, in the interest of reform, it was all right, but if it was his boy that played such tricks he would take an ax to him, and the boy went out, apparently encouraged, saying he hadn't seen the old man since the day before, and he was almost afraid to meet him.

CHAPTER XXVI

Searching for sewer gas—The powerful odor of limberger cheese at church—The after meeting—Fumigating the house—The bad boy resolves to board at an hotel.

"WHAT was the health officer doing over to your house this morning?" said the grocery man to the bad boy, as the youth was firing frozen potatoes at the man who collects garbage in the alley.

"O, they are searching for sewer gas and such things and they have got plumbers and other society experts till you can't rest, and I came away for fear they would find the sewer gas and warm my jacket. Say, do you think it is right, when anything smells awfully to always lay it to a boy?"

"Well, in nine cases out of ten they would hit it right, but what do you think is the trouble over to your house, honest?"

"Sh-h! Now don't breathe a word of it to a living soul or I am a dead boy. You see I was over to the dairy fair at the exposition building Saturday night, and when they were breaking up, me and my chum helped to carry boxes of cheese and firkins of butter, and a cheese-man gave each of us a piece of limberger cheese, wrapped up in tin foil. Sunday morning I opened my piece, and it made me tired. O, it was the offulest smell I ever heard of, except the smell when they found a tramp who hung himself in the woods on the Whitefish Bay road, and had been dead three weeks. It was just like a old back number funeral. Pa and Ma were just getting ready to go to church, and I cut off a piece of cheese and put it in the inside pocket of Pa's vest, and I

put another in the lining of Ma's muff, and they went to
church.   I went down to church, too, and sat on a back
seat with my chum, looking just as pious as though I was
taking up a collection.   The church was pretty warm,
and by the time they got up to sing the first hymn Pa's
cheese began to smell a match against Ma's cheese.   Pa held
one side of the hymn book and Ma held the other, and Pa
he always sings for all that is out, and when he braced himself and sang 'Just as I am,' Ma thought Pa's voice was
tinctured a little with billiousness and she looked at him, and
hunched him and told him to stop singing and breathe
through his nose, cause his breath was enough to stop a
clock.   Pa stopped singing and turned around kind of cross
towards Ma, and then he smelled Ma's cheese, and he turned
his head the other way and said, 'Whew,' and they didn't
sing any more, but they looked at each other as though they
smelled frowy.   When they sat down they sat as far apart
as they could get, and Pa sat next to a woman who used to
be a nurse in a hospital, and when she smelled Pa's cheese
she looked at him as though she thought he hed the small-
pox, and she held her handkerchief to her nose.   The man
in the other end of the pew, that Ma sat near, he was a
stranger from Racine, who belongs to our church, and he
looked at Ma sort of queer, and after the minister prayed,
and they got up to sing again, the man took his hat and
went out, and when he came by me he said something in a
whisper about a female glue factory.

"Well, sir, before the sermon was over everybody in that
part of the church had their handkerchiefs to their noses,
and they looked at Pa and Ma scandalous, and the two ush-
ers they come around in the pews looking for a dog, and
when the minister got over his sermon, and wiped the perspiration off his face, he said he would like to have the
trustees of the church stay after meeting, as there was some
business of importance to transact.   He said the question of
proper ventilation and sewerage for the church would be
brought up, and that he presumed the congregation had

noticed this morning that the church was unusually full of
sewer gas. He said he had spoken of the matter before, and
he expected it would be attended to before this. He said
he was a meek and humble follower of the lamb, and was

HE SAID HE WAS A WEAK AND HUMBLE FOLLOWER OF THE LAMB.

willing to cast his lot wherever the Master decided, but
he would be blessed if he would preach any longer in a
church that smelled like a bone boiling establishment. He
said religion was a good thing, but no person could enjoy
religion as well in a fat rending establishment as he could in

a flower garden, and as far as he was concerned he had got
enough. Everybody looked at everybody else, and Pa
looked at Ma as though he knew where the sewer gas came
from, and Ma looked at Pa real mad, and me and my chum
lit out, and went home and distributed my cheese all around.
I put a slice in Ma's bureau drawer, down under her under-
clothes, and a piece in the spare room, under the bed, and a
piece in the bath-room in the soap-dish, and a slice in the
album on the parlor table, and a piece in the library in a book,
and I went to the dining-room and put some under the table,
and dropped a piece under the range in the kitchen. I tell
you the house was loaded for bear. Ma came home from
church first, and when I asked where Pa was, she said she
hoped he had gone to walk around a block to air hisself. Pa
came home to dinner, and when he got a smell of the house
he opened all the doors, and Ma put a comfortable around
her shoulders and told Pa he was a disgrace to civilization.
She tried to get Pa to drink some carbolic acid. Pa finally
convinced Ma it was not him, and then they decided it was
the house that smelled so, as well as the church, and all Sunday afternoon they went visiting, and this morning Pa went
down to the health office and got the inspector of nuisances to
come up to the house, and when he smelled around a spell
he said there was dead rats in the main sewer pipe, and they
sent for plumbers, and Ma went out to a neighbors to
borry some fresh air, and when the plumbers began to dig
up the floor in the basement I came over here. If they find
any of that limberg cheese it will go hard with me. The
hired girls have both quit, and Ma says she is going to break
up keeping house and board. That is just into my hand. I
want to board at a hotel, where you can have bill-of-fare
and tooth picks, and billiards, and everything. Well I guess
I will go over to the house and stand in the back door and
listen to the mocking bird. If you see me come flying out
of the alley with my coat tail full of boots you can bet they
have discovered the sewer gas."

CHAPTER XXVII

The bad boy don't think the grocer fit for heaven—He is very severe on his old friend—The need of a new revised edition—The bad boy turns reviser—His Pa reaches for the poker—A special providence—The sled slewed!—His Pa under the mules.

"WELL, I guess I will go to hell. I will see you later," said the bad boy to the grocery man, as he held a cracker under the faucet of the syrup keg, and then sat down on a soap box by the stove and proceeded to make a lunch, while the grocery man charged the boy's father with a gallon of syrup and a pound of crackers.

"What do you mean, you profane wretch, talking about meeting me later in Hades?" said the indignant grocery man. "I expect to pass by the hot place where you are sizzling, and go to the realms of bliss, where there is one continued round of happiness, and angels playing on golden harps and singing hymns of praise."

"Why, Pa says I will surely go to hell, and I thought you would probably be there, as it costs something to get to heaven, and you can get to the other place for nothing. Say, you would be a healthy delegate to go to heaven, with a lot of girl angels, wouldn't you, smelling of frowy butter, as you always do, and kerosene, and herring, and bar soap, and cheese, and rotten potatoes. Say, an angel wouldn't stay on the same golden street with you, without holding her handkerchief to her nose, and you couldn't get in there, anyway, cause you would want to pay your entrance fee out of the store."

"Say, you get out of here, condemn you. You are getting sassy. There is no one that is more free hearted than I am," said the grocery man.

"O, give us a *siesta*. I am on to you bigger than an
elevator. When they had the oyster sociable at the church
you gave four pounds of musty crackers with worms in, and
they tasted of kerosene, and when the minister prayed for
those who had generously contributed to the sociable, you
raised up your head as though you wanted them all to know
he meant you. If a man can get to heaven on four pounds
of musty crackers, done up in a paper that has been around
mackerel, then what's the use of a man being good, and
giving sixteen ounces to the pound? But, there, don't
blush and cry. I will use my influence to get your feet onto
the golden streets of the New Jerusalem, but you have
got to quit sending those small potatoes to our house,
with a few big ones on top of the basket. I'll tell you
how it was that Pa told me I would go to hell. You see
Pa has been reading out of an old back number bible,
and Ma and me argued with him about getting a new
revised edition. We told him that the old one was all out
of style, and that all the neighbors had the newest cut in
bibles, with dolman sleeves, and gathered in the back, and
they put on style over us, and we could not hold up our
heads in society when it was known that we were wearing
the old last year's bible. Pa kicked against it, but finally
got one. I thought I had as much right to change things in
the revised bible, as the other fellows had to change the old
one, so I pasted some mottoes and patent-medicine advertisements in it, after the verses. Pa never reads a whole
chapter, but reads a verse or two and skips around. Before
breakfast, the other morning, Pa got the new bible and
started to read the ten commandments and some other
things. The first thing Pa struck was, 'Verily I say unto
you, try St. Jacob's oil for rheumatism.' Pa looked over his
specs at Ma, and then looked at me, but I had my face
covered with my hands, sort of pious. Pa said he didn't
think it was just the thing to put advertisements in the
bible, but Ma said she didn't know as it was any worse
than to have a patent medicine notice next to Beecher's ser-

mon in the religious paper. Pa sighed and turned over a
few leaves, and read, 'Thou shalt not covet thy neighbor's
wife, nor his ox, if
you love me as I love
you no knife can cut
our love in two.' That
last part was a motto
that I got out of a
paper of candy. Pa
said that the senti-
ment was good, but
he didn't think the re-
visers had improved
the old command-
ment very much.
Then Pa turned over
and read, 'Take a lit-
tle wine for the stom-
ach's sake, and keep
a bottle of Reed's
Gilt Edged tonic on
your side-board, and
you can defy malaria,
and chills and fever.'

PA FOLLOWED ME AS FAR AS THE
SIDEWALK.

Pa was hot. He looked at it again, and noticed that the
tonic commandment was on yellow paper, and the corner
curled up and Pa took hold of it, and the paste that I stuck
it on with was not good, and it come off, and when I saw Pa
lay down the bible, and put his spectacles in the case, and
reach for the fire poker, I knew he was not going to pray, and
I looked out the window and yelled dog fight, and I lit out,
and Pa followed me as far as the sidewalk, and it was that
morning when it was so slippery, and Pa's feet slipped out
from under him, and he stood on his neck, and slid around
on his ear, and the special providence of sleet on the sidewalk
saved me. Say, do you believe in special providence? What

was the use of that sleet on the sidewalk, if it was not to save sinners?"

"O, I don't know anything about special providence," said the grocery man, "but I know you have got two of your pockets filled with them boneless raisins since you have been talking, and my opinion is you will steal. But, say, what is your Pa on crutches for? I see him hobbling down town this morning. Has he sprained his ankle?"

"Well, I guess his ankle got sprained with all the rest. You see, my chum and me went bobbing, and Pa said he supposed he used to be the greatest bobber, when he was a boy, that ever was. He said he used to slide down a hill that was steeper than a church steeple. We asked him to go with us, and we went to that street that goes down by the depot, and we had two sleds hitched together, and there were more'n a hundred boys, and Pa wanted to steer, and he got on the front sled, and when we got about half way down the sled slewed, and my chum and me got off all right, but Pa got shut up between the two sleds, and the other boys behind they all run over Pa and one sled runner caught him in the trousers' leg, and dragged him over the slippery ice clear to the bottom, and the whole lay-out run into the street car, and the mules got wild and kicked, and Pa's suspenders broke, and when my chum and me got down there was Pa under the car, and a boy's boots was in Pa's shirt bosom, and another boy was straddle of Pa's neck, and the crowd rushed up from the depot, and got Pa out, and began to yell 'fire,' and 'police,' and he kicked at a boy that was trying to get his sled out of the small of Pa's back, and a policeman came along and pushed Pa and said, 'Go away from here, ye owld divil, and let the b'ys enjoy themselves;' and he was going to arrest Pa, when me and my chum told him we would take Pa home. Pa said the hill was not steep enough for him or he wouldn't have fell off. He is offul stiff to-day, but he says he will go skating with us next week, and show us how to skate. Pa means well, but he don't realize that he is getting stiff and can't be as kitteny as he used to be. He is very kind to me. If I had some fathers I would have been a broken-backed disfigured angel long ago. Don't you think so?"

The grocery man said he was sure of it, and the boy got out with his boneless raisins, and pocket full of lump sugar.

CHAPTER XXVIII

The bad boy carves a turkey—His Pa's fame as a skater—The old man essays to skate on rollers—His wild capers—He spreads himself—Holidays a condemned nuisance—The bad boy's Christmas presents.

"WHAT is that stuff on your shirt bosom, that looks like soap grease?" said the grocery man to the bad boy, as he came into the grocery the morning after Christmas.

The boy looked at his shirt front, put his fingers on the stuff and smelled of his fingers, and then said, "O, that is nothing but a little of the turkey dressing and gravy. You see after Pa and I got back from the roller skating rink yesterday, Pa was all broke up, and he couldn't carve the turkey, and I had to do it, and Pa sat in a stuffed chair with his head tied up and a pillow amongst his legs, and he kept complaining that I didn't do it right. Gol darn a turkey any way. I should think they would make a turkey flat on the back, so he would lay on a greasy platter without skating all around the table. It looks easy to see Pa carve a turkey, but when I speared into the bosom of that turkey, and began to saw on it, the turkey rolled around as though it was on castors, and it was all that I could do to keep it out of Ma's lap. But I rassled with it till I got off enough white meat for Pa and Ma, and dark meat enough for me, and I dug out the dressing, but most of it flew into my shirt bosom, cause the string that tied up the place where the dressing was concealed about the person of the turkey, broke prematurely, and one oyster hit Pa in the eye, and he said I was as awkward as a cross-eyed girl trying to kiss a man with a hair lip. If I ever get to be the head of a family I shall carve turkeys with a corn sheller."

142

"But what broke your Pa up at the roller skating rink?" asked the grocery man.

"O, everything broke him up. He is split up so Ma buttons the top of his pants to his collar button, like a bicycle rider. Well, he had no business to have told me and my

EVERYBODY GOT OUT OF THE WAY EXCEPT A GIRL.

chum that he used to be the best skater in North America, when he was a boy. He said he skated once from Albany to New York in an hour and eighty minutes. Me and my chum thought that if Pa was such a terror on skates we could get him to put on a pair of roller skates, and enter him as the 'great unknown,' and clean out the whole gang.

We told Pa that he must remember that roller skates were different from ice skates, and that maybe he couldn't skate on them, but he said it didn't make any difference what they were as long as they were skates, and he would just paralyze the whole crowd. So we got a pair of big roller skates for him, and while we were strapping them on, Pa he looked at the skaters glide around on the smooth wax floor just as though they were greased. Pa looked at the skates on his feet, after they were fastened, sort of forlorn like, the way a horse thief does when they put shackles on his legs, and I told him if he was afraid he couldn't skate with them, we would take them off, but he said he would beat anybody there was there, or bust a suspender. Then we straightened Pa up, and pointed him toward the middle of the room, and he said 'leggo,' and we just give him a little push to start him, and he began to go. Well, by gosh, you'd a dide to have seen Pa try to stop. You see, you can't stick in your heel and stop, like you can on ice skates, and Pa soon found that out, and he began to turn sideways, and then he threw his arms and walked on his heels, and he lost his hat, and his eyes began to stick out, cause he was going right toward an iron post. One arm caught the post, and he circled around it a few times, and then he let go and began to fall, and sir, he kept falling all across the room, and everybody got out of the way, except a girl, and Pa grabbed her by the polonaise, like a drowning man grabs at straws, though there wasn't any straws in her polonaise as I know of, but Pa just pulled her along as though she was done up in shawl-strap, and his feet went out from under him and he struck on his shoulders and kept a going, with the girl dragging along like a bundle of clothes. If Pa had had another pair of roller skates on his shoulders, and castors on his ears, he couldn't have slid along any better. Pa is a short, big man, and as he was rolling along on his back, he looked like a sofa with castors on, being pushed across the room by a girl. Finally Pa came to the wall and had to stop, and the girl fell right across him with her roller skates in his neck, and she called him an old brute, and told him if he didn't let go of her polonaise she would murder him. Just then my chum and me got there, and we amputated Pa from the girl, and lifted him up and told him for heaven's sake to let

I GUESS IT KNOCKED THE BREATH OUT OF HIM.

us take off the skates, 'cause he couldn't skate any more than a cow, and Pa was mad and said for us to let him alone, and he could skate all right, and we let go, and he struck out again. Well, sir, I was ashamed. An old man like Pa ought to know better than to try to be a boy. This last time Pa said he was going to spread himself, and if I am any judge of a big spread, he did spread himself. Somehow the skates had got turned around sideways on his feet; and his feet got to going in different directions, and Pa's feet were getting so far apart that I was afraid I would have two Pa's half the size, with one leg apiece.

"I tried to get him to take up a collection of his legs, and get them both in the same ward but his arms flew around and one hit me on the nose, and I thought if he wanted to strike the best friend he had, he could run his old legs hisself. When he began to separate I could hear the bones crack, but maybe it was his pants, but anyway he came down on the floor like one of those fellows in a circus who spreads hisself, and he kept going and finally he surrounded an iron post with his legs, and stopped, and looked pale, and the proprietor of the rink told Pa if he wanted to give a flying trapeze performance he would have to go to the gymnasium, and he couldn't skate on his shoulders any more, cause other skaters were afraid of him. Then Pa said he would kick the liver out of the proprietor of the rink, and he got up and steadied himself, and he tried to kick the man, but both heels went up to onct, and Pa turned a back somersault and struck right on his vest in front. I guess it knocked the breath out of him, for he didn't speak for a few minutes, and then he wanted to go home, and we put him in a street car, and he laid down on the hay and rode home. O, the work we had to get Pa's clothes off. He had cricks in his back, and everywhere, and Ma was away to one of the neighbors, to look at the presents, and I had to put liniment on Pa, and I made a mistake and got a bottle of furniture polish, and put it on Pa and rubbed it in, and when Ma came home, Pa smelled like a coffin at a charity funeral, and Ma said there was no way of getting that varnish off of Pa till it wore off. Pa says holidays are a condemned nuisance anyway. He will have to stay in the house all this week."

"You are pretty rough on the old man," said the grocery man, "after he has been so kind to you and given you nice presents."

"Nice presents nothing.   All I got was a 'Come to Jesus' Christmas card, with brindle fringe, from Ma, and Pa gave me a pair of his old suspenders, and a calender with mottoes for every month, some quotations from scripture, such as 'Honor thy father and thy mother,' and 'Evil communications corrupt two in a bush,' and 'A bird in the hand beats two pair.' Such things don't help a boy to be good. What a boy wants is club skates, and seven shot revolvers, and such things.   Well, I must go and help Pa roll over in bed, and put on a new porous plaster.   Good-bye."

CHAPTER XXIX

HIS PA GOES CALLING

His Pa starts forth—A picture of the old man "full"—Politeness at a winter picnic—Assaulted by sandbaggers—Resolved to drink no more coffee—A girl full of "aig-nogg."

Say, you are getting too all-fired smart," said the grocery man to the bad boy as he pushed him into a corner by the molasses barrel, and took him by the neck and chocked him so his eyes stuck out. "You have driven away several of my best customers, and now, confound you, I am going to have your life," and he took up a cheese knife and began to sharpen it on his boot.

"What's the—gurgle—matter?" asked the choking boy, as the grocery man's fingers let up on his throat a little, so he could speak. "I hain't done nothin."

"Didn't you hang up that dead gray Tom cat by the heels, in front of my store, with the rabbits I had for sale? I didn't notice it until the minister called me out in front of the store, and pointing to the rabbits, asked what good fat cats were selling for. By crimus, this thing has got to stop. You have got to move out of this ward or I will."

The boy got his breath and said it wasn't him that put the cat up there. He said it was the policeman, and he and his chum saw him do it and he just come in to tell the grocery man about it, and before he could speak he had his neck nearly pulled off. The boy began to cry and the grocery man said he was only joking, and gave him a box of sardines, and they made up. Then he asked the boy

how his Pa put in his New Years, and the boy sighed and
said:

"We had a sad time at our house New Years. Pa in-

HE SAID IT WAS A FRIEND OF HIS.

sisted on making calls, and Ma and me tried to prevent it,
but he said he was of age and guessed he could make calls if
he wanted to, so he looked at the morning paper and got the
names of all the places where they were going to receive,
and he turned his paper collar, and changed ends with his

cuffs, and put some arnica on his handkerchief, and started
out. Ma told him not to drink anything, and he said he
wouldn't, but he did. He was full the third place he went
to. O, *so* full. Some men can get full and not show it, but
when Pa gets full, he gets so full his back teeth float, and the
liquor crowds his eyes out, and his mouth gets loose and
wiggles all over his face, and he laughs all the time, and the
perspiration just oozes out of him, and his face gets red, and
he walks *so* wide. O, he disgraced us all. At one place he
wished the hired girl a happy New Year more than twenty
times, and hung his hat on her elbow, and tried to put on
a rubber hall mat for his overshoes. At another place he
walked up a lady's train, and carried away a card basket full
of bananas and oranges. Ma wanted my chum and me to
follow Pa and bring him home, and about dark we found
him in the door yard of a house where they have statues in
front of the house, and he grabbed me by the arm, and mis-
took me for another caller, and insisted on introducing me to
a marble statue without any clothes on. He said it was a
friend of his, and it was a winter picnic. He hung his hat on
an evergreen, and put his overcoat on the iron fence, and I
was so mortified I almost cried. My chum said if his Pa
made such a circus of himself he would sand-bag him. That
gave me an idea, and when we got Pa most home I went and
got a paper box covered with red paper, so it looked just
like a brick, and a bottle of tomato ketchup, and when we
got Pa up on the steps at home I hit him with the paper
brick, and my chum squirted the ketchup on his head, and
demanded his money, and then he yelled murder, and we lit
out, and Ma and the minister, who was making a call on her,
all the afternoon, they came to the door and pulled Pa in.
He said he had been attacked by a band of robbers, and they
knocked his brains out, but he whipped them, and then Ma
saw the ketchup brains oozing out of his head, and she
screamed, and the minister said, 'Good heavens he is murdered,' and just then I came in the back door and they sent
me after the doctor, and they put Pa on the lounge and tied

up his head with a towel to keep the brains in, and Pa began to snore, and when the doctor came in it took them half an hour to wake him, and then he was awful sick to his stummick, and then Ma asked the doctor if he would live, and the doc. analyzed the ketchup and smelled of it and told Ma he would be all right if he had a little Worcester sauce to put on with the ketchup, and when he said Pa would pull through, Ma looked awful sad. Then Pa opened his eyes and saw the minister and said that was one of the robbers that jumped on him, and he wanted to whip the minister, but the doc. held Pa's arms, and Ma sat on his legs, and the minister said he had got some other calls to make, and he wished Ma a happy new year in the hall, much as fifteen minutes. His happy new year to Ma is most as long as his prayers. Well, we got Pa to bed, and when we undressed him we found nine napkins in the bosom of his vest, that he had picked up at the places where he called   He is all right this morning, but he says it is the last time he will drink coffee when he makes New Year's calls."

"Well, then you didn't have much fun yourself on New Years. That's too bad," said the grocery man, as he looked at the sad-eyed youth. "But you look hard. If you were old enough I should say you had been drunk, your eyes are so red."

"Didn't have any fun eh? Well, I wish I had as many dollars as I had fun. You see, after Pa got to sleep Ma wanted me and my chum to go to the houses that Pa had called at and return the napkins he had kleptomaniaced, so we dressed up and went. The first house we called at the girls were sort of demoralized. I don't know as I ever saw a girl drunk, but those girls acted queer. The callers had stopped coming, and the girls were drinking something out of shaving cups that looked like lather, and they said it was 'aig-nogg.' They laffed and kicked up their heels wuss nor a circus, and their collars got unpinned, and their faces was red, and they put their arms around me and my chum and hugged us and asked us if we didn't want some of the custard. You'd a dide to see me and my chum drink that lather. It looked just like soap suds with nutmaig in it, but by gosh it got in its work sudden. At first I was afraid

I WAS NOT AFRAID NO MORE.

when the girls hugged me, but after I had drank a couple of shaving cups full of the 'aig-nogg' I wasn't afraid no more, and I hugged a girl so hard she catched her breath and panted, and said, 'O don't.' Then I kissed her, and she is a great big girl, bigger'n me, but she didn't care. Say, did you ever kiss a girl full of aig-nogg? If you did it would break up your grocery business. You would want to waller in bliss instead of selling mackerel. My chum ain't no slouch either. He was sitting in a stuffed chair holding another New Year's girl, and I could hear him kiss her so it sounded like a cutter scraping on bare ground. But the girl's Pa came in and said he guessed it was time to close the place, unless they had a license for an all night house, and me and my chum went out. But *wasn't* we sick when we got out doors. O, it seemed as though the pegs in my boots was the only thing that kept them down, and my chum he liked to dide. He had been to dinner and supper and I had only been skating all day, so he had more to contend with than I did. O, my, but that lets me out on aig-nogg. I don't know how I got home, but I got in bed with Pa, cause Ma was called away to attend a baby matinee in the night. I don't know how it is, but there never is anybody in our part of the town that has a baby but they have it in the night, and they send for Ma. I don't know what she has to be sent for every time for. Ma ain't to blame for all the young ones in this town, but she has got up a reputashun, and when we hear the bell ring in the night Ma gets up and begins to put on her clothes, and the next morning she comes in the dining room with a shawl over her head; and says, 'It's a girl and weighs ten pounds,' or a boy, if it's a boy baby. Ma was out on one of her professional engagements, and I got in bed with Pa. I had heard Pa blame Ma about her cold feet, so I got a piece of ice about as big as a raisin box, just zactly like one of Ma's feet, and I laid it right against the small of Pa's back. I couldn't help laffin, but pretty soon Pa began to squirm and he said, 'Why'n 'ell don't you warm them feet before you come to bed?' and then he hauled back his leg and kicked me clear out in the middle of the floor, and said if he married again he would marry a woman who had lost both of her feet in a railroad accident. Then I put the ice back in the bed with Pa and went to my room, and in the morning Pa said he sweat more'n a pail full in the night. Well you must excuse me. I have an engagement to shovel snow off the sidewalk. But before I go, let me advise you not to drink aig-nogg, and don't sell tom cats for rabbits," and he got out the door just in time to miss the rutabaga that the grocery man threw at him.

CHAPTER XXX

HIS PA DISSECTED

The miseries of the mumps—No pickles thank you—One more effort to reform the old man—The bad boy plays medical student—Proceeds to dissect his Pa—"Gentlemen I am not dead!"—Saved from the scalpel!—"No more whisky for you."

"I UNDERSTAND your Pa has got to drinking again like a fish," says the grocery man to the bad boy, as the youth came in the grocery and took a hand full of dried apples. The boy ate a dried apple and then made up a terrible face, and the grocery man asked him what he was trying to do with his face. The boy caught his breath and then said:

"Say, don't you know any better than to keep dried apples where a boy can get hold of them when he has got the mumps? You will kill some boy yet by such dum carelessness. I thought there were sweet dried apples, but they are sour as a boarding-house keeper, and they make me tired. Didn't you ever have the mumps? Gosh, but don't it hurt though? You have got to be darned careful when you have the mumps, and not go out bob-sledding, or skating, or you will have your neck swell up biggern a milk pail. Pa says he had the mumps once when he was a boy and it broke him all up."

"Well, never mind the mumps, how about your Pa spreeing it? Try one of those pickles in the jar there, won't you? I always like to have a boy enjoy himself when he comes to see me," said the grocery man, winking to a man who was filling an old fashioned tin box with tobacco out of the pail, who winked back as much as to say, "If that boy eats a pickle on top of them mumps we will have a circus, sure."

"You can't play no pickle on me, not when I have the mumps. Ma passed the pickles to me this morning, and I

took one mouthful, and like to had the lockjaw. But Ma
didn't do it on purpose, I guess. She never had the mumps
and didn't know how discouraging a pickle is. Darn if I
didn't feel as though I had been struck in the butt of the
ear with a brick. But about Pa. He has been fuller'n a
goose ever since New Year's day. I thing it's wrong for
women to tempt feeble minded persons with liquor on New
Year's. Now me and my chum, we can take a drink and
then let it alone. We have got brains, and know when we
have got enough, but Pa, when he gets to going don't ever

FOR GOD'S SAKE, GENTLEMEN, WHAT
DOES THIS MEAN?

stop until he gets so sick that he can't keep his stummick
inside of hisself. It is getting so they look to me to brace Pa
up every time he gets on a tear, and I guess I fixed him
this time so he will never touch liquor again. I scared him
so his bald head turned gray in a single night."

"What under the heavens have you done to him now?"
says the grocery man, in astonishment. "I hope you haven't
done anything you will regret in after years."

"Regret nothing," said the boy, as he turned the lid of
the cheese box back and took the knife and sliced off a
piece of cheese, and took a few crackers out of a barrel, and
sat down on a soap box by the stove, "You see Ma was

annoyed to death with Pa. He would come home full, when
she had company, and lay down on the sofa and snore, and
he would smell like a distillery. It hurt me to see ma cry, and
I told her I would break Pa of drinking if she would let me,
and she said if I would promise not to hurt Pa to go ahead,
and I promised not to. Then I got my chum and another
boy, quite a big boy, to help, and Pa is all right. We went
down to the place where they sell arms and legs to folks
who have served in the army, or a saw mill, or a threshing
machine, and lost their limbs, and we borrowed some arms
and legs, and fixed up a dissecting room. We fixed a long
table in the basement, big enough to lay Pa out on you
know, and then we got false whiskers and mustaches, and
when Pa came in the house drunk and laid down on the sofa,
and got to sleep, we took him and laid him out on the table,
and took some trunk straps, and a sircingle and strapped
him down to the table. He slept right along all through it,
and we had another table with the false arms and legs on,
and we rolled up our sleeves, and smoked pipes, just like I
read that medical students do when they cut up a man.
Well, you'd a dide to see Pa look at us when he woke up.
I saw him open his eyes, and then we began to talk about
cutting up dead men. We put hickory nuts in our mouths
so our voices would sound different, so he wouldn't know us,
and I was telling the other boys about what a time we had
cutting up the last man we bought. I said he was awful
tough, and when we had got his legs off, and had taken out
his brain, his friends came to the dissecting room and
claimed the body, and we had to give it up, but I saved the
legs. I looked at Pa on the table and he began to turn pale,
and he squirmed around to get up, but found he was fast.
I had pulled his shirt up under his arms, while he was asleep,
and as he began to move, and I took an icicle, and in the dim
light of the candles, that were sitting on the table in beer
bottles, I drew the icicle across Pa's stummick, and I said to
my chum, 'Doc, I guess we had better cut open this old
duffer and see if he died from inflammation of the stummick,

from hard drinking, as the coroner said he did.' Pa shuddered all over when he felt the icicle going over his bare stummick, and he said, 'For God's sake, gentlemen, what does this mean? I am not dead.'

"The other boys looked at Pa with astonishment, and I said, 'Well, we bought you for dead, and the coroner's jury said you were dead, and by the eternal, we ain't going to be fooled out of a corpse when we buy one, are we doc?' My chum said not if he knowed hisself, and the other students said, 'Of course he is dead. He thinks he is alive, but he died day before yesterday, fell dead on the street, and his folks said he had been a nuisance and they wouldn't claim the corpse, and we bought it at the morgue.' Then I drew the icicle across him again, and I said, 'I don't know about this, doctor.

THAT'S A PRETTY NARROW ESCAPE, OLD MAN.

I find the blood follows the scalpel as I cut through the cuticle. Hand me the blood sponge please.' Pa

began to wiggle around, and we looked at him, and my
chum raised his eye-lid, and looked solemn, and Pa said,
'Hold on, gentlemen. Don't cut into me any more, and I
can explain this matter. This is all a mistake. I was only
drunk.' We went in a corner and whispered, and Pa kept
talking all the time. He said if we would postpone the hog
killing he could send and get witnesses to prove that he was
not dead, but that he was a respectable citizen, and had a
family. After we held a consultaticn I went to Pa and told
him that what he said about being alive might possibly be
true, though we had our doubts. We had found such cases
before in our practice east, where men seemed to be alive,
but it was only temporary. Before we had got them cut up
they were dead enough for all practical purposes. Then I
laid the icicle across Pa's abdomen, and went on to tell him
that even if he *was* alive, it would be better for him to play
that he was dead, because he was such a nuisance to his
family that they did not want him, and I was telling him
that I had heard that in his lifetime he was very cruel to his
boy, a bright little fellow who was at the head of his class in
Sunday school, and a pet wherever he was known, when Pa
interrupted me and said, 'Doctor, please take that carving
knife off my stummick, for it makes me nervous. As for
that boy of mine, he is the condemndest little whelp in town,
and he isn't no pet anywhere. Now, you let up on this dissecting business, and I will make it all right with you.' We
held another consultation and then I told Pa that we did not
feel that it was doing justice to society to give up the body
of a notorious drunkard, after we had paid twenty dollars
for the corpse. If there was any hopes that he would reform
and try and lead a different life, it would be different, and I
said to the boys, 'Gentlemen, we must do our duty. Doc,
you dismember that leg, and I will attend to the stomach
and the upper part of the body. He will be dead before we
are done with him. We must remember that society has
some claims on us, and not let our better natures be worked
upon by the *post mortem* promises of a dead drunkard.'

Then I took my icicle and began fumbling around the abdomen portion of Pa's remains, and my chum took a rough piece of ice and began to saw his leg off, while the other boy took hold of the leg and said he would catch it when it dropped off. Well, Pa kicked like a steer. He said he wanted to make one more appeal to us, and we acted sort of impatient, but we let up to hear what he had to say. He said if we would turn him loose he would give us ten dollars more than we paid for his body, and that he would never drink another drop as long as he lived. Then we whispered some more, and then told him we thought favorably of his last proposition, but he must swear, with his hand on the leg of a corpse we were then dissecting, that he would never drink again, and then he must be blindfolded and be conducted several blocks away from the dissecting room, before we could turn him loose. He said that was all right, and so we blindfolded him, and made him take a bloody oath, with his hand on a piece of ice that we told him was a piece of another corpse, and then we took him out of the house and walked him around the block four times, and left him on a corner, after he had promised to send the money to an address that I gave him. We told him to stand still five minutes after we left him, then remove the blindfold, and go home. We watched him from behind a board fence, and he took off the handkerchief, looked at the name on a street lamp, and found he was not far from home. He started off saying, 'That's a pretty narrow escape, old man. No more whisky for you.' I did not see him again until this morning, and when I asked him where he was last night he shuddered and said, 'None of your darn business. But I never drink any more, you remember that.' Ma was tickled and she told me I was worth my weight in gold. Well, good-day. That cheese is musty." And the boy went and caught on a passing sleigh.

CHAPTER XXXI

HIS PA JOINS A TEMPERANCE SOCIETY

The grocery man sympathizes with the old man—Warns the bad boy that he may have a step-father!—The bad boy scorns the idea—Introduces his Pa to the grand "worthy dude!"—The solemn oath—The brand plucked from the burning.

"DON'T you think my Pa is showing his age a good deal more than usual?" asked the bad boy of the grocery man, as he took a smoked herring out of the box and peeled off the skin with a broken bladed jack-knife, and split it open and ripped off the bone, threw the head at a cat, and took some crackers and began to eat.

"Well, I don't know but he does look as though he was getting old," said the grocery man, as he took a piece of yellow wrapping paper, and charged the boy's poor old father with a dozen herrings and a pound of crackers; "but there is no wonder he is getting old. I wouldn't go through what your father has, the last year, for a million dollars. I tell you, boy, when your father is dead, and you get a step-father, and he makes you walk the chalk mark, you will realize what a bonanza you have fooled yourself out of by killing off your father. The way I figure it, your father will last about six months, and you ought to treat him right, the little time he has to live."

"Well, I am going to," said the boy, as he picked the herring bones out of his teeth with a piece of match that he sharpened with his knife. "But I don't believe in borrowing trouble about a step-father so long before hand. I don't think Ma could get a man to step into Pa's shoes as long as I lived, not if she was inlaid with diamonds, and owned a brewery. There are brave men, I know, that are on the marry, but none of them would want to be brevet

160

father to a cherubim like me, except he got pretty good wages. And then, since Pa was dissected he is going to lead a different life, and I guess I will make a man of him, if he holds out. We got him to join the Good Templars last night."

"No, you don't tell me," said the grocery man, as he thought that his trade in cider for mince pies would be cut off. "So you got him in the Good Templars, eh?"

"Well, he thinks he has joined the Good Templars, so it is all the same. You see my chum and me have been going to a private gymnasium, on the west side, kept by a dutchman, and in a back room he has all the tools for getting up muscle. There, look at my arm," said the boy, as he rolled up his sleeve and showed a muscle about as big as an oyster. "That is the result of training at the gymnasium. Before I took lessons I hadn't any more muscle than you have got. Well, the dutchman was going to a dance on the south side the other night, and he asked my chum to tend the gymnasium, and I told Pa if he would join the Good Templars that night there wouldn't be many at the lodge, and he wouldn't be so embarrassed, as I was one of the officers of the lodge I would put it to him light, and he said he would go, so my chum got five other boys to help us put him through. So we steered him down to the gymnasium, and made him rap on the storm door outside, and I said, 'Who comes there?' and he said it was a pilgrim who wanted to jine our sublime order. I asked him if he had made up his mind to turn from the ways of a hyena, and adopt the customs of the truly good, and he said if he knew his own heart, he had, and then I told him to come in out of the snow and take off his pants. He kicked a little at taking off his pants, because it was cold out there in the storm-door dog house, but I told him they all had to do it. The princes, potentates and paupers all had to come to it. He asked me how it was when we initiated a woman, and I told him women never took that degree. He pulled off his pants, and wanted a check for them, but I told him the

11

Grand Mogul would hold his clothes, and then I blind-folded him, and with a base ball club I pounded on the floor as I walked around the gymnasium, while the lodge, headed by my chum, sung 'We won't go home till morning.' I stopped in front of the ice-water tank and said, 'Grand Worthy Duke, I bring before you a pilgrim who has drank of the dregs until his stomach won't hold water, and who desires to swear off.' The Grand Mogul asked me if he was worthy and well qualified, and I told him that he had been drunk more or less since the reunion last summer, which ought to qualify him. Then the Grand Mogul made Pa repeat the most blood-curdling oath, in which Pa agreed, if he ever drank another drop, to allow anybody to pull his toe-nails out with tweezers, to have his liver dug out and fed to dogs, his head chopped off, and his eyes removed. Then the Mogul said he would brand the candidate on the bare back with the initial letters of our order, 'G. T.,' that all might read how a brand had been snatched from the burning. You'd a dide to see Pa flinch when I pulled up his shirt, and got ready to brand him.

"My chum got a piece of ice out of the water cooler, and just as he clapped it on Pa's back I burned a piece of horse's hoof in the candle and held it to Pa's nose, and I guess Pa actually thought it was his burning skin that he smelled. He jumped about six feet and said, 'Great heavens, what you dewin!' and then he began to roll over a barrel which I had arranged for him. Pa thought he was going down cellar, and he hung to the barrel, but he was on top half the time. When Pa and the barrel got through fighting I was beside him, and I said, 'Calm yourself, and be prepared for the ordeal that is to follow.' Pa asked how much of this dum fooling there was, and said he was sorry he joined. He said he could let licker alone without having the skin all burned off his back. I told Pa to be brave and not weaken, and all would be well. He wiped the perspiration off his face on the end of his shirt, and we put a belt around his body and hitched it to a tackle, and pulled him up so his

feet were just off the floor, and then we talked as though
we were away off, and I told my chum to look out that Pa
did not hit the gas fixtures, and Pa actually thought he was
being hauled clear up to the roof. I could see he was scared
by the complexion of his hands and feet, as they clawed the

BIMEBY WE LET HIM DOWN.

air. He actually sweat so the drops fell on the floor.
Bimeby we let him down, and he was awfully relieved,
thought his feet were not more than two inches from the
floor any of the time. We were just going to slip Pa down
a board with slivers in to give him a realizing sense of the
rough road a reformed man was to travel, and got him

straddle of the board, when the dutchman came home from the dance, fullern a goose and he drove us boys out, and we left Pa, and the dutchman said, 'Vot you vas doing here mit dose boys, you old duffer, and vere vas your pants?' and Pa pulled off his handkerchief from his eyes, and the dutchman said if he didn't get out in a holy minute he would kick the stuffing out of him, and Pa got out. He took his pants and put them on in the alley, and then we come up to Pa and told him that was the third time the drunken dutchman had broke up our lodge, but we should keep on doing good until we had reformed every drunkard in Milwaukee, and Pa said that was right, and he would see us through if it cost every dollar he had. Then we took him home, and when Ma asked if she couldn't join the lodge too, Pa said, 'Now you take my advice, and don't you ever join no Good Templars. Your system could not stand the racket. Say, I want you to put some cold cream on my back.' I think Pa will be a different man now, don't you?"

The grocery man said if he was that boy's Pa for fifteen minutes, he would be a different boy, or there would be a funeral, and the boy took a handful of soft-shelled almonds and few layer raisins, and skipped out.

CHAPTER XXXII

HIS PA'S MARVELOUS ESCAPE

The grocery man has no vaseline—The old man provides three fire
escapes—One of the escapes tested—His Pa scandalizes the church
—"She's a darling!"—Worldly music in the courts of Zion.

"Got any vaseline?" said the bad boy to the grocery man,
as he went into the store one cold morning, leaving the door
open, and picked up a cigar stub that had been thrown down
near the stove, and began to smoke it.

"Shut the door, dum you. Was you brought up in a saw
mill? You'll freeze every potato in the house. No, I haven't
got vaseline. What do you want of vaseline?" said the
grocery man, as he sat the syrup keg on a chair by the stove
where it would thaw out.

"Want to rub it on Pa's legs," said the boy, as he tried
to draw smoke through the cigar stub.

"What is the matter with your Pa's legs? Rheumatiz?"

"Wuss nor rheumatiz," said the boy, as he threw away
the cigar stub and drew some cider in a broken tea cup.
"Pa has got the worst looking hind legs you ever saw. You
see, since there has been so many fires Pa has got offul
scared, and he has bought three fire escapes, made out of
rope with knots in them, and he has been telling us every day
how he could rescue the whole family in case of fire. He
told us to keep cool, whatever happened, and to rely on him.
If the house got on fire we were all to rush to Pa, and he
would save us. Well, last night Ma had to go to one of the
neighbors where they was going to have twins, and we didn't
sleep much, cause Ma had to come home twice in the night
to get saffron, and an old flannel petticoat that I broke in
when I was a kid, cause the people where Ma went did not
know as twins was on the bill of fare, and they only had

165

flannel petticoat for one. Pa was cross at being kept awake, and told Ma he hoped when all the children in Milwaukee were born, and got grown up, she would take in her sign and not go around nights and act as usher to baby matinees. Pa says there ought to be a law that babies should arrive only on the regular day trains, and not wait for the midnight express. Well, Pa he got asleep, and he slept till about eight o'clock in the morning, and the blinds were closed, and it was dark in his room, and I had to wait for my breakfast till I was hungry as a wolf, and the girl told me to wake Pa up, so I went up-stairs, and I don't know what made me think of it, but I had some of this powder they make red fire with in the theater, that me and my chum had the 4th of July, and I put it in a washdish in the bath-room, and I touched it off and hollered fire. I was going to wake Pa up and tell him it was all right and laugh at him. I guess there was too much fire, or I yelled too loud, cause Pa jumped out of bed and grabbed a rope and rushed through the hall toward the back window, that goes out on the shed. I tried to say something, but Pa ran over me and told me to save myself, and I got to the back window to tell him there was no fire just as he let himself out of the window. He had one end of the rope tied to the leg of the washstand, and he was climbing down the back side of the shed by the kitchen, with nothing on but his nightshirt, and he was the horriblest looking object ever was, with his legs flying and trying to stick his toe nails into the rope and side of the house. I don't think a man looks well in society with nothing on but his nightshirt. I didn't blame the hired girls for being scared when they saw Pa and his legs coming down outside the window, and when they yelled I went down to the kitchen, and they said a crazy man with no clothes on but a pillow slip around his neck was trying to kick the window in, and they ran into the parlor, and I opened the door and let Pa in the kitchen. He asked me if anybody else was saved, and then I told him there was no fire, and he must have dreamed that he was in hell, or somewhere. Well, Pa was astonished, and said he must be wrong in the head, and I left him thawing himself by the stove while I went after his pants, and his legs were badly chilled, but I guess nothin' was froze. He lays it all to Ma, and says if she would stay at home and let people run their own baby shows, there would be more comfort in the house. Ma came in with a shawl over her head, and a bowl full of something that s m e l l e d frowy, and after she had told us what the result of her visit was, she sent me after vaseline to rub Pa's legs. Pa says he has demonstrated that if a man is cool and collected, in case of fire, and goes deliberately at work to save himself, he will come out all right."

I DIDN'T BLAME THE HIRED GIRLS FOR BEING SCARED.

"Well, you are the meanest boy I ever heard of," said the grocery man. "But what about your Pa's dancing a clog dance in church Sunday? The minister's hired girl was in here after some codfish yesterday morning, and she said the minister said your Pa had scandalized the church the worst way."

"O, he didn't dance in church. He was a little excited, that's all. You see, Pa chews tobacco, and it is pretty hard on him to sit all through a sermon without taking a chew, and he gets nervous. He always reaches around in his pistol pocket, when they stand up to sing the last time, and feels in his tobacco box and gets out a chew, and puts it in his mouth when the minister pronounces the benediction, and then when they get out doors he is all ready to spit. He always does that. Well, my chum had a present, on Christmas, of a music box, just about as big as Pa's tobacco box, and all you have to do is to touch a spring and it plays, 'She's a Daisy, She's a Dumpling.' .I borrowed it and put it in Pa's pistol pocket, and when the choir got most through singing, Pa reached his hand in his pocket, and began to fumble around for a chew. He touched the spring, and just as everybody bowed their heads to receive the benediction, and it was so still you could hear a gum drop, the music box began to play, and in the stillness it sounded as loud as a church organ. Well, I thought Ma would sink. The minister heard it, and everybody looked at Pa, too, and Pa turned red, and the music box kept up, 'She's a Daisy,' and the minister looked mad and said 'Amen,' and the people began to put on their coats, and the minister told the deacon to hunt up the source of that worldly music, and they took Pa into the room back of the pulpit and searched him, and Ma says Pa will have to be churched. They kept the music box, and I have got to carry in coal to get money enough to buy my chum a new music box. Well, I shall have to go and get that vaseline or Pa's legs will suffer. Good-day."

CHAPTER XXXIII

HIS PA JOKES WITH HIM

The bad boy caught at last—How to grow a mustache—Tar and cayenne pepper—The grocery man's fate is sealed—Father and son join in a practical joke—Soft soap on the steps—Downfall of ministers and deacons—Ma to the rescue!—The bad boy gets even with his Pa.

"What on earth is that you have got on your upper lip?" said the grocery man to the bad boy, as he came in and began to peel a rutabaga, and his upper lip hung down over his teeth, and was covered with something that looked like shoemaker's wax, 'You look as though you had been digging potatoes with your nose."

"O, that is some of Pa's darn smartness. I asked him if he knew anything that would make a boy's mustache grow. and he told me the best thing he ever tried was tar, and for me to rub it on thick when I went to bed, and wash it off in the morning. I put it on last night, and by gosh I can wash it off. Pa told me all I had to do was to use a scouring brick, and it would come off, and I used the brick, and it took the skin off, and the tar is there yet, and, say, does my lip look very bad?"

The grocery man told him it was the worst looking lip he ever saw, but he could cure it by rubbing a little cayenne pepper in the tar. He said the tar would neutralize the pepper, and the pepper would loosen the tar, and act as a cooling lotion to the lacerated lip. The boy went to a can of pepper behind the counter, and stuck his finger in and rubbed a lot of it on his lip, and then his hair began to raise, and he began to cry, and rushed to the water-pail and ran his face into the water to wash off the pepper. The grocery man

169

laughed, and when the boy had got the pepper washed off, and had resumed his rutabaga, he said:

"That seals your fate. No man ever trifles with the feelings of the bold buccaneer of the Spanish main, without living to rue it. I will lay for you old man, and don't you forget it. Pa thought he was smart when he got me to put tar on my lip, to bring my mustache out, and to-day he lays on a bed of pain, and to-morrow your turn will come. You will regret that you did not get down on your knees and beg my pardon. You will be sorry that you did not prescribe cold cream for my bruised lip, instead of cayenne pepper. Beware, you base twelve ounces to the pound huckster, you gimlet-eyed seller of dog-sausage, you sanded sugar idiot, you small potato three card monte sleight of hand rotten egg fiend, you villain that sells smoked sturgeon and dogfish for smoked halibut. The avenger is on your track."

"Look here, young man, don't you threaten me, or I will take you by the ear and walk you through green fields, and beside still waters, to the front door, and kick your pistol pocket clear around so you can wear it for a watch pocket in your vest. No boy can frighten me, by crimus! But tell me, how did you get even with your Pa?"

"Well, give me a glass of cider and we will be friends and I will tell you. Thanks! Gosh, but that cider is made out of mouldy dried apples and sewer water," and he took a handful of layer raisins off the top of a box to take the taste out of his mouth, and while the grocer charged a peck of rutabagas, a gallon of cider and two pounds of raisins to the boy's Pa, the boy proceeded: "You see, Pa likes a joke the best of anybody you ever saw, if it is on somebody else, but he kicks like a steer when it is on him. I asked him this morning if it wouldn't be a good joke to put some soft soap on the front step, so the letter carrier would slip up and spill hisself, and Pa said it would be elegant. Pa is a democrat, and he thinks that anything that will make it unpleasant for republican office holders, is legitimate, and he encouraged me to paralyze the letter-carrier. The letter-carrier is as old a man as Pa, and I didn't want to humiliate him, but I just wanted Pa to give his consent, so he couldn't kick if he got caught in his own trap. You see? Well, this morning the minister and two of the deacons called on Pa, to have a talk with him about his actions in church, on two or three occasions, when he pulled out the pack of cards with his handkerchief, and played the music box and they had a pretty hot time in the back parlor, and finally they settled it, and were going to sing a hymn, when Pa handed them a little hymn book, and the minister opened it and turned pale and said, 'What's this?' and they looked at it and it was a book of Hoyle's games instead of a hymn book. Gosh, wasn't the minister mad! He had started to read a hymn and he quit after he read two lines where it said, 'In a game of four handed euchre, never trump your partner's ace, but rely on the ace to take the trick on suit.' Pa was trying to explain how the book came to be there, when the minister and deacons started out, and then I poured the two quart tin pail full of soft soap on the front step. It was this white soap,

THE MINISTER AND TWO DEACONS.

just the color of the step, and when I got it spread I went down in the basement. The visitors came out and Pa was trying to explain to them about Hoyle, when one of the deacons stepped in the soap, and his feet flew up and he struck on his pants and slid down the steps. The minister said, 'Great heavens, deacon, are you hurt? let me assist you,' and he took two quick steps, and you have seen these fellows in a nigger show that kick each other head over heels and fall on their ears, and stand on their heads and turn round like a top. The minister's feet slipped and the next I saw he was standing on his head in his hat, and his legs were sort of wilted and fell limp by his side, and he fell over on his stomach. You talk about spreading the gospel in heathen lands! It is nothing to the way you can spread it with two quarts of soft soap. The minister didn't look pious a bit, when he was trying to catch the railing, he looked as though he wanted to murder every man on earth, but it may be he was tired.

"Well, Pa was paralyzed, and he and the other deacon rushed out to pick up the minister and the first old man, and when they struck the step they went kiting. Pa's feet somehow slipped backward, and he turned a somersault and struck full length on his back, and one heel was across the minister's neck, and he slid down the steps, and the other deacon fell all over the other three, and Pa swore at them, and it was the worst looking lot of pious people I ever saw. I think if the minister had been in the woods somewhere, where nobody could have heard him, he would have used language. They all seemed mad at each other. The hired girl told Ma there was three tramps out on the sidewalk fighting Pa, and Ma she took the broom and started to help Pa, and I tried to stop Ma, 'cause her constitution is not very strong and I didn't want her to do any flying trapeze bizness, but I couldn't stop her, and she went out with the broom and a towel tied around her head. Well, I don't know where Ma did strike, but when she came in she said she had palpitation of the heart, but that was not the place where she put the arnica. O, but she *did* go through the air like a bullet through cheese, and when she went down the steps a bumpity-bump, I felt sorry for Ma. The minister.

TALK ABOUT SPREADING THE GOSPEL.

had got so he could sit up on the sidewalk, with his back against the lower step, when Ma came sliding down, and one of the heels of her gaiters hit the minister in the hair, and the other foot went right through between his arm and his side, and the broom like to pushed his teeth down his throat.

But he was not mad at Ma. As soon as he see it was Ma he said, 'Why, sister, the wicked stand in slippery places, don't they?' and Ma she was mad and said for him to let go her stocking, and then Pa was mad and he said, 'Look-a-here, you sky pilot, this thing has gone far enough,' and then a policeman came along, and first he thought they were all drunk, but he found they were respectable, and he got a chip and scraped the soap off of them, and they went home, and Pa and Ma they got in the house some way, and just then the letter-carrier came along, but he didn't have any letters for us, and he didn't come onto the steps, and then I went up stairs and I said, 'Pa, don't you think it is real mean, after you and I fixed the soap on the steps for the letter-carrier, he didn't come on the steps at all?' and Pa was scraping the soap off his pants with a piece of shingle, and the hired girl was putting liniment on Ma, and heating it in for palpitation of the heart, and Pa said, 'You dam idjut, no more of this, or I'll maul the liver out of you,' and I asked him if he didn't think soft soap would help a mustache to grow, and he picked up Ma's work-basket and threw it at my head, as I went down stairs, and I came over here. Don't you think my Pa is unreasonable to get mad at a little joke that he planned himself?"

The grocery man said he didn't know, and the boy went out with a pair of skates over his shoulder, and the grocery man is wondering what joke the boy will play on him to get even for the cayenne pepper.

CHAPTER XXXIV

HIS PA GETS MAD

A boom in court plaster—The bad boy declines being mauled!—The old man gets a hot box—The bad boy borrows a cat!—The battle!—"Helen blazes"—The cat victorious!—The bad boy draws the line at kindling wood!

"I WAS down to the drug store this morning, and saw your Ma buying a lot of court-plaster, enough to make a shirt, I should think. What's she going to do with so much court-plaster?" asked the grocery man of the bad boy, as he came in and pulled off his boots by the stove and emptied

I BORROWED A CAT.

out a lot of snow, that had collected as he walked through a drift, which melted and made a bad smell.

"O, I guess she is going to patch Pa up so he will hold water. Pa's temper got him in the worst muss you ever see, last night. If that museum was here now they would hire Pa and exhibit him as the tattooed man. I tell you I have got too old to be mauled as though I was a kid, and any man who attacks me from this out wants to have his peace made with the insurance companies, and know that his calling and election is sure, because I am a bad man, and don't you forget it." And the boy pulled on his boots and looked so cross and desperate that the grocery man asked him if he wouldn't try a little new cider.

"Good heavens!" said the grocery man, as the boy swallowed the cider, and his face resumed its natural look, and the piratical frown disappeared with the cider. "You have not stabbed your father, have you? I have feared that one thing would bring on another, with you, and that you would yet be hung."

"Naw, I haven't stabbed him. It was another cat that stabbed him. You see, Pa wants me to do all the work around the house. The other day he bought a load of kindling wood, and told me to carry it into the basement. I have not been educated up to kindling wood, and I didn't do it. When supper time came, and Pa found that I had not carried in the kindling wood, he had a hot box, and he told me that if that wood was not in when he came back from the lodge, that he would warm my jacket. Well, I tried to hire some one to carry it in, and got a man to promise to come in the morning and carry it in and take his pay in groceries, and I was going to buy the groceries here and have them charged to Pa. But that wouldn't help me out that night. I knew when Pa came home he would search for me. So I slept in the back hall on a cot. But I didn't want Pa to have all his trouble for nothing, so I borrowed an old tom cat that my chum's old maid aunt owns, and put the cat in my bed. I thought if Pa came in my room after me, and found that by his unkindness I had changed to a tom cat, he would be sorry. That is the biggest cat you ever see, and the worst fighter in our ward. It isn't afraid of anything, and can whip a Newfoundland dog quicker than you can put sand in a barrel of sugar. Well, about eleven o'clock I heard Pa tumble over the kindling wood, and I knew by the remark he made, as the wood slid around under him, that there was going to be a cat fight real quick. He came up to Ma's room, and sounded Ma as to whether Hennery had retired to his virtuous couch. Pa is awful sarcastic when he tries to be. I could hear him take off his clothes, and hear him say, as he picked up a trunk strap, 'I guess I will go up to

PA'S SHIRT WAS NO PROTECTION AT ALL.

his room and watch the smile on his face, as he dreams of the angels. I yearn to press him to my aching bosom.' I thought to myself, 'Maybe you won't yearn so much directly.' He come up stairs, and I could hear him breathing hard. I looked around the corner and could see he just had on his shirt and pants, and his suspenders were hanging down, and his bald head shone like a calcium light just before it explodes. Pa went in my room, and up to the bed, and I could hear him say, 'Come out here and bring in that kindling wood, or I will start a fire on your base-burner with this strap.' And then there was a yowling such as I never heard before, and Pa said, 'Helen Blazes,' and the furniture in my room began to fall around and break. O, *my!* I think Pa took the tom cat right by the neck, the way he does me, and that left all the cat's feet free to get in their work. By the way the cat squalled as though it was being choked, I know Pa had him by the neck. I suppose the cat thought Pa was a whole flock of Newfoundland dogs, and the cat had a record on dogs, and it kicked awful. Pa's shirt was no protection at all in a cat fight, and the cat just walked all around Pa's stomach, and Pa yelled 'Police,' and, Fire,' and 'Turn on the hose,' and he called Ma, and the cat yowled. If pa had had the presence of mind enough to have dropped the cat, or rolled it up in the mattress, it would have been all right, but a man always gets rattled in time of danger, and he held onto the cat and started down stairs yelling murder, and he met Ma coming up.

"I guess Ma's night cap, or something frightened the cat some more, cause he stabbed Ma on the night-shirt with one hind foot, and Ma said, 'Mercy on us,' and she went back, and Pa stumbled on a hand-sled that was on the stairs, and they all fell down, and the cat got away and went down in the coal bin and yowled all night. Pa and Ma went into their room, and I guess they anointed themselves with vaseline, and Pond's extract, and I went and got into my bed, cause it was cold out in the hall, and the cat had warmed my bed as well as it had warmed Pa. It was all I could do to go to sleep, with Pa and Ma talking all night, and this morning I came down the back stairs, and haven't been to breakfast, cause I don't want to see Pa when he is vexed. You let the man that carries in the kindling wood have six shillings worth of groceries and charge them to Pa. I have passed the kindling wood period in a boy's life, and have arrived at the coal period. I will carry in coal, but I draw the line at kindling wood."

"Well, you are a cruel, bad boy," said the grocery man, as he went to the book and charged the six shillings.

"O, I don't know. I think Pa is cruel. A man who will take a poor kitty by the neck, that hasn't done any harm, and tries to chastise the poor thing with a trunk strap, ought to be looked after by the humane society. And if it is cruel to take a cat by the neck, how much more cruel is it to take a boy by the neck, that had diphtheria only a few years ago, and whose throat is tender. Say, I guess I will accept your invitation to take breakfast with you," and the boy cut off a piece of bologna and helped himself to the crackers, and while the grocery man was out shoveling off the snow from the sidewalk, the boy filled his pockets with raisins and loaf sugar, and then went out to watch the man carry in his kindling wood.

CHAPTER XXXV

HIS PA AN INVENTOR

The bad boy a martyr—The dog collar in the sausage—A patent stove —The patent tested!—His Pa a burnt offering—Early breakfast!

"HA! Ha! Now I have got you," said the grocery man to the bad boy, the other morning, as he came in, jumped upon the counter and tied the end of a ball of twine to the tail of a dog, and "sicked" the dog on another dog that was following a passing sleigh, causing the twine to pay out until the whole ball was scattered along the block. "Condemn you, I've a notion to choke the liver out of you. Who tied that twine to the dog's tail?"

The boy choked up with emotion, and the tears came into his eyes and he said he didn't know anything about the twine or the dog. He said he noticed the dog come in, and wag his tail around the twine, but he supposed the dog was a friend of the family and did not disturb him. "Everybody lays everything that is done to me," said the boy, as he put his handkerchief to his nose, "and they will be sorry for it when I die. I have a good notion to poison myself by eating some of your glucose sugar."

"Yes, and you do about everything that is mean. The other day a lady came in and told me to send up to her house some of my country sausage, done up in muslin bags, and while she was examining it she noticed something hard inside the bags, and asked me what it was, and I opened it, and I hope to die if there wasn't a little brass padlock and a piece of red morrocco dog collar imbedded in the sausage.

"Now, how do you suppose that got in there?" and the grocery man looked savage.

The boy looked interested and put on an expression as though in deep thought, and finally said: "I suppose the

180

farmer that put up the sausage did not strain the dog meat. Sausage meat ought to be strained."

The grocery man pulled in about half a block of twine, after the dog had run against a fence and broke it, and told the boy he knew perfectly well how the brass padlock came to be in the sausage, but thinking it was safer to have the good will of the boy than the ill will, he offered him a handful of prunes.

"No," said the boy, "I have sworn off on mouldy prunes. I am no kindergarten any more. For years I have eaten rotten peaches around this store, and everything you couldn't sell, but I have turned over a new leaf now, and after this nothing is too good for me. Since Pa has got to be an inventor, we are going to live high."

"What's your Pa invented? I saw a hearse and t h r e e hacks go up on your street the other day and I thought maybe you had killed your Pa."

"Not much, there will be more than three hacks when I kill Pa, and don't you forget it. Well sir, Pa has struck a fortune, if he can make the thing work. He has got an idea about coal stoves that will bring him several million dollars if he gets a royalty of five dollars on every cook stove in the world. His idea is to have a coal stove on casters, with the pipe made to telescope out and in, and rubber hose for one joint, so you can pull the stove all around the room and warm any particular place. Well, sir, to hear Pa tell about it, you would think it would revolutionize the country, and maybe it will when he gets it perfected, but he came near burning the house up, and scared us half to death this morning, and burned his shirt off, and he is all covered with cotton with sweet oil on, and he smells like salad dressing.

"You see Pa had a pipe made and some castors put on our coal stove, and he tied a rope to the hearth of the stove and had me put in some kindling wood and coal last night, so he could draw the stove up to the bed and light the fire without getting up. Ma told him he would put his foot in it, and he told her to dry up, and let him run the stove business. He said it took a man with brain to run a patent right, and Ma she pulled the clothes over her head and let Pa do the fire act. She has been building the fires for twenty years, and thought she would let Pa see how good it was. Well, Pa pulled the stove to the bed, and touched off the kindling wood. I guess may-be I got a bundle of kindling wood that the hired girl had put kerosene on, cause it blazed up awful and smoked, and the blaze bursted out the doors and windows of the stove, and Pa yelled fire, and I jumped out of bed and rushed in and he was the scartest man you ever see and you'd a dide to see how he kicked when I threw a pail of water on his legs and put his shirt out. Ma did not get burned, but she was pretty wet, and she told Pa she would pay the five dollars royalty on that stove and take the castors off and let it remain stationary. Pa says he will make it work if he burns the house down. I think it was real mean in Pa to get mad at me because I threw cold water

on him instead of warm water, to put his shirt out. If I
had waited till I could heat water to the right temperature I
would have been an orphan, and Pa would have been a burnt
offering. But some men always kick at everything. Pa
has given up business entirely and says he shall devote the
remainder of his life curing himself of the different troubles

PA SAID IT MADE A MAN FEEL GOOD TO GET UP EARLY.

that I get him into. He has retained a doctor by the year,
and he buys liniment by the gallon."

"What was it about your folks getting up in the middle
of the night to eat? The hired girl was over here after
some soap the other morning, and she said she was going to
leave your house."

"Well, that was a picnic. Pa said he wanted breakfast

earlier than we were in the habit of having it, and he said I might see to it that the house was awake early enough. The other night I awoke with the awfulest pain you ever heard of. It was that night that you gave me and my chum the bottle of pickled oysters that had begun to work. Well, I couldn't sleep, and I thought I would call the hired girls, and they got up and got breakfast to going, and then I rapped on Pa and Ma's door and told them the breakfast was getting cold, and they got up and came down. We eat breakfast by gas light, and Pa yawned and said that it made a man feel good to get up and get ready for work before daylight, the way he used to on the farm, and Ma she yawned and agreed with Pa, 'cause she has to, or have a row. After breakfast we sat around for an hour, and Pa said it was a long time getting daylight, and bimeby Pa looked at his watch. When he began to pull out his watch I lit out and hid in the storeroom, and pretty soon I heard Pa and Ma come up stairs and go to bed, and then the hired girls, they went to bed, and when it was all still, and the pain had stopped inside my clothes, I went to bed, and I looked to see what time it was and it was two o'clock in the morning. We got dinner at eight o'clock in the morning and Pa said he guessed he would call up the house after this, so I have lost another job and it was all on account of that bottle of pickled oysters you gave me. My chum says he had the colic too, but he didn't call up his folks. It was all he could do to get up hisself. Why don't you sometimes give away something that is not spoiled?"

The grocery man said he guessed he knew what to give away, and the boy went out and hung up a sign in front of the grocery, that he had made on wrapping paper with red chalk, which read, "Rotten eggs, good enough for custard pies, for 18 cents a dozen."

CHAPTER XXXVI

HIS PA GETS BOXED

A parrot for sale—The old man is down on the grocer—"A contrite heart beats a bob-tail flush!"—Polly's responses—Can a parrot go to hell?—The old man gets another black eye—Duffy hits for keeps —Nothing like an oyster for a black eye.

"You don't want to buy a good parrot, do you?" said the bad boy to the grocery man, as he put his wet mittens on the top of the stove to dry and kept his back to the stove so he could watch the grocery man, and be prepared for a kick, if the man should remember the rotten-egg sign that the boy put up in front of the grocery, last week.

"Naw, I don't want no parrot. I had rather have a fool boy around than a parrot. But what's the matter with your Ma's parrot? I thought she wouldn't part with him for anything."

"Well, she wouldn't until Wednesday night; but now she says she will not have him around, and I may have half I can get for him. She told me to go to some saloon, or some disreputable place and sell him, and I thought maybe he would about suit you," and the boy broke into a bunch of celery, and took out a few tender stalks and rubbed them on a codfish, to salt them, and began to bite the stalks, while he held the sole of one wet boot up against the stove to dry it, making a smell of burned leather that came near turning the stomach of the cigar sign.

"Look-a-here, boy, don't you call this a disreputable place. Some of the best people in this town come here," said the grocery man, as he held up the cheese-knife and grated his teeth as though he would like to jab it into the youth.

"O, that's all right, they come here 'cause you trust; but

185

you make up what you lose by charging it to other people, Pa will make it hot for you the last of the week. He has been looking over your bill, and comparing it with the hired girl, and she says we haven't ever had a prune, or a dried apple, or a raisin, or any cinnamon, or crackers and cheese out of your store, and he says you are worse than the James Brothers, and that you used to be a three card monte man; and he will have you arrested for highway robbery, but you can settle that with Pa. I like you, because you are no ordinary sneak thief. You are a high-toned, gentlemanly sort of a bilk, and wouldn't take anything you couldn't lift. O, keep your seat, and don't get excited. It does a man good to hear the truth from one who has got the nerve to tell it.

"But about the parrot. Ma has been away from home for a week, having a high old time in Chicago, going to theaters and things, and while she was gone, I guess the hired girl or somebody learned the parrot some new things to say. A parrot that can only say 'Polly wants a cracker,' don't amount to anything—what we need is new style parrots that can converse on the topics of the day, and say things original. Well, when Ma got back, I guess her conscience hurt her for the way she had been carrying on in Chicago, and so when she heard the basement of the church was being frescoed, she invited the committee to hold the Wednesday evening prayer meeting at our house. First, there were four people came, and Ma asked Pa to stay to make up a quorum and Pa said seeing he had two pair, he guessed he would stay in, and if Ma would deal him a queen he would have a full hand. I don't know what Pa meant; but he plays draw poker sometimes. Anyway, there were eleven people come including the minister, and after they had talked about the neighbors a spell, and Ma had showed the women a new tidy she had worked for the heathen, with a motto on it which Pa had taught her: 'A contrite heart beats a bob-tail flush,'— and Pa had talked to the men about a religious silver mine he was selling stock in, which he advised them as a friend to buy for the glory of the church, they all went in the back parlor, and the minister led in prayer. He got down on his knees right under the parrot's cage, and you'd a dide to see Polly hang on to the wires of the cage with one foot, and drop an apple core on the minister's head. Ma shook her handkerchief at Polly, and looked sassy, and Polly got up

MA SHOOK HER HANDKERCHIEF AT POLLY.

on the perch, and as the minister got warmed up, and began to raise the roof, Polly said, 'O, dry up.' The minister had his eyes shut, but he opened one of them a little and looked at Pa. Pa was tickled at the parrot, but when the minister looked at Pa as though it was him that was making irreverent remarks, Pa was mad.

"The minister got to the 'Amen,' and Polly shook hisself and said, 'What you giving us?' and the minister got up and brushed the bird seed off his knees, and he looked mad. I thought Ma would sink with mortification, and I was sitting on a piano stool, looking as pious as a Sunday School superintendent the Sunday before he skips out with the bank's funds; and Ma looked at me as though she thought it was me that had been tampering with the parrot. Gosh, I never said a word to that parrot, and I can prove it by my chum.

"Well, the minister asked one of the sisters if she wouldn't pray, and she wasn't engaged, so she said, 'With pleasure,' and she kneeled down, but she corked herself, 'cause she got one knee on a cast iron dumb bell that I had been practicing with. She said 'O my,' in a disgusted sort of a way, and then she began to pray for the reformation of the youth of the land, and asked for the spirit to descend on the household, and particularly on the boy that was such a care and anxiety to his parents, and just then Polly said, 'O, pull down your vest.' Well, you'd a dide to see that woman look at me. The parrot cage was partly behind the window curtain, and they couldn't see it, and she thought it was me. She looked at Ma as though she was wondering why she didn't hit me with a poker, but she went on, and Polly said, 'Wipe off your chin,' and then the lady got through and got up, and told Ma it must be a great trial to have an idiotic child, and then Ma she was mad and said it wasn't half so bad as it was to be a kleptomaniac, and then the woman got up and said she wouldn't stay no longer, and Pa said to me to take that parrot out doors, and that seemed to make them all good natured again. Ma said to take the parrot and give it to the poor. I took the cage and pointed my finger at the parrot and it looked at the woman and said 'Old catamaran,' and the woman tried to look pious and resigned, but she couldn't. As I was going out the door the parrot ruffed up his feathers and said, 'Dammit, set 'em up,' and I hurried out with the cage for fear he would say something bad, and the folks all held up their hands and said it was scandalous.

Say, I wonder if a parrot can go to hell with the rest of the community. Well, I put the parrot in the woodshed, and after they all had their innings, except Pa, who acted as umpire, the meeting broke up, and Ma says it's the last time she will have that gang at her house."

"That must have been where your Pa got his black eye," said the grocery man, as he charged the bunch of celery to the boy's Pa. "Did the minister hit him, or was it one of the sisters?"

THEN HE GAVE HIM A SIDE WINDER IN BOTH EYES.

"O, he didn't get his black eye at prayer meeting!" said the boy, as he took his mittens off the stove and rubbed them to take the stiffening out. "It was from boxing. Pa told my chum and me that it was no harm to learn to box; 'cause we could defend ourselves, and he said he used to be a holy terror with the boxing gloves when he was a boy, and he has been giving us lessons. Well, he is no slouch, now I tell you, and handles himself pretty well for a church member. I read in the paper how Zack Chandler played it on Conkling by getting Jem Mace, the prize fighter, to knock him silly, and I asked Pa if he wouldn't let me bring a poor boy who had no father to teach him boxing, to our house to learn to box, and Pa said, 'Certainly, fetch him along.' He said he would be glad to do anything for a poor orphan. So I went down in the Third ward and got an Irish boy by the name of Duffy, who can knock the socks off of any boy in the ward. He fit a prize fight once. It would have made you laugh to see Pa telling him how to hold his hands, and how to guard his face. He told Duffy not to be afraid, but to strike right out and hit for keeps. Duffy said he was afraid Pa would get mad if he hit him, and Pa said, 'Nonsense, boy, knock me down if you can, and I will laugh, "ha! ha!"' Well, Duffy he hauled back and gave Pa one in the nose and another in both eyes, and cuffed him on the ear and punched him in the stomach, and lammed him in the mouth and made his teeth bleed, and then he give him a side-winder in both eyes, and Pa pulled off the boxing gloves and grabbed a chair, and we adjourned and went down-stairs as though there was a panic. I haven't seen Pa since. Was his eye very black?"

"Black, I should say so," said the grocery man. "And his nose seemed to be trying to look into his left ear. He was at the market buying beefsteak to put on it."

"O, beefsteak is no account. I must go and see him and tell him that an oyster is the best thing for a black eye. Well, I must go. A boy has a pretty hard time running a house the way it should be run," and the boy went out and hung up a sign in front of the grocery: *"Frowy Butter a Speshulty!"*

PECK'S BAD BOY

AND HIS PA

VOL. II

FIRST AND ONLY COMPLETE EDITION

BY

GEORGE W. PECK

AUTHOR OF

"PECK'S FUN," "PECK'S SUNSHINE," "PECK'S BOSS BOOK," ETC.

WITH 100 ILLUSTRATIONS BY TRUE WILLIAMS

THE GROCERY MAN

AND

PECK'S BAD BOY

———

CHAPTER I

VARIEGATED DOGS

*The bad boy sleeps on the roof—A man doesn't know anything at
forty-eight—The old man wants some Pollynurious water. The
dyer's dogs—Procession of the dogs—Pink, blue, green and white—
"Well I'm dem'd"—His Pa don't appreciate.*

"How do you and your Pa get along now?" asked the
grocery man of the bad boy, as he leaned against the counter
instead of sitting down on a stool, while he bought a bottle
of liniment.

"O, I don't know. He don t seem to appreciate me.
What he ought to have is a deaf and dumb boy, with only
one leg, and both arms broke—then he could enjoy a quiet
life. But I am too gay for Pa, and you needn't be surprised
if you never see me again. I talk of going off with a circus.
Since I played the variegated dogs on Pa, there seems to
have been a coldness in the family, and I sleep on the roof."

"Variegated dogs," said the store keeper, "what kind of
a game is that? You have not played another Daisy trich
on your Pa, have you?

"Oh, no, it was nothing of that kind. You know Pa

thinks he is smart. He thinks because he is forty-eight years old he knows it all; but it don't seem to me as though a man of his age, that had sense, would let a tailor palm off on him a pair of pants so tight that he would have to use a button-hook to button them; but they can catch him on everything, just as though he was a kid smoking cigarettes. Well, you know Pa drinks some. That night the new club opened he came home pretty fruitful, and next morning his head ached so he said he would buy me a dog if I would go down town and get a bottle of pollynurious water for him. You know that dye house on Grand avenue, where they have got the four white spitz dogs. When I went after the penurious water, I noticed they had been coloring their dogs with the dye stuff, and I put up a job with the dye man's little boy to help me play it on Pa. They had one dog dyed pink, another blue, another red, and another green, and I told the boy I would treat him to ice cream if he would let one out at a time, when I came down with Pa, and call him in and let another out, and when we started to go away, to let them all out. What I wanted to do was to paralyze Pa, and make him think he had got 'em, got dogs the worst way. So, about ten o'clock, when his head got cleared off, and his stomach got settled, he changed ends with his cuffs, and we came down town, and I told him I knew where he could get a splendid white spitz dog for me, for five dollars; and if he would get it, I would never do anything disrespectful again, and would just sit up nights to please him, and help him up stairs and get seltzer for him. So we went by the dye house and just as I told him I didn't want anything but a white dog, the door opened, and the pink dog came out and barked at us, and I said, 'That's him' and the boy called him back. Pa looked as though he had the colic, and his eyes stuck out, and he said 'Hennery, that is a pink dog!' and I said 'No, it is a white dog, Pa,' and just then the green dog came out, and I asked Pa if it wasn't a pretty white dog, and Pa, he turned pale and said, 'Hell, boy, that is a green dog— what's got into the dogs?' I told him he must be color blind, and was feeling in my pocket for a strap to tie the dog, and telling him he must be careful of his health or he would see

TOLD HIM THERE WAS ONLY DOG AND A CAT.

something worse than green dogs, when the green dog went in, and the blue dog came rushing out and barked at Pa. Well, Pa leaned against a tree box, and his eyes stuck out like stops on an organ, and the sweat was all over his face in drops as big as kernels of hominy.

"I think a boy ought to do everything he can to make it pleasant for his Pa, don't *you?* And yet, some parents don't realize what a comfort a boy is. The blue dog was called in, and just as Pa wiped the perspiration off his forehead, and rubbed his eyes, and put on his specs, the red maroon dog came out. Pa acted as if he was tired, and sat down on a horse block. Dogs *do* make some people tired, don't they? He took hold of my hand, and his hand trembled just as though he was putting a gun wad in the collection plate at church, and he said, 'My son, tell me truly, is that a red dog?'

"A fellow has got to lie a little if he is going to have any fun with his Pa, and I told him it was a white dog, and I could get it for five dollars. He straightened up just as the dog went into the house, and said, 'Well, I'm dem'd;' and just then the boy let all the dogs out and sicked them on a cat, which ran up a shade tree right near Pa, and they rushed all around us—the blue dog going between his legs, and the green dog trying to climb the tree, and the pink dog barking, and the red dog standing on his hind feet.

"Pa was weak as a cat, and told me to go right home with him, and he would buy me a bicycle. He asked me how many dogs there were, and what was the color of them. I s'pose I did awful wrong, but I told him there was only one dog, and a cat, and the dog was white.

"Well, sir, Pa acted just as he did the night Hancock was beat, and he had to have the doctor to give him something to quiet him (the time he wanted me to go right down town and buy a hundred rat traps, but the doctor said never mind, I needn't go). I took him home, and Ma soaked his feet, and give him some ginger tea, and while I was gone after the doctor he asked Ma if she ever saw a green dog.

"That was what made all the trouble. If Ma had kept her mouth shut I would have been all right, but she up and told him that they had a green dog, and a blue dog, and all

colors of spitz dogs down at the dyers. They dyed them just for an advertisement, and for him to be quiet, and he would feel better when he got over it. Pa was all right when I got back and told him the doctor had gone to Wauwatosa, and I had left an order on his slate. Pa said he would leave an order on my slate. He took a harness tug and used it for breeching on me. I don't think a boy's Pa ought to wear a harness on his son, do you? He said he would learn me to play rainbow dogs on him. He said I was a liar, and he expected to see me wind up in Congress. Say, is Congress anything like Waupun or Sing Sing? No, I can't stay, thank you, I must go down to the office and tell Pa I have reformed, and freeze him out of a circus ticket. He is a good enough man, only he don't appreciate a boy that has got all the modern improvements. Pa and Ma are going to enter me in the Sunday school. I guess I'll take first money, don't you?"

And the bad boy went out with a visible limp, and a look of genius cramped for want of opportunity.

CHAPTER II

HIS PA PLAYS JOKES

A man shouldn't get mad at a joke—The magic bouquet—The grocery man takes a turn—His Pa tries the bouquet at church—One for the old maid—A fight ensues—The bad boy threatens the grocery man —A compromise.

"Say, do you think a little practical joke does any hurt?" asked the bad boy of the grocery man, as he came in with his Sunday suit on, and a bouquet in his button-hole, and pried off a couple of figs from a new box that had been just opened.

"No sir," said the grocery man, as he licked off the syrup that dripped from a quart measure, from which he had been filling a jug. "I hold that a man who gets mad at a practical joke, that is, one that does not injure him, is a fool, and he ought to be shunned by all decent people. That's a nice bouquet you have in your coat. What is it, pansies? Let me smell of it," and the grocery man bent over in front of the boy to take a whiff at the bouquet. As he did so a stream of water shot out of the innocent looking bouquet and struck him full in the face, and run down over his shirt, and the grocery man yelled murder, and fell over a barrel of axe helves and scythe snaths, and then groped around for a towel to wipe his face.

"You condemn skunk," said the grocery man to the boy, as he took up an axe helve and started for him, "What kind of a golblasted squirt gun have you got there? I will maul you, by thunder," and he rolled up his shirt sleeves.

"There, keep your temper. I took a test vote of you on the subject of practical jokes, before the machine began to play upon the conflagration that was raging on your whiskey nose, and you said that a man who would get mad at a

198

joke was a fool, and now I know it. Here let me show it to you. There is a rubberhose runs from the bouquet, inside my coat to my pants pocket, and there is a bulb of rubber, that holds about half a pint, and when a feller smells of the posey. I squeeze the bulb, you you see the result. It's fun, where you don't squirt it on a person that gets mad."

IT STRUCK HER RIGHT ON THE NOSE.

The grocery man said he would give the boy half a pound of figs if he would lend the bouquet to him for half an hour, to play it on a customer, and the boy fixed it on the grocery man, and turned the nozzle so it would squirt right back into the grocery man's face. He tried it on the first customer that came in, and got it right in his own face, and then the bulb in his pants pocket got to leaking, and the rest of the

water ran down the grocery man's trousers' leg, and he gave
it up in disgust, and handed it back to the boy.

"How was it your Pa had to be carried home from
the sociable in a hack the other night?" asked the grocery
man, as he stood close to the stove so his pants leg would
dry. "He has not got to drinking again, has he?"

"O, no," said the boy, as he filled the bulb with vinegar,
to practice on his chum. "It was this bouquet that got Pa
into the trouble. You see I got Pa to smell of it, and I
just filled him chuck full of water. He got mad and called
me all kinds of names, and said I was no good on earth, and
I would fetch up in state's prison, and then he wanted to
borrow it to wear to the sociable. He said he would have
more fun than you could shake a stick at, and I asked him if
he didn't think he would fetch up in state's prison, and he
said it was different with a man. He said when a man
played a joke there was a certain dignity about it that was
lacking in a boy. So I lent it to him, and we all went to
the sociable in the basement of the church. I never see Pa
more kitteny than he was that night. He filled the bulb
with ice water, and the first one he got to smell of his button-
hole bouquet was an old maid who thinks Pa is a heathen,
but she likes to be made something of by anybody that wears
pants, and when Pa sidled up to her and began talking about
what a great work the christian wimmen of the land were
doing in educating the heathen, she felt real good, and then
she noticed Pa's posey in his button-hole and she touched it,
and then she reached over her beak to smell of it. Pa he
squeezed the bulb, and about half a teacupful of water
struck her right in the nose, and some went into her strangle
place, and O, my, didn't she yell. The sisters gathered
around her and they said her face was all covered with perspiration, and the paint was coming off, and they took her
in the kitchen, and she told them Pa had slapped her with a
dish of ice cream, and the wimmen told the minister and the
deacons, and they went to Pa for an explanation, and Pa
told them it was not so, and the minister got interested and

got near Pa, and Pa let the water go at him, and hit him in the eye, and then a deacon got a dose, and Pa laughed; and then the minister, who used to go to college, and be a hazer, and box, he got mad and squared off and hit Pa three times right by the eye, and one of the deacons kicked Pa, and Pa got mad and said he could clean out the whole shebang, and began to pull off his coat, when they bundled him out doors, and Ma got mad to see Pa abused, and she

IF I WAS A PROVISION PIRATE.

left the sociable, and I had to stay and eat ice cream and things for the whole family. Pa says that settles it with him. He says they haven't got any more christian charity in that church than they have in a tannery. His eyes are just getting over being black from the sparring lessons, and now he has got to go through oysters and beefsteak cure again. He says it is all owing to me."

"Well, what has all this got to do with your putting up signs in front of my store, 'Rotten Eggs,' and 'Frowy Butter a specialty?'" said the grocery man as he took the boy by the ear and pulled him around. "You have got an idea you are smart, and I want you to keep away from here. The next time I catch you in here I shall call the police and have you pulled. Now git!"

The boy pulled his ear back on the side of his head where it belonged, took out a cigarette and lit it, and after puffing smoke in the face of the grocery cat that was sleeping on the cover to the sugar barrel he said:

"If I was a provision pirate that never sold anything but what was spoiled so it couldn't be sold in a first-class store, who cheated in weights and measures, who bought only wormy figs and decayed cod-fish, who got his butter from a fat rendering establishment, his cider from a vinegar factory, and his sugar from a glucose factory, I would not insult the son of one of the finest families. Why, sir, I could go out on the corner, and when I saw customers coming here, I could tell a story that would turn their stomachs, and send them to the grocery on the next corner. Suppose I should tell them that the cat sleeps in the dried apple barrel, that the mice made nests in the prune box, and rats run riot through the raisins, and that you never wash your hands except on Decoration day and Christmas, that you wipe your nose on your shirt sleeves, and that you have the itch, do you think your business would be improved? Suppose I should tell customers that you buy sour kraut of a wooden-shoed Polacker, who makes it of pieces of cabbage that he gets by gathering swill and sells that stuff to respectable people, could you pay your rent? If I should tell that you put lozengers in the collection plate at church, and charge the minister forty cents a pound for oleomargarine, you would have to close up. Old man, I am onto you, and now you apologize for pulling my ear."

The grocery man turned pale during the recital, and finally said the bad boy was one of the best little fellows in this town, and the boy went out and hung up a sign in front: "Girl wanted to cook."

CHAPTER III

HIS PA STABBED

The grocery man sets a trap in vain—A boom in liniment—His Pa goes to the Langtry show—The bad boy turns burglar—The old man stabbed—His account of the fray—A good single handed liar.

"I HEAR you had burglars over to your house last night," said the grocery man to the bad boy, as he came in and sat on the counter right over a little gimlet hole, where the grocery man had fixed a darning needle so that by pulling a string the needle would fly up through the hole and run into the boy about an inch. The grocery man had been laying for the boy about two days, and now that he had got him right over the hole the first time, it made him laugh to think how he would make him jump and yell, and as he edged off and got hold of the string the boy looked unconscious of impending danger. The grocery man pulled, and the boy sat still. He pulled again, and again, and finally the boy said:

"Yes, it is reported that we had burglars over there. O, you needn't pull that string any more. I heard you was setting a trap for me, and I put a piece of board inside my pants, and thought I would let you exercise yourself. Go ahead, if it amuses you. It don't hurt me."

The grocery man looked sad, and then smiled a sickly sort of a smile, at the failure of his plan to puncture the boy, and then he said, "Well, how was it? The policeman didn't seem to know much about the particulars. He said there was so much deviltry going on at your house that nobody could tell when anything was serious, and he was inclined to think it was a put up job."

"Now let's have an understanding," says the boy. "Whatever I say you are not to give me away. It's a go, is it? I have always been afraid of you, because you have a sort of decayed egg look about you. You are like a peck of potatoes with the big ones on top, a sort of strawberry box with the bottom raised up, so I have thought you would go back on a fellow. But if you won't give this away, here goes. You see, I heard Ma tell Pa to bring up another bottle of liniment last night. When Ma corks herself, or has a pain

"I HAVE RECEIVED MY DEATH WOUND."

anywhere, she just uses liniment for all that is out, and a pint bottle don't last more than a week. Well, I told my chum, and we laid for Pa. This liniment Ma uses is offul hot, and almost blisters. Pa went to the Langtry show, and did not get home till eleven o'clock, and me and my chum decided to teach Pa a lesson. I don't think it is right for a man to go to the theaters and not take his wife or his little boy.

"So we concluded to burgle Pa. We agreed to lay on the stairs, and when he came up my chum was to hit him on the head with a dried bladder, and I was to stab him on his breast pocket with a stick, and break the liniment bottle, and make him think he was killed.

"It couldn't have worked better if we had rehearsed it. We had talked about burglars at supper time, and got Pa nervous, so when he came up stairs and was hit on the head with the bladder, the first thing he said was 'Burglars, by mighty,' and he started to go back, and I hit him on the breast pocket, where the bottle was, and then we rushed by him, down stairs, and I said in a stage whisper, 'I guess he's a dead man,' and we went down cellar and up the back stairs to my room and undressed. Pa hollered to Ma that he was murdered, and Ma called me, and I came down in my night-shirt, and the hired girl she came down, and Pa was on the lounge, and he said his life-blood was fast ebbing away. He held his hand on the wound, and said he could feel the warm blood trickling clear down to his boots. I told Pa to stuff some tar into the wound, such as he told me to put on my lip to make my mustache grow, and Pa said, 'My boy, this is no time for trifling. Your Pa is on his last legs. When I came up stairs I met six burglars, and I attacked them, and forced four of them down, and was going to hold them and send for the police, when two more, that I did not know about, jumped on me ,and I was getting the best of them when one of them struck me over the head with a crowbar, and the other stabbed me in the heart with a butcher knife. I have received my death wound, my boy and my hot southern blood, that I offered up so freely for my country in her time of need, is passing from my body, and soon your Pa will be only a piece of poor clay. Get some ice and put on my stomach, and all the way down, for I am burning up.' I went to the water pitcher and got a chunk of ice and put inside Pa's shirt, and while Ma was tearing up an old skirt to stop the flow of blood, I asked Pa if he felt better, and if he could describe the villains who

had murdered him. Pa gasped and moved his legs to get
them cool from the clotted blood, he said, and he went on,
'One of them was about six feet high, and had a sandy

THE DEACON GOT OFF THE COUNTER WITH HIS HAND CLASPED.

mustache. I got him down and hit him on the nose, and if
the police find him, his nose will be broke. The second one
was thick set, and weighed about two hundred. I had him

down and my boot was on his neck, and I was knocking two more down when I was hit. The thick set one will have the mark of boot heels on his throat. Tell the police when I'm gone, about the boot heel marks.'

"By this time Ma had got the skirt tore up and she stuffed it under Pa's shirt, right where she said he was hit, and Pa was telling us what to do to settle his estate, when Ma began to smell the liniment, and she found the broken bottle in his pocket, and searched Pa for the place where he was stabbed, and then she began to laugh, and Pa got mad and said he didn't see as a death-bed scene was such an almighty funny affair; and then she told him he was not hurt, but that he had fallen on the stairs and broke his bottle, and that there was no blood on him, and he said, 'Do you mean to tell me my body and legs are not bathed in human gore?' and then Pa got up and found it was only the liniment. He got mad and asked Ma why she didn't fly around and get something to take that liniment off his legs, as it was eating them right through to the bone; and then he saw my chum put his head in the door, with one gallus hanging down, and Pa looked at me, and then he said, 'Look-a-here, if I find out it was you boys that put up this job on me, I'll make it so hot for you that you will think liniment is ice cream in comparison. I told Pa it didn't look reasonable that me and my chum could be six burglars, six feet high, with our noses broke, and boot-heel marks on our neck, and Pa he said for us to go to bed all-fired quick, and give him a chance to rinse off that liniment, and we retired. Say, how does my Pa strike you as a good single-handed liar?" and the boy went up to the counter, while the grocery man went after a scuttle of coal.

In the meantime one of the grocery man's best customers—a deacon in the church—had come in and sat down on the counter over the darning needle, and as the grocery man came in with the coal, the boy pulled the string, and went out the door and tipped over a basket of rutabages, while the deacon got down on the counter with his hands clasped, and anger in every feature, and told the grocery man he could whip him in two minutes. The grocery man asked what was the matter, and the deacon hunted up the source from whence the darning needle came through the counter, and as the boy went across the street, the deacon and the grocery man were rolling on the floor, the grocery man trying to hold the deacon's fists while he explained about the darning needle and that it was intended for the boy. How it came out the boy did not wait to see.

CHAPTER IV

HIS PA BUSTED

The craze for mining stock—What's a bilk?—The pious bilk—The old man invests—The deacons and even the hired girls invest—Hot maple syrup for one—Getting a man's mind off his troubles.

"SAY, can't I sell you some stock in a silver mine?" asked the bad boy of the grocery man, as he came in the store and pulled from his breast pocket a document printed on parchment paper, and representing several thousand dollars stock in a silver mine.

"Look-a-here," said the grocery man, as he turned pale, and thought of telephoning to the police station for a detective, "you haven't been stealing your father's mining stock, have you? Great heavens, it has come at last! I have known all the time that you would turn out to be a burglar, or a defaulter or robber of some kind. Your father has the reputation of having a bonanza in a silver mine, but if you go lugging his silver stock around he will soon be ruined. Now you go right back home and put that stock in your Pa's safe, like a good boy."

"Put it in the safe! O, no, we keep it in a box stall now, in the barn. I will trade you this thousand dollars in stock for two heads of lettuce, and get Pa to sign it over to you, if you say so. Pa told me I could have the whole trunk full if I wanted it, and the hired girls are using the silver stock to clean the windows, and kindle fires, and Pa has quit the church, and says he won't belong to any concern that harbors bilks. What's a bilk?" said the boy, as he opened a candy jar and took out four sticks of hoarhound candy.

"A bilk," said the grocery man, as he watched the boy, "is a fellow that plays a man for candy, or money, or any-

thing, and don't intend to return an equivalent. You are a
small sized bilk. But what's the matter with your Pa and
the church, and what has the silver mine stock got to do
with it?"

"Well, you remember that exhorter that was here last
fall, that used to board around with the church people all
the week and talk about Zion and laying up treasures where
the moths wouldn't gnaw them, and they wouldn't get rusty,
and where thieves wouldn't pry off the hinges. He was the
one that used to go home with Ma from prayer meetings,

AND PA USED TO SIT UP NIGHTS TO LOOK AT IT.

when Pa was down town, and who wanted to pay off the
church debt in solid silver bricks. He's the bilk. I guess
if Pa should get him by the neck he would jerk nine kinds
of revealed religion out of him. O, Pa is hotter than he
was when the hornets took the lunch off of him. When you
strike a pious man on the pocket-book it hurts him. That
fellow prayed and sang like an angel, and boarded around
like a tramp. He stopped at our house over a week, and
he had specimens of rock that were chuck full of silver and
gold, and he and Pa used to sit up nights and look at it.
You could pick pieces of silver out of the rock as big as

buck shot, and he had some silver bricks that were beautiful.
He had been out in Colorado and found a hill full of silver
rock, and he wanted to form a stock company and dig out
millions of dollars. He didn't want anybody but pious men
that belonged to the church, in the company, and I think
that was one thing that caused Pa to unite with the church
so suddenly. I know he was as wicked as could be a few
days before he joined the church; but this revivalist, with
his words about the beautiful beyond where all shall dwell
together in peace and sing praises; and his description of
that Colorado mountain where the silver stuck out so you
could hang your hat on it, converted Pa. That man's scheme
was to let all the church people who were in good standing,
and who had plenty of money, into the company, and when
the mine begun to return dividends by the car load, they
could give largely to the church and pay the debts of all
the churches, and put down carpets and fresco the ceiling.
The man said he felt that he had been steered on to that
silver mine by a higher power, and his idea was to work it
for the glory of the cause. He said he liked Pa and would
make him vice-president of the company. Pa, he bit like
a bass, and I guess he invested five thousand dollars in
stock, and Ma, she wanted to come in, and she put in a
thousand dollars that she had laid up to buy some diamond
ear-rings, and the man gave Pa a lot of stock to sell to other
members of the church. They all went into it, even the minister. He drew his salary ahead, and all of the deacons
they came in, and the man went back to Colorado with about
thirty thousand dollars of good, pious money. Yesterday
Pa got a paper from Colorado, giving the whole snap away,
and the pious man has been spending the money in Denver,
and whooping it up. Pa suspected something was wrong
two weeks ago, when he heard that the pious man had
been on a toot in Chicago, and he wrote to a man in Denver, who used to get full with Pa years ago when they were
both on the turf; and Pa's friend said the man that sold
the stock was a fraud, and that he didn't own no mine, and

that he borrowed the samples of ore and silver bricks from a pawnbroker in Denver. I guess it will break Pa up for a while, though he is well e n o u g h fixed with mort-gages and things; but it hurts him to be took in. He lays it all to Ma— she says if she hadn't let that ex-horter for the sil-ver mine go home with her t h i s would not have occurred, and Ma says she believes Pa was in partner-ship with the man to beat her out of her thousand dol-lars that she was going to buy a pair of diamond ear-rings with. O, it is a terror over

I TOLD PA IF HE WOULD PUT SOME TAR ON HIS LEGS.

to the house now. Both of the hired girls put in all money they had, and took stock and they threaten to sue Pa for arson, and they are going to leave to-night, and Ma will have to do the work. Don't you never try to get rich quick," said the boy as he peeled a herring, and took a couple of crackers.

"Never you mind me," said the grocery man, "they don't catch me on any of their silver mines; but I hope this will have some influence on you and teach you to respect your Pa's feelings, and not play jokes on him while he is feeling so bad over his being swindled."

"O, I don't know about that, I think when a man is in trouble, if he has a good little boy to take his mind from his troubles, and get him mad at something else, it rests him. Last night we had hot maple syrup and biscuit for supper, and Pa had a saucer full in front of him, just a steaming. I could see he was thinking too much about his mining stock, and I thought if there was anything I could do to take his mind off of it and place it on something else, I would be doing a kindness that would be appreciated. I sat on the right of Pa, and when he wasn't looking I pulled the table cloth so the saucer of red hot maple syrup dropped off in his lap. Well, you'd a dide to see how quick his thoughts turned from his financial troubles to his physical misfortunes. There was about a pint of hot syrup, and it went all over his lap, and you know how hot melted maple sugar is, and how it sort of clings to anything. Pa jumped up and grabbed hold of his pants' legs to pull them away from hisself, and he danced around and told Ma to turn the hose on him, and then he took a pitcher of ice-water and poured it down his pants, and he said the condemned old table was getting so rickety that a saucer wouldn't stay on it, and I told Pa if he would put some tar on his legs, the same kind that he told me to put on my lip to make my mustache grow, the syrup wouldn't burn so; and then he cuffed me, and I think he felt better. It is a great thing to get a man's mind off his troubles, but where a man hasn't got any mind, like you, for instance—"

At this point the grocery man picked up a fire poker, and the boy went out in a hurry and hung up a sign in front of the grocery:

> *CASH PAID*
>
> *FOR FAT DOGS.*

CHAPTER V

"I GUESS your Pa's losses in the silver mine have made him crazy, haven't they?" said the grocery man to the bad boy, as he came into the store with his eye-winkers singed off, and powder marks on his face, and began to play on the harmonica, as he sat down on the end of a stick of stove wood, and balanced himself.

"O, I guess not. He has hedged. He got in with a deacon of another church, and sold some of his stock to him, and Pa says if I will keep my condemned mouth shut he will unload the whole of it, if the churches hold out. He goes to a new church every night there is prayer meeting or anything, and makes Ma go with him to give him tone, and after meeting she talks with the sisters about how to piece a bed quilt, while Pa gets in his work selling silver stock. I don't know but he will order some more stock from the factory, if he sells all he has got," and the boy went on playing, "There's a land that is fairer than day."

"But what was he skipping up street for the other night with his hat off, grabbing at his coat tails as though they were on fire? I thought I never saw a pussy man run any faster. And what was the celebration down on your street about that time. I thought the world was coming to an end," and the grocery man kept away from the boy, for fear he would explode.

"O, that was only a Fenian scare. Nothing serious. You see Pa is a sort of half Englishman. He claims to be an American citizen when he wants office, but when they talk about a draft he claims to be a subject of Great Britain, and he says they can't touch him. Pa is a darned smart man, and don't you forget it. They don't any of them get ahead of Pa much. Well, Pa has said a good deal about the wicked Fenians, and that they ought to be pulled, and all that, and when I read the story in the papers about the explosion in the British Parliament, Pa was hot. He said the damnirish was ruining the whole world. He didn't dare to say it at the table, or our hired girl would have knocked him silly with a spoonful of mashéd potatoes, 'cause she is a nirish girl, and she can lick any Englishman in this town. Pa said there ought to have been somebody there to have taken that bomb up and throwed it in the sewer before it exploded. He said that if he should ever see a bomb he would grab it right up and throw it away where it wouldn't hurt anybody. Pa has me read the papers to him nights, 'cause his eyes have got splinters in 'em, and after I had read all there was in the paper, I made up a lot more and pretended to read it, about how it was rumored that the Fenians here in Milwaukee were going to place dynamite bombs at every house where an Englishman lived, and at a given signal blow them all up. Pa looked pale around the gills, but he said he wasn't scared.

"Pa and Ma were going to call on a she-deacon that night, that has lots of money in the bank, to see if she didn't want to invest in a dead sure paying silver mine, and me and my chum concluded to give them a send-off. We got my big black injy rubber foot ball, and painted '*Diny-mite*' in big white letters on it, and tied a piece of tarred rope to it for a fuse, and got a big fire-cracker, one of those old Fourth of July horse scarers, and a basket full of broken glass. We put the foot ball in front of the step and lit the tarred rope and got under the step with the fire-crackers and the basket, where they go down into the basement. Pa and Ma came out of the front door and down the steps, and Pa saw the foot ball and the burning fuse, and he said 'Great God, Hanner, we are blowed up!' and he started to run, and Ma she stopped to

"GREAT GOD! HANNER, WE ARE BLOWED UP."

look at it. Just as Pa started to run I touched off the fire-cracker, and my chum arranged it to pour out the broken glass on the brick pavement just as the fire-cracker went off.

Well, everything went just as we expected, except Ma.
She had examined the foot ball and concluded it was not
dangerous, and was just giving it a kick as the fire-cracker
went off, and the glass fell, and the fire-cracker was so near
her that it scared her, and when Pa looked around Ma was
flying across the sidewalk, and Pa heard the noise and he
thought the house was blown to atoms. O, you'd a dide to see
him go around the corner. You could play crokay on his
coat-tail, and his face was as pale as Ma's when she goes to
a party. But Ma didn't scare much. As quick as she
stopped against the hitching post she knew it was us boys,
and she came down there, and maybe she didn't maul me.
I cried and tried to gain her sympathy by telling her the
fire-cracker went off before it was due, and burned my eyebrows off, but she didn't let up until I promised to go and
find Pa.

"I tell you, my Ma ought to be engaged by the British
government to hunt out the dynamite fiends. She would
corral them in two minutes. If Pa had as much sand as Ma
has got, it would be warm weather for me. Well, me and
my chum went and headed Pa off or I guess he would be
running yet. We got him up by the lake shore, and he
wanted to know if the house fell down. He said he would
leave it to me if he ever said anything against the Fenians,
and I told him that he had always claimed that the Fenians
were the nicest men in the world, and it seemed to relieve
him very much. When he got home and found the house
there he was tickled, and when Ma called him an old bald-
headed coward, and said it was only a joke of the boys with
a foot ball, he laughed right out, and said he knew it all
the time, and he ran to see if Ma would be scared. And
then he wanted to hug me, but it wasn't my night to hug
and I went down to the theater. Pa don't amount to much
when there is trouble. The time Ma had them cramps, you
remember, when you got your cucumbers first last season,
Pa came near fainting away, and Ma said ever since they had
been married when anything ailed her, Pa has had pains

just the same as she has, only he grunted more, and thought
he was going to die.   Gosh, if I was a man I wouldn't be
sick every time one of the neighbors had a back ache, would
you?

"Well, you can't tell.   When you have been married
twenty or thirty years you will know a good deal more than
you do now.   You think you know it all, now, and you are
pretty intelligent for a boy that has been brought up care-
lessly, but there are things that you will learn after a
while that will astonish
you.   But what ails your
Pa's teeth? The hired girl
was over here to get some
corn meal for gruel, and
she said your Pa was
gumming it, since he lost
his teeth."

"O, about the teeth.
That was too bad.   You
see my chum has got a
dog that is old and his
teeth have all come out in
front, and this morning I
borried Pa's teeth before
he got up, to see if we
couldn't fix them in the
dog's mouth, so he could
eat better. Pa says it is an
evidence of a kind heart

HE LOOKED JUST LIKE PA WHEN HE
TRIES TO SMILE.

for a boy to be good to dumb animals, but it is a darned
mean dog that will go back on a friend. We tied the teeth
in the dog's mouth with a string that went around his upper
jaw, and another around his under jaw, and you'd a dide
to see how funny he looked when he laffed.   He looked just
like Pa when he tried to smile so as to get me to come up
to him so he can lick me. The dog pawed his mouth a
spell to get the teeth out, and then we gave him a bone

with some meat on, and he began to gnaw the bone, and the
teeth came off the plate, and he thought it was pieces of
the bone, and he swallowed the teeth.   My chum noticed it
first, and he said we had got to get in our work pretty quick
to save the plates and I thinl we were in luck to save them.
I held the dog, and my chum, who was better acquainted
with him, untied the strings and got the gold plates out, but
there were only two teeth left, and the dog was happy.
He woggled his tail for more teeth, but we hadn't any more.
I am going to give him Ma's teeth some day.   My chum
says when a dog gets an appetite for anything you have
got to keep giving it it him or he goes back on you.
But I think my chum played dirt on me.   We sold the gold
plates to a jewelry man, and my chum kept the money.
I think, as long as I furnished the goods, he ought to have
given me something besides the experience, don't you?
After this I don't have no more partners, you bet."   All this
time the boy was marking on a piece of paper, and soon after
he went out the grocery man noticed a crowd outside, and on
going out he found a sign hanging up which read:

> *WORMY FIGS*
>
> *FOR PARTIES.*

CHAPTER VI

HIS PA AN ORANGEMAN.

The grocery man shamefully abused—He gets hot—Butter, oleomargarine and axle grease—the old man wears orange on St. Patrick's day—He has to run for his life—the bad boy at Sunday school—Ingersoll and Beecher voted out—"Mary had a little lamb."

"Say, will you do me a favor?" asked the bad boy of the grocery man, as he sat down on the soap box and put his wet boots on the stove.

"Well, y-e-s," said the grocery man hesitatingly, with a feeling that he was liable to be sold. "If you will help me catch the villain who hangs up those disreputable signs in front of my store, I will. What is it?"

"I want you to lick this stamp and put it on this letter. It is to my girl and I want to fool her," and the boy handed over the letter and stamp, and while the grocery man was licking it and putting it on, the boy filled his pockets with dried peaches out of a box.

"There, that's a small job," said the grocery man, as he pressed the stamp on the letter with his thumb and handed it back. "But how are you going to fool her?"

"That's just the business," said the boy, as he held the letter to his nose and smelled of the stamp. "That will make her tired. You see every time she gets a letter from me she kisses the stamp, because she thinks I licked it. When she kisses this stamp and gets the fumes of plug tobacco, and stale beer, and limberger cheese, and mouldy potatoes, it will knock her down, and then she will ask me what ailed the stamp, and I will tell her I got you to lick it, and then it will make her sick, and her parents will stop trading here. O, it will paralyze her. Do you know, you smell like a glue factory. Gosh, I

221

can smell you all over the store. Don't you smell anything
that smells spoiled?"

The grocery man thought he did smell something that
was rancid, and he looked around the stove and finally kicked
the boy's boot off the stove and said, "It's your boot burning
Gracious, open the door! It smells like a hot box on a
caboose. Whew! And there comes a couple of my best
lady customers." The ladies came in and held their handkerchiefs to their noses, and while they were trading the
boy said, as though continuing the conversation:

"Yes, Pa says that last oleomargarine I got here is nothing but axle grease. Why don't you put your axle grease
in a different kind of a package? The only way you can
tell axle grease from oleomargarine is in spreading it on pancakes. Pa says axle grease will spread, but your alleged butter just rolls right up and acts like lip salve, or ointment, and
is only fit to use on a sore—"

At this point the ladies went out of the store in disgust,
without buying anything, and the grocery man took a dried
codfish by the tail and went up to the boy and took him by
the neck. "Golblast you, I have a notion to kill you. You
have driven away more custom from this store than your
neck is worth. Now you git," and he struck the boy across
the back with the codfish.

"That's just the way with you all," says the boy, as he
put his sleeve up to his eyes and pretended to cry, "when a
fellow is up in the world, there is nothing too good for him,
but when he gets down you maul him with a codfish. Since
Pa drove me out of the house, and told me to go shirk
for my living, I haven't had a kind word from anybody.
My chum's dog won't even follow me, and when a fellow
gets so low down that a dog goes back on him there is nothing left for him to do but to loaf around a grocery, or sit on
a jury, and I am too young to sit on a jury, though I know
more than some of the dead beats that lay around the court
to get on a jury. I am going to drown myself, and my death
will be laid to you. They will find evidences of codfish on

my clothing, and you will be arrested for driving me to a
suicide's grave. Good-bye. I forgive you," and the boy
started for the door.

"Hold on here," says the grocery man, feeling that he
had been too harsh. "Come back here, and have some maple
sugar. What did your Pa drive you away from home for?"

THE GROCERYMAN TOOK A DRIED CODFISH BY THE TAIL.

"O, it was on account of St. Patrick's Day," said the bad
boy as he bit off half a pound of maple sugar, and dried his
tears. "You see, Pa never sees Ma buy a new silk handkerchief, but he wants it. T'other day Ma got one of these
orange-colored handkerchiefs, and Pa immediately had a
sore throat and wanted to wear it, and Ma let him put it on.
I thought I would break him of taking everything nice that
Ma got, so when he went down town with the orange handkerchief on his neck, I told some of the St. Patrick boys in

the Third ward, who had green ribbons on, that the old
duffer that was putting on style was an orange-man, and he
said he could whip any St. Patrick's Day man in town. The
fellers laid for Pa, and when he came along one of them
threw a barrel at Pa, and another pulled the yellow handkerchief off his neck, and they all yelled 'Hang him,' and one
grabbed a rope that was on the sidewalk where they were
moving a building, and Pa got up and dusted. You'd a dide
to see Pa run. He met a policeman and said more'n a hundred men had tried to murder him, and they had mauled
him, and stolen his yellow handkerchief. The policeman told
Pa his life was not safe, and he better go home and lock
himself in, and he did, and I was telling Ma about how I
got the boys to scare Pa, and he heard it, and he told me
that settled it. He said I had caused him to run more foot
races than any champion pedestrian, and had made his life
unbearable, and now I must go it alone. Now I want you
to send a couple of pounds of crackers over to the house,
and have your boy tell the hired girl that I have gone down
to the river to drown myself, and she will tell Ma, and Ma
will tell Pa, and pretty soon you will see a bald-headed pussy
man whooping it up toward the river with a rope. They
may think at times that I am a little tough, but when it
comes to parting forever, they weaken."

"Well, the teacher says you are a hardened infidel," said
the grocery man, as he charged the crackers to the boy's Pa.
"He says he had to turn you out to keep you from ruining
the morals of the other scholars. How was that?"

"It was about speaking a piece. When I asked him
what I should speak, he told me to learn some speech of
some great man, some lawyer or statesman, so I learned
one of Bob Ingersoll's speeches. Well, you'd a dide to see
the teacher and the school committee, when I started in on
Bob Ingersoll's lecture, the one that was in the paper when
Bob was here. You see I thought if a newspaper that all the
pious folks takes in their families, could publish Ingersoll's
speech, it wouldn't do any hurt for a poor little boy who

ain't knee high to a giraffe, to speak it in school, but they made me dry up. The teacher is a republican, and when Ingersoll was speaking around here on politix, the time of the election, the teacher said Bob was the smartest man this

THE POLICEMAN TOLD PA TO GO HOME AND LOCK HIMSELF IN.

country ever produced. I heard him say that in a corcus, when he went bumming around the ward settin' 'em up nights, 'specting to be superintendent of schools. He said Bob Ingersoll just took the cake, and I think it was darned mean in him to go back on Bob and me, too, just 'cause there was no 'lection. The school committee made the teacher stop me, and they asked me if I didn't know any other piece to speak, and I told them I knew one of Beecher's, and they

15

let me go ahead, but it was one of Beecher's new ones where he said he didn't believe in any hell, and afore I got warmed up they said that was enough of that, and I had to wind up on 'Mary had a Little Lamb.' None of them didn't kick on Mary's Lamb and I went through it, and they let me go home. That's about the safest thing a boy can speak in school now-days, either 'Mary had a Little Lamb,' or 'Twinkle, Twinkle Little Star.' That's about up to the average intelleck of the committee. But if a boy tries to branch out as a statesman, they choke him off. Well, I am going down to the river, and I will leave my coat and hat by the wood yard, and get behind the wood, and you steer Pa down there and you will see some tall weeping over them clothes, and maybe Pa will jump in after me, and then I will come out from behind the wood and throw in a board for him to swim ashore on. Good-bye. Give my pocket comb to my chum," and the boy went out and hung up a sign in front of the grocery as follows:

> *POP CORN THAT THE CAT HAS SLEPT*
>
> *IN, CHEAP FOR*
>
> *POP CORN BALLS FOR SOCIABLES.*

Bad Boy's Chum.

CHAPTER VII

HIS MA DECEIVES HIM

The bad boy in search of saffron—"Well, it's a girl if you must know"
—The bad boy is grieved at his Ma's deception —"S-h-h tootsy go
to sleep"—"By low, baby"—That settled it with the cat—A baby!
bah! it makes me tired.

"Give me ten cents worth of saffron, quick," said the bad
boy to the grocery man, as he came in the grocery on a gallop, early one morning, with no collar on and no vest. He
looked as though he had been routed out of bed in a hurry
and had jumped into his pants and boots, and put on his
coat and hat on the run.

"I don't keep saffron," said the grocery man as he picked
up a barrel of ax-handles the boy had tipped over in his
hurry. "You want to go over to the drug store on the corner, if you want saffron. But what on earth is the mat—"

At this point the boy shot out of the door, tripping over a
basket of white beans and disappearing in the drug store.
The grocery man got down on his knees on the sidewalk and
scooped up the beans, occasionally looking over to the drug
store, and just as he got them picked up, the boy came out
of the drug store and walked deliberately towards his home
as though there was no particular hurry. The grocery man
looked after him, took up an ax-handle, spit on his hands,
and shouted to the boy to come over pretty soon, as he
wanted to talk with him. The boy did not come to the grocery till towards night; but the grocery man had seen him
running down town a dozen times during the day and once
he rode up to the house with the doctor, and the grocer sur-
mised what was the trouble. Along towards night the boy
came in in a dejected sort of a tired way, sat down on a
barrel of sugar, and never spoke.

227

"What is it, a boy or girl?" said the grocery man, winking at an old lady with a shawl over her head, who was trying to hold a paper over a pitcher of yeast with her thumb.

"How in blazes did you know anything about it?" said the boy, as he looked around in astonishment, and with some indignation. "Well, it's a girl, if you must know, and that's enough," and he looked down at the cat playing on the floor with a potato, his face a picture of dejection.

"O, don't feel bad about it," said the grocery man, as he opened the door for the old lady. "Such things are bound to occur; but you take my word for it, that young one is going to have a hard life unless you mend your ways. You will be using it for a cork to a jug, or to wad a gun with, the first thing your Ma knows."

"I wouldn't touch the darn thing with the tongs," said the boy as he rallied enough to eat some crackers and cheese. "Gosh, this cheese tastes good. I hain't had nothing to eat since morning. I have been all over this town trolling for nurses. They think a boy hasn't got any feelings. But I wouldn't care a goldarn, if Ma hadn't been sending me for neuralgia medicine, and hay fever stuff all winter, when she wanted to get rid of me. I have come into the room lots of times when Ma and the sewing girl were at work on some flannel things, and Ma would hide them in a basket and send me off after medicine. I was deceived up to about four o'clock this morning, when Pa come to my room and pulled me out of bed to go over on the West Side after some old woman that knew Ma, and they have kept me whooping ever since. What does a boy want of a sister, unless it is a big sister? I don't want no sister that I have got to hold, and rock, and hold a bottle for. This affair breaks me all up," and the boy picked the cheese out of his teeth with a sliver he cut from the counter.

"Well, how does your Pa take it?" asked the grocery man, as he charged the boy's Pa with cheese, and saffron and a number of such things.

"O, Pa will pull through. He wanted to boss the whole

concern until Ma's chum, an old woman that takes snuff,
fired him out into the hall. Pa sat there on my hand-sled,
a perfect picture of despair, and I thought it would be a
kindness to play it on him. I found the cat asleep in the
bathroom, and I rolled the cat up in a shawl and brought it
out to Pa and told him the nurse wanted him to hold the
baby. It seemed to do Pa good to feel
that he was indispensable around the
house, and he took the cat on his lap as
tenderly as you ever saw a
mother hold her infant. Well,
I got in the back hall,
where he couldn't see
me, and pretty soon
the cat began to wake
up and stretch him-
self, and Pa said,
'S-h-h-tootsy, go to
sleep now, and let its
Pa hold it,' and Pa
rocked back a n d
forth on the hand-
sled and began to
sing 'By, low, baby.'
That settled it with
the cat. Well, some
cats can't stand mu-
sic, anyway, and the
more the cat wanted
to get out of the

SCAT YOU BRUTE.

shawl the harder Pa   sung, and bimeby I heard
something rip, and Pa yelled, 'Scat you brute,' and
when I looked around the corner of the hall the
cat was bracing hisself against Pa's vest with his toe
nails, and yowling and Pa fell over the sled and began to
talk about the hereafter like the minister does when he gets
excited in church, and then Pa picked up the sled, and

seemed to be looking for me or the cat, but both of us was offul scarce. Don't you think there are times when boys and cats are kind of few around their accustomed haunts? Pa don't look as though he was very smart, but he can hold a cat about as well as the next man. But I am sorry for Ma. She was just getting ready to go to Florida for her neuralgia, and this will put a stop to it, 'cause she has to stay and take care of that young one. Pa says I will have a nice time this summer pushing the baby wagon. By the great horn spoons, there has got to be a dividing line somewhere between business and pleasure, and I strike the line at wheeling a baby. I had rather catch a string of perch than to wheel all the babies ever was. They needn't procure no baby on my account, if it is to amuse me. I don't see why babies can't be sawed off onto people that need them in their business. Our folks don't need a baby any more than you need a safe, and there are people just suffering for babies. Say, how would it be to take the baby some night and leave it on some old bachelor's door-step? If it had been a bicycle, or a breech-loading shot-gun, I wouldn't have cared, but a baby! Bah! It makes me tired. I'd druther have a prize package. Well, I am sorry Pa allowed me to come home after he drove me away last week. I guess all he wanted me to come back for was to humiliate me, and send me on errands. Well, I must go and see if he and the cat have made up."

And the boy went out and put a paper sign in front of the store:

> *LEAVE **YOUR** MEASURE FOR*
>
> *SAFFRON TEA.*

CHAPTER VIII

THE BABY AND THE GOAT

The bad boy thinks his sister will be a fire engine—"Old number two"
—Baby requires goat milk—The goat is frisky—Takes to eating
Roman candles—The old man, the hired girl and the goat—The bad
boy becomes teller in the livery stable.

"Well, how is the baby?" asked the grocery man of
the bad boy, as he came into the grocery smelling very
"horsey," and sat down on the chair with the back gone,
and looked very tired.

"O, darn the baby.
Everybody asks me
about the b a b y as
though it was mine. I
don't pay no attention
to the darn thing, ex-
cept to notice the fool-
ishness going on around
the house. Say, I guess
that baby will grow up
to be a fire engine. The
nurse coupled the baby
onto a section of rub-
ber hose that runs down
into a bottle of milk,
and it began to get up
steam and pretty soon
the milk began to disap-
pear, just like the water

OLD NUMBER TWO.

does when a fire engine couples onto a hydrant.
Pa calls the baby 'Old Number Two.' I am 'Number One,' and if Pa had a hook and ladder truck and a

231

hose cart, and a fire gong he would imagine he was chief engineer of the fire department.   But the baby kicks on this
milk wagon milk, and howls like a dog that's got lost.   The
doctor told Pa the best thing he could do was to get a goat,
but Pa said since we 'nishiated him into the Masons with
the goat he wouldn't have a goat around no how.   The doc.
told Pa the other kind of a goat, I think it was a Samantha
goat he said, wouldn't kick with its head, and Pa sent me
up into the Polack settlement to see if I couldn't borrow a
milk goat for a few weeks.   I got a woman to lend us her
goat till the baby got big enough to chew beef, for a dollar
a week, and paid a dollar in advance, and Pa went up in
the evening to help me to get the goat.   Well, it was the
darndest mistake you ever see.   There was two goats so near
alike you could not tell which was the goat we leased, and
the other goat was the chum of our goat, but it belonged to
a nirish woman.   We got a bed cord hitched around the
Irish goat, and that goat didn't recognize the lease, and
when we tried to jerk it along it rared right up, and made
things real quick for Pa.   I don't know what there is about a
goat that makes it get so spunky, but that goat seemed to
have a grudge against Pa from the first.   If there were any
places on Pa's manly form that the goat did not explore,
with his head, Pa don't know where the places are.   O, it
lammed him and when I laffed Pa got mad.   I told him
every man ought to furnish his own goats, when he had a
baby, and I let go the rope and started off, and Pa said he
knew how it was, I wanted him to get killed.   It wasn't
that, but I saw the Irish woman that owned the goat coming
around the corner of the house with a cistern pole.   Just as
Pa was getting the goat out of the gate the goat got cross-
ways of the gate, and Pa yanked, and doubled the goat right
up, and I thought he had broke the goat's neck, and the
woman thought so too, for she jabbed Pa with the cistern
pole just below the belt and she tried to get a hold on Pa's
hair, but he had her there.   No woman can get the advantage
of Pa that way, 'cause Ma has tried it.   Well, Pa explained

it to the woman and she let Pa off if he would pay her two
dollars for damages to her goat, and he paid it, and then we
took the nanny goat, and it went right along with us. But I
have my opinion of a baby that will drink goat's milk. Gosh,
it is like this stuff that comes in a spoiled cocoanut. The
baby hasn't done anything but blat since the nurse coupled
it onto the goat hydrant. I had to take all my playthings out
of the basement to keep the goat from eating them. I guess
the milk will taste of powder and singed hair now. The
goat got to eating some Roman candles me and my chum
had laid away in the coal bin, and chewed them around the
furnace, and the powder leaked out and a coal fell out of
the furnace on the hearth, and you'd a dide to see Pa and the
hired girl and the goat. You see Pa can't milk nothing but
a milk wagon, and he got the hired girl to milk the goat,
and they were just hunting around the basement for the goat
with a tin cup, when the fireworks went off. Well, there
was balls of green, and red and blue fire, and spilled powder
blazed up, and the goat just looked astonished, and looked
on as though it was sorry so much good fodder was spoiled,
but when its hair began to burn, the goat gave one snort and
went between Pa and the hired girl like it was shot out of a
cannon, and it knocked Pa over a wash boiler into the coal
bin and the hired girl in amongst the kindling wood,
and she crossed herself and repeated the catechism,
and the goat jumped up on the brick furnace, and they
couldn't get it down. I heard the celebration and went down
and took Pa by the pants and pulled him out of the coal bin,
and he said he would surrender and plead guilty of being the
biggest fool in Milwaukee. I pulled the kindling wood off
the hired girl, and then she got mad, and said she would
milk the goat or die. O, that girl has got sand. She used
to work in a glass factory. Well, sir, it was a sight worth
two shillings admission, to see that hired girl get up on a
step ladder to milk that goat on top of the furnace, with
Pa sitting on a barrel of potatoes, bossing the job. They are
going to fix a gang plank to get the goat down off the fur-

nace. The baby kicked on the milk last night. I guess besides tasting of powder and burnt hair, the milk was too warm on account of the furnace. Pa has got to grow a new lot of hair on the goat, or the woman won't take it back. She don't want no bald goat. Well, they can run the baby and goat to suit themselves, 'cause I have resigned. I have gone into business. Don't you smell anything that would lead you to surmise that I had gone into business? No drug store this time," and the boy got up and put his thumbs in the armholes of his vest, and looked proud.

"O, I don't know as I smell anything except the faint odor of a horse blanket. What you gone into, anyway?" and the grocery man put the wrapping paper under the counter, and put the red chalk in his pocket, so the boy couldn't write any sign to hang up outside.

"You hit it the first time. I have accepted a situation of teller in a livery stable," said the boy, as he searched around for the barrel of cut sugar, which had been removed.

"Teller in a livery stable! Well, that is a new one on me. What is a teller in a livery stable?" and the grocery man looked pleased, and pointed the boy to a barrel of seven cent sugar.

"Don't you know what a teller is in a livery stable? It is the same as a teller in a bank. I have to grease the harness, oil the buggies, and curry off the horses, and when a man comes in to hire a horse I have to go down to the saloon and tell the livery man. That's what a teller is. I like the teller part of it; but greasing harness is a little too rich for my blood, but the livery man says that if I stick to it I will be governor some day, 'cause most all the great men have begun life taking care of horses. It all depends on my girl whether I stick or not. If she likes the smell of horses I shall be a statesman, but if she objects to it and sticks up her nose, I shall not yearn to be governor, at the expense of my girl. It beats all, don't it, that wimmin settle every great question? Everybody does everything to please wimmin, and if they kick on anything that settles it. But I must go and umpire that game between Pa and the hired girl and the goat. Say, can't you come over and see the baby? 'Taint bigger than a small satchel," and the boy waited till the grocery man went to draw some vinegar, when he slipped **out** and put up a sign written on a shingle with white chalk:

> *YELLOW SAND WANTED*
> *FOR*
> *MAPLE SUGAR.*

CHAPTER IX

A FUNERAL PROCESSION

The bad boy on crutches—"You ought to see the minister!"—An eleven dollar funeral—The minister takes the lines—An earthquake— After the earthquake was over—The policeman fans the minister —A minister should have sense.

"WELL, great Julius Cæsar's bald-headed ghost, what's the matter with you?" said the grocery man to the bad boy, as he came into the grocery on crutches, with one arm in a sling, one eye blackened, and a strip of court plaster across his face. "Where was the explosion, or have you been in a fight, or has your Pa been giving you what you deserve, with a club? Here, let me help you; there, sit down on that keg of apple-jack. Well, by the great guns, you look as though you had called somebody a liar. What's the matter?" and the grocery man took the crutches and stood them up against the showcase.

"O, there's not much the matter with me," said the boy in a voice that sounded all broke up, as he took a big apple off a basket, and began peeling it with his upper front teeth. "If you think I'm a wreck, you ought to see the minister; they had to carry him home in installments, the way they buy sewing machines. I am all right, but they have got to stop him up with oakum and tar, before he will hold water again."

"Good gracious, you have not had a fight with the minister, have you? Well, I have said all the time, and I stick to it, that you would commit a crime yet, and go to state's prison. What was the fuss about?" and the grocery man laid the hatchet out of the boy's reach for fear he would get excited and kill him.

236

"O, it was no fuss, it was in the way of business. You see the livery man that I was working for promoted me. He let me drive a horse to haul sawdust for bedding, first, and when he found I was real careful he let me drive an

e x p r e s s wagon to haul trunks. Day before y e s t e r d a y, I think it was—yes, I was in bed all day yesterday — day before yesterday there was a funeral, and our stable furnished the outfit. It was only a common, eleven dollar funeral so they let me go to drive the horse for the minister — y o u know, the buggy that goes ahead of the hearse. They gave me an old horse that is thirty years old, that has not been off a walk since nine years ago, and they told me to give him

MY LITTLE MAN I GUESS YOU'D BETTER DRIVE.

a loose rein, and he would go along all right. It' the same old horse that used to pace so fast on the avenue, years ago, but I didn't know it. Well, I wasn't to blame. I just let him walk along as though he was hauling sawdust, and gave him a loose rein. When we got off the pavement, the fellow that drives the hearse, he was in a hurry, 'cause his folks was going to have ducks for dinner, and he wanted to get back, so he kept driving along side of my buggy, and telling me to hurry up. I wouldn't do it 'cause the livery

man told me to walk the horse. Then the minister, he got
nervous, and said he didn't know as there was any use of
going so slow, because he wanted to get back in time to get
his lunch and go to a minister's meeting in the afternoon, but
I told him we would all get to the cemetery soon enough if
we took it cool, and as for me I wasn't in no sweat. Then
one of the drivers that was driving the mourners, he came
up and said he had to get back in time to run a wedding
down to the one o'clock train, and for me to pull out a little.
I have seen enough of disobeying orders, and I told him a
funeral in the hand was worth two weddings in the bush, and
as far as I was concerned, this funeral was going to be conducted in a decorous manner, if we didn't get back till the
next day. Well, the minister said, in his regular Sunday
school way, 'My little man, let me take hold of the lines,'
and like a darned fool I gave them to him. He slapped the
old horse on the crupper with the lines and then jerked up, and
the old horse stuck up his off ear, and then the hearse driver
told the minister to pull hard and saw on the bit a little, and
the old horse would wake up. The hearse driver used to
drive the old pacer on the track, and he knew what he wanted. The minister took off his black kid gloves and put his
umbrella down between us, and pulled his hat down tight on
his head, and began to pull and saw on the bit. The old
cripple began to move along sort of sideways, like a hog
going to war, and the minister pulled some more, and the
hearse driver, who was behind, he said, so you could hear
him clear to Waukesha, 'Ye-e-up,' and the old horse kept
going faster, then the minister thought the procession was
getting to quick, and he pulled harder, and yelled 'Who-a,'
and that made the old horse worse, and I looked through
the little window in the buggy top, behind, and the hearse
was about two blocks behind, and the driver was laughing,
and the minister he got pale and said, 'My little man I guess
you'd better drive,' and I said, 'Not much, Mary Ann, you
wouldn't let me run this funeral the way I wanted to, and
now you can boss it, if you will let me get out,' but there

was a street car ahead, and all of a sudden there was an earthquake, and when I come to there were about six hundred people pouring water down my neck, and the hearse was hitched to the fence, and the hearse driver was asking if my leg was broke, and a policeman was fanning the minister with a plug hat that looked as though it had been struck by a pile driver, and some people were hauling our buggy into the gutter, and some men were trying to take old pacer out of the windows of the street-car, and then I guess I fainted away again. O, it was worse than telescoping a train loaded with cattle."

"Well, I swan," said the grocery man as he put some eggs in a funnel shaped brown paper for a servant girl, "What did the minister say when he come to?"

"Say! What could he say? He just yelled 'Whoa,' and kept sawing with his hands, as though he was driving. I heard that the policeman was going to pull him for fast driving, till he found it was an accident. They told me, when they carried me home in a hack, that it was a wonder everybody was not killed, and when I got home Pa was going to sass me, until the hearse driver told him it was the minister that was to blame. I want to find out if they got the minister's umbrella back. The last I see of it the umbrella was running up his trouser's leg, and the point came out by the small of his back. But I am all right, only my shoulder sprained, and my legs bruised, and my eye black. I will be all right, and shall go to work to-morrow, 'cause the livery man says I was the only one in the crowd that had any sense. I understand the minister is going to take a vacation on account of his liver and nervous prostration. I would if I was him. I never saw a man that had nervous prostration any more than he did when they fished him out of the barbed wire fence, after we struck the street car. But that settles the minister business with me. I don't drive for no more preachers. What I want is a quiet party that wants to go on a walk," and the boy got up and hopped on one foot toward his crutches, filling his pistol pocket with figs as he hobbled along.

"Well, sir," said the grocery man, as he took a chew of tobacco out of a pail, and offered some to the boy, knowing that was the only thing in the store the boy would not take, "Do you know I think some of these ministers have about as little sense on worldly matters, as anybody? Now, the idea of that man jerking on an old pacer. It don't make any difference if the pacer was a hundred years old, he *would* pace if he was jerked on."

"You bet," said the boy, as he put his crutches under his arms and started for the door. "A minister may be sound on the atonement, but he don't want to saw on an old pacer. He may have the subject of infant baptism down finer than a cambric needle, but if he has ever been to college, he ought to have learned enough not to say '*ye-up*' to an old pacer that has been the boss of the road in his time. A minister may be endowed with sublime power to draw sinners to repentance, and make them feel like getting up and dusting for the beautiful beyond, and cause them, by his eloquence, to see angels bright and fair in their dreams, and chariots of fire flying through the pearly gates and down the golden streets of New Jerusalem, but he wants to turn out for a street car all the same, when he is driving a 2:20 pacer. The next time I drive a minister to a funeral, he will walk," and the boy hobbled out and hung out a sign in front of the grocery:

> *SMOKED DOG FISH AT HALIBUT*
>
> *PRICES, GOOD ENOUGH*
>
> *FOR COMPANY.*

CHAPTER X

THE OLD MAN MAKES A SPEECH

The grocery man and the bad boy have a fuss—The Bohemian Band—
The bad boy organizes a serenade—"Baby mine"—The old man
eloquent—The Bohemians create a famine—The Y. M. C. A.
announcement.

"THERE, you drop that," said the grocery man to the
bad boy, as he came limping into the store and began to
fumble around a box of strawberries. "I have never kicked
at your eating my codfish, and crackers and cheese, and
herring, and apples, but there has got to be a dividing line
somewhere, and I make it at strawberries at six shillings
a box, and only two layers in a box. I only bought one
box, hoping some plumber or gas man would come along
and buy it, and by gum, everybody that has been in the store
has sampled a strawberry out of that box, shivered as though
it was sour and gone off without asking the price," and the
grocery man looked mad, took a hatchet and knocked in the
head of a barrel of apples, and said: "There, help yourself to
dried apples."

"O, I don't want your strawberries or dried apples," said
the boy, as he leaned against a show case and looked at a bar
of red, transparent soap. "I was only trying to fool you.
Say, that bar of soap is old enough to vote. I remember
seeing it in your show case when I was about a year old, and
Pa came in here with me and held me up to the show case
to look at that tin tobacco box, and that round zinc looking-
glass, and the yellow wooden pocket comb, and the soap
looks just the same, only a little faded. If you would wash
yourself once in a while your soap wouldn't dry up on your
hands," and the boy sat down on the chair without any back,
feeling that he was even with the grocery man.

241

"You never mind the soap. It is paid for and that is more than your father can say about the soap that has been used in his house the past month," said the grocery man, as he split up a box to kindle the fire. "But we won't quarrel. What was it I heard about a band serenading your father, and his inviting them in to lunch?"

"Don't let that get out or Pa will kill me dead. It was a joke. One of those Bohemian bands that goes about town playing tunes for pennies, was over on the next street, and I told Pa I guessed some of his friends who had heard we had a baby at the house, had hired a band and was coming in a few minutes to serenade him and he better prepare to make a speech. Pa is proud of being a father at his age, and he thought it no more than right for the neighbors to serenade him, and he went to loading himself for a speech, in the library, and me and my chum went out and told the leader of the band there was a family up there that wanted to have some music, and they didn't care for expense, so they quit blowing where they was and came right along. None of them could understand English except the leader, and he only understood enough to go and take a drink when he is invited. My chum steered the band up to our house and got them to play 'Babies on our Block,' and 'Baby Mine,' and I stopped all the men who were going home and told them to wait a minute and they would see some fun; so when the band got through the second tune, and the Prussians were emptying the beer out of the horns, and Pa stepped out on the porch, there was more nor a hundred people in front of the house. You'd a dide to see Pa, when he put his hand in the breast of his coat, and struck an attitude. He looked like a congressman, or a tramp. The band was scared, 'cause they thought he was mad, and some of them were going to run, thinking he was going to throw pieces of brick house at them, but my chum and the leader kept them. Then Pa sailed in. He commenced, 'Fellow Citizens,' and then went away back to Adam and Eve, and worked up to the present day, giving a history of the notable people who had acquired children, and kept the crowd interested. I felt sorry for Pa, 'cause I knew how he would feel when he came to find out how he had been sold. The Bohemians in the band that couldn't understand English, they looked at each other, and wondered what it was all about,

PA STEPPED OUT ON THE PORCH.

and finally Pa wound up by stating that it was every citizen's duty to own children of his own, and then he invited the band and the crowd in to take some refreshments. Well, you ought to have seen that band come in the house. They fell over each other getting in, and the crowd went home, leaving Pa and my chum and me and the band. Eat? Well, I should smile. They just reached for things and talked Bohemian. Drink? O, no. I guess they didn't pour

it down. Pa opened a dozen bottles of champagne, and
they fairly bathed in it, as though they had a fire inside.
Pa tried to talk with them about the baby, but they couldn't
understand, and finally they got full and started out, and the
leader asked Pa for three dollars, and that broke him.
Pa told the leader he supposed the gentlemen who had got
up the serenade had paid for the music and the leader pointed
to me and said I was the gentleman that got it up. Pa
paid him, but he had a wicked look in his eye, and me and
my chum lit out, and the Bohemians came down the street
bilin' full, with their horns on their arms, and they were
talking Bohemian for all that was out. They stopped in
front of a vacant house, and began to play; but you couldn't
tell what tune it was they were so full, and a policeman came
along and drove them home. I guess I will sleep at the
livery stable to-night, 'cause Pa is so offul unreasonable
when anything costs him three dollars besides the champagne."

"Well, you have made a pretty mess of it," said the grocery man. "It's a wonder your Pa does not kill you. But
what is it I hear about the trouble at the church? They
lay that foolishness to you."

"It's all a lie. They lay everything to me. It was some
of them ducks that sing in the choir. I was just as much surprised as anybody when it occurred. You see our minister
is laid up from the effects of the ride to the funeral, when
he tried to run over a street car, and an old deacon who had
symptoms of being a minister in his youth, was invited to
take the minister's place, and talk a little. He is an absent
minded old party, who don't keep up with the events of the
day, and who ever played it on him knew that he was too
pious to even read the daily papers. There was a notice of
a choir meeting to be read, and I think the tenor smuggled in
the other notice between that and the one about the weekly
prayer meeting. Anyway, it wasn't me, but it like to broke
up the meeting. After the deacon read the choir notice he
took up the other one and read, 'I am requested to announce

that the Y. M. C. Association will give a friendly entertainment with soft gloves, on Tuesday evening, to which all are invited. Brother John Sullivan, the eminent Boston revivalist, will lead the exercises, assisted by Brother Slade, the Maori missionary from Australia. There will be no slugging, but a collection will be taken up at the door to defray expenses.' Well, I thought the people in church would sink through the floor. There was not a person in the church except the poor old deacon, but who understood that some wicked wretch had deceived him, and I know by the way the tenor tickled the soprano that he did it. I may be mean, but everything I do is innocent, and I wouldn't be as mean as a choir singer for two dollars. I felt real sorry for the old deacon, but he never knew what he had done, and I think it would be real mean to tell him. He won't be at the slugging match. That remark about taking up a collection settled the deacon. I must go down to the stable, now, and help grease a hack, so you will have to excuse me. If Pa comes here looking for me, tell him you heard I was going to drive a picnic party out to Waukesha, and may not be back in a week. By that time Pa will have got over that Bohemian serenade," and the boy filled his pistol pocket with dried apples, and went out and hung a sign in front of the grocery:

STRAWBERRIES, TWO SHILLINGS

A SMELL,

AND ONE SMELL IS ENOUGH.

CHAPTER XI

GARDENING UNDER DIFFICULTIES

The grocery man is deceived—The bad boy don't like moving—Goes into the coloring business—The old man thoroughly disguised—Uncle Tom and Topsy—The old man arrested—What the grocery man thinks—The bad boy moralizes on his fate—Resolves to be good.

"See here, you boy, get out of here," said the grocery man to the bad boy, as he came in the store with his face black and shining, "I don't want any other boys around here.

"O, philopena," said the bad boy as he put his hands on his knees and laughed so the candy jars rattled on the shelves. "You didn't know me. I am the same boy that comes in here and talks your arm off," and the boy opened the cheese box and cut off a piece of cheese so natural that the grocery man had no difficulty in recognizing him.

"What in the name of the seven sleeping sisters have you got on your hands and face?" said the grocery man, as he took the boy by the ear and turned him around. "You would pass in a colored prayer meeting, and no one would think you were galvanized. What you got up in such an outlandish rig for?"

"Well, I'll tell you, if you will keep watch at the door. If you see a bald-headed colored man coming along the street with a club, you whistle, and I will fall down cellar. The bald-headed colored man will be Pa. You see, we moved yesterday. Pa told me to get a vacation from the livery stable, and we would have fun moving. But I don't want any more fun. I know when I have got enough fun. Pa carried all the light things, and when it came to lifting, he had a crick in the back. Gosh, I never was so tired as I was last night, and I hope we have got settled, only some of the goods haven't turned up yet. A drayman took one load over on the West Side, and delivered them to a house that seemed to be expecting a load of household furniture. He thought it was all right, if everybody that was moving got a load of

THE POLICEMAN TOOK PA BY THE NECK.

goods. Well, after we got moved Pa said we must make a garden, and we said we would go out and spade up the ground and sow peas, and radishes and beets. There was some neighbors lived in the next house to our new one, that was all wimmin, and Pa don't like to have them think he had to work, so he said it would be a good joke to disguise

ourselves as tramps and the neighbors would think we had
hired some tramps to dig in the garden. I told Pa of a boss
scheme to fool them. I suggested that we take some of his
shoe blacking that is put on with a sponge, and black our
faces, and the neighbors would think we had hired an old
colored man and his boy to work in the garden. Pa said it
was immense, and he told me to go and black up, and if it
worked he would black hisself. So I went and put this burnt
cork on my face, 'cause it would wash off, and Pa looked
at me and said it was wack, and for me to fix him up too.
So I got the bottle of shoe blacking and painted Pa so he
looked like a colored coal heaver. Actually, when Ma saw
him she ordered him off the premises, and when he laffed
at her and acted sassy, she was going to throw biling water
on Pa. But I told her the scheme and she let up on Pa.
O, you'd a dide to see us out in the garden. Pa
looked like Uncle Tom, and I looked like Topsy, only I
ain't that kind of a colored person. We worked till a boy
throwed some tomato cans over the alley fence and hit me,
and I piled over the fence after him and left Pa. It was my
chum, and when I had caught him we put up a job to get Pa
to chase us. We throwed some more cans, and
Pa come out and my chum started, and I after
him, and Pa after both of us. He chased us two blocks
and then we got behind a policeman, and my chum told
the policeman it was a crazy old colored man that wanted to
kidnap us, and the policeman took Pa by the neck and was
going to club him, but Pa said he would go home and be-
have. He was offul mad, and he went home, and we looked
through the alley fence and Pa was trying to wash off the
blacking. You see that blacking won't wash off. You have
to wear it off. Pa would wash his face with soap suds,
and then look in the glass, and he was blacker every time he
washed, and when Ma laffed at him he said the offulest
words, something like 'Sweet spirit hear my prayer,' then
he washed himself again. I am going to leave my burnt cork
cork on, 'cause if I washed it off Pa would know there had

been some smouging somewhere. I asked the shoe store man
how long it would take the blacking to wear off, and he said
it ought to wear off in a week. I guess Pa won't go out
doors much, unless it is in the night. I am going to get him
to let me go off in the country fishing, till mine wears off,
and when I get out of town I will wash up. Say, you don't
think a little blacking hurts a man's complexion, do you, and
you don't think a man ought to get mad because it won't
wash off, do you?"

"O, probably it don't hurt the complexion," said the
grocery man, as he sprinkled some fresh water on the wilted
lettuce, so it would look fresh while the hired girl was buying some, "and yet it is mighty unpleasant, where a man
has got an engagement to go to a card party, as I know your
Pa has to-night. As to getting mad about it, if I was your
Pa I would take a barrel stave and shatter your castle scandalous. What kind of a fate do you think awaits you when
you die, anyway?"

"Well, I am mixed on the fate that awaits me when I
die. If I should go off sudden, with all my sins on my
head, and this burnt cork on my face, I should probably be
a neighbor to you down below, and they would give me a
job as fireman, and I should feel bad for you every time
I chucked in another chunk of brimstone, and thought of you
trying to swim dog-fashion in the lake of fire,
and straining your eyes to find an iceberg that you
could crawl on to cool your parched hind legs. If
I don't die slow so I will have time to repent
and be saved, I shall be toasted brown. That's what the
minister says, and they wouldn't pay him two thousand
dollars a year and give him a vacation to tell anything that
was not so. I tell you it is painful to think of that place
that so many pretty fair average people here are going to
when they die. Just think of it, a man that swears just
once, if he don't hedge, and take it back will go to the bad
place. If a person steals a pin, just a small, no account pin,
he is as bad as if he stole all there was in a bank, and he

stands the best chance of going to the bad place. You see, if a fellow steals a little thing like a pin, he forgets to repent, 'cause it don't seem to be worth while to make so much fuss about. But if a fellow robs a bank, or steals a whole lot of money from orphans, he knows it is a mighty serious matter, and he gets in his work repenting, too quick, and he is liable to get to the good place, while you, who have only stole a few potatoes out of a bushel that you sold to the orphan asylum, will forget to repent, and you will sizzle. I tell you, the more I read about being good, and going to heaven, the more I think a fellow can't be too careful, and from this out you won't find a better boy than I am. When I come in here after this and take a few dried peaches or crackers and cheese, you charge it right up to Pa, and then I won't have it on my mind and have to answer for it at the great judgment day. I am going to shake my chum, cause he chews tobacco, which is wicked, though I don't see how that can be, when the minister smokes, but I want to be on the safe side. I am going to be good or bust a suspender, and hereafter you can point to me as the boy who has seen the folly of an ill-spent life, and if there is such a thing as a fifteen year old boy, who has been a terror, going to heaven, I am the hairpin. I tell you, when I listen to the minister tell about the angels flying around there, and I see pictures of them purtier than any girl in this town, with chubby arms and dimples in the elbows and shoulders, and long golden hair, and think of myself here cleaning off horses in a livery stable and smelling like an old harness, it makes me tired, and I wouldn't miss going there for ten dollars. Say, you would make a healthy angel, for a back street of the new Jerusalem, but you would give the whole crowd away unless you washed up, and sent that shirt to the Chinese laundry. Yes, sir, hereafter you will find me as good as I know how to be. Now I am going to wash up and go and help the minister move."

As the boy went out the grocery man sat for several minutes thinking of the change that had come over the bad boy, and wondered what had brought it about and then he went to the door to watch him as he wended his way across the street with his head down, as though in deep thought, and the grocery man said to himself, "That boy is not as bad as some people think he is," and then he looked around and saw a sign hanging up in front of the store. written on a piece of box cover, with a blue pencil:

> *SPOILED*
> *CANNED HAM AND TONGUE*
> *GOOD ENOUGH*
> *FOR CHURCH PICNICS.*

and he looked after the boy who was slipping down an alley and said: "The condemn little whelp. Wait till I catch him."

CHAPTER XII

THE OLD MAN SHOOTS THE MINISTER

The bad boy tries to lead a different life—Murder in the air—The old man and his friends give themselves away—Dreadful stories of their wicked youth—The chicken coop invaded—The old man to the rescue—The minister and the deacons salted.

"SAY, I thought you was going to try to lead a different life," said the grocery man to the bad boy, as the youth came in with his pockets full of angle worms, and wanted to borrow a baking powder can to put them into, while he went fishing, and he held a long angle worm up by the tail and let it wiggle so it frightened a girl that had come in after two cents worth of yeast, so she dropped her pitcher and went out of the grocery as though she was chased by an anaconda.

"I am going to lead a different life; but a boy can't change his whole course of life in a minute, can he? Grown persons have to go on probation for six months before they can lead a different life, and half the time they lose their cud before the six months expire, and have to commence again. When it is so all fired hard for a man that is endowed with sense to break off being bad, you shouldn't expect too much from a boy. But I am going to do as well as could be expected—I ain't half as bad as I was! Gosh, why don't you burn a rag? That yeast that the girl spilled on the floor smells like it was sick. I should think that bread that was raised with that yeast would smell like this cooking butter you sell to hired girls."

"Well, never you mind the cooking butter. I know my business. If people want to use poor butter when they have company, and then blow up the grocer before folks, I can stand it if they can. But what is this I hear about your Pa fighting a duel with the minister in your back yard, and wounding him in the leg, and then trying to drown himself in the cistern? One of your new neighbors was in here this morning, and told me there was murder in the air at your house last night, and they are going to have the police pull your place as a disorderly house. I think you were at the bottom of the whole business!"

"O, it's all a darned lie and those neighbors will find they better keep still about us, or we will lie about them a little. You see, since Pa got that blacking on his face he don't go out any, and to make it pleasant for him Ma invited in a few friends to spend the evening. Ma has got up around, and the baby is a daisy, only it smells like a goat on account of drinking the goat's milk. Ma invited the minister

MA WENT TO THE HEAD OF THE STAIRS AND TOLD PA.

among the rest, and after supper the men went up into Pa's library to talk. O, you think I am bad, don't you, but of the nine men at our house last night I am an angel compared with what they were when they were boys. I got into the bath-room to untangle my fish line, and it is next to Pa's room, and I could hear everything they said, but I went away 'cause I thought the conversation would hurt my morals. They would all steal, when they were boys, but darned if I ever

stole. Pa has stolen over a hundred wagon loads of water-
melons, one deacon used to rob orchards, another one shot
tame ducks belonging to a farmer, and another tipped over
grindstones in front of the village store, at night, and broke
them, and run, and another used to steal eggs, and go out
in the woods and boil them, and the minister was the worst
of the lot, 'cause he took a seine, with some other boys, and
went to a stream where a neighbor was raising brook trout,
and cleaned the stream out, and to ward off suspicion, he
went to the man next day and paid him a dollar to let him
fish in the stream, and then kicked because there were no
trout, and the owner found the trout were stolen and laid it
to some Dutch boys. I wondered, when those men were
telling their experience, if they ever thought of it now when
they were preaching and praying, and taking up collections.
I should think they wouldn't say a boy was going to hell
right off 'cause he was a little wild nowadays, when he has
such an example. Well, lately, somebody has been burgling
our chicken coop, and Pa loaded an old musket with rock
salt, and said he would fill the fellow full of salt if he
caught him, and while they were talking up stairs Ma heard
a rooster squawk, and she went to the stairway and told Pa
there was somebody in the hen house. Pa jumped up and
told the visitors to follow him, and they would see a man
running down the alley full of salt, and he rushed out with
the gun, and the crowd followed him. Pa is shorter than the
rest, and he passed under the first wire clothes line in the
yard all right, and was going for the hen house on a jump,
when his neck caught the second wire clothes line just as the
minister and two of the deacons caught their necks under
the other wire. You know how a wire, hitting a man on
the throat, will set him back, head over appetite. Well, sir,
I was looking out of the back window, and I wouldn't be
positive, but I think they all turned double back somersaults,
and struck on their ears. Anyway, Pa did, and the gun must
have been cocked, or it struck the hammer on a stone, for
it went off, and it was pointed toward the house, and three

of the visitors got salted. The minister was hit the worst,
one piece of salt taking him in the hind leg, and the other
in the back, and he yelled as though it was dynamite. I suppose when you shoot a man with salt, it smarts, like when you
get corned beef brine on your chapped hands. They all
yelled and Pa seemed to have been knocked silly, some way,
for he pranced around and seemed to think he had killed

I THOUGHT OF THE CISTERN.

them. He swore at the wire clothes line, and then I missed
Pa and heard a splash like when you throw a cat in the river,
and then I thought of the cistern, and I went down and we
took Pa by the collar and pulled him out. O, he was awful
damp. No, sir, it was no duel at all, but a naxident, and I
didn't have anything to do with it. The gun wasn't loaded
to kill, and the salt only went through the skin, but those
men *did* yell. Maybe it was my chum that stirred up the
chickens, but I don't know. He has not commenced to lead

a different life yet, and he might think it would make our folks sick if nothing occurred to make them pay attention. I think where a family has been having a good deal of exercise, the way ours has, it hurts them to break off too suddenly. But the visitors went home, real quick, after we got Pa out of the cistern, and the minister told Ma he always felt when he was in our house, as though he was on the verge of a yawning crater, ready to be engulfed any minute, and he guessed he wouldn't come any more. Pa changed his clothes and told Ma to have them wire clothes lines changed for rope ones. I think it is hard to suit Pa, don't you?"

"O, your Pa is all right. What he needs is rest. But why are you not working at the livery stable? You haven't been discharged, have you?" And the grocery man laid a little lump of concentrated lye, that looked like maple sugar on a cake of sugar that had been broken, knowing the boy would nibble it.

"No, sir, I was not discharged, but when a livery man lends me a kicking horse to take my girl out riding, that settles it. I asked the boss if I couldn't have a quiet horse that would drive himself if I wound the lines around the whip, and he let me have one he said would go all day without driving. You know how it is, when a fellow takes a girl out riding he don't want his mind occupied holding lines. Well, I got my girl in, and we went out on the Whitefish Bay road, and it was just before dark, and we rode along under the trees, and I wound the lines around the whip, and put one arm around my girl, and patted her under the chin with my other hand, and her mouth looked so good, and her blue eyes looked up at me and twinkled as much as to dare me to kiss her, and I was all of a tremble, and then my hand wandered around by her ear and I drew her head up to me and gave her a smack. Say, that was no kind of a horse to give to a young fellow to take a girl out riding . Just as I smacked her I felt as though the buggy had been struck by a pile-driver, and when I looked at the horse he was running away and kicking the buggy, and the lines were dragging on the ground. I was scared, I tell you. I wanted to jump out but my girl threw her arms around my neck and screamed, and said we would die together, and just as we were going to die the buggy struck a fence and the horse broke loose and went off, leaving us in the buggy tumbled down by the dash board, but we were not hurt. The old horse stopped and went to chewing grass and looked up at me as though he wanted to say 'philopena.' I tried to catch him, but he wouldn't catch, and then we waited till dark and walked home, and I told the livery man what I thought of such treatment, and he said that if I had attended to my driving, and not kissed the girl, I would have been all right. He said I ought to have told him I wanted a horse that wouldn't shy at kissing, but how did I know I was going to get up courage to kiss her? A livery man ought to take it for granted that when a young fellow goes out with his girl he is going to kiss her, and give him a horse according. But I quit him at once. I won't work for a man that hasn't got sense. Gosh! What kind of maple sugar is that? Jerusalem! Whew, give me some water! O, my, it is taking the skin off my mouth!"

The grocery man got him some water and seemed sorry that the boy had taken the lump of concentrated lye by mistake, and when the boy went out the grocery man pounded his hands on his knees and laughed, and presently he went out in front of the store and found a sign:

FRESH LETIS, BEEN PICKED

MORE'N A WEEK

TUFFER'N TRIPE.

CHAPTER XIII

THE BAD BOY A THOROUGHBRED

The bad boy with a black eye—A poor friendless girl excites his pity—
Proves himself a gallant knight—The old man is charmed at his
son's courage—The grocery man moralizes—Fifteen Christs in Milwaukee—The tables turned—The old man wears the boy's old
clothes.

"AH, ha, you have got your deserts at last," said the
grocery man to the bad boy, as he came in with one eye
black, and his nose peeled on one side, and sat down on a
board across the coal scuttle, and began whistling as uncon-
cerned as possible. "What's the matter with your eye?"

"Boy tried to gouge it out without my consent," and the
bad boy took a dried herring out of the box and began peeling it. "He is in bed now, and his ma is poulticing him, and
she says he will be out about the last of next week."

"O, you are going to be a prize fighter, ain't you?" said
the grocery man, disgusted. "When a boy leaves a job
where he is working, and goes to loafing around, he becomes
a fighter the first thing. What your Pa ought to do is bind
you out with a farmer, where you would have to work all
the time. I wish you would go away from here, because you
look like one of these fellows that comes up before the police
judge Monday morning, and gets thirty days in the house
of correction. Why don't you go out and loaf around a
slaughter house, where you would look appropriate?" and
the grocery man took a hair-brush and brushed some sugar
and tea that was on the counter, into the sugar barrel.

"Well, if you have got through with your sermon, I
will toot a little on my horn," and the boy threw the remains
of the herring over behind a barrel of potatoes, and wiped
his hands on a coffee sack. "If you had this black eye, and

got it the way I did, it would be a more priceless gem in the crown of glory you hope to wear, than any gem you can get by putting quarters in the collection plate, with the holes filled with lead, as you did last Sunday, when I was watching you. O, didn't you look pious when you picked that filled quarter out, and held your thumb over the place where the lead was? The way of the black eye was this. I got a job tending a soda water fountain, and last night, just before we closed, there was two or three young loafers in the place, and a girl came in for a glass of soda. Five years ago she was one of the brightest scholars in the ward school, when I was in the intermediate department. She was just as handsome as a peach, and everybody liked her. At recess she used to take my part when the boys knocked me around, and she lived near us. She had a heart as big as that cheese box, and I guess that's what's the matter. Anyway, she left school, and then it was said she was going to get married to a fellow who is now in the dude business, but he went back on her, and after awhile her ma turned her out doors, and for a year or two she was jerking beer in a concert saloon, until the mayor stopped concerts. She tried hard to get sewing to do, but they wouldn't have her, I guess 'cause she cried so much when she was sewing, and the tears wet the cloth she was sewing on. Once I asked Pa why Ma didn't give her some sewing to do, and he said for me to dry up and never speak to her if I met her on the street. It seemed tough to pass her on the street when she had tears in her eyes as big as marbles, and not speak to her when I know her so well, and she had been so kind to me at school just 'cause the dude wouldn't marry her, but I wanted to obey Pa, so I used to walk around a block when I see her coming, 'cause I didn't want to hurt her feelings. Well, last night she came in the store, looking pretty shabby, and wanted a glass of soda, and I gave it to her, and O, how her hand trembled when she raised the glass to her lips, and how wet her eyes were, and how pale her face was. I choked up so I couldn't speak

when she handed me the nickel, and when she looked up at
me and smiled just like she used to, and said I was getting
to be almost a man since we went to school at the old school
house, and put her handkerchief to her eyes, by gosh my
eyes got so full I couldn't tell whether it was a nickel or a
lozenger she gave me. Just then one of those loafers began
to laugh at her, and call ner names, and say the police
ought to take her up for a stray, and he made fun of her
until she cried some more, and I got hot, and went around
to where he was, and told him if he said another unkind
word to that girl I would maul him. He laughed and asked
if she was my sister, and I told him that a poor, friendless
girl, who was sick and in distress, and who was insulted,
ought to be every boy's sister, for a minute, and any boy who
had a spark of manhood, should protect her, and then he
laughed and said I ought to be one of the Little Sisters
of the Poor, and he took hold of her faded shawl and pulled
the weak girl against the show case, and said something
mean to her, and she looked as though she wanted to die,
and I mashed that boy one right on the nose. Well, the air
seemed to be full of me for a minute, 'cause he was bigger
than me, and he got me down, and got his thumb in my eye.
I guess he was going to take my eye out, but I turned him
over and got on top, and I mauled him until he begged,
but I wouldn't let him up till he asked the girl's pardon, and
swore he would whip any boy that insulted her, and then I let
him up and the girl thanked me; but I told her I couldn't speak
to her, 'cause she was tough, and Pa didn't want me to speak
to anybody who was tough; but if anybody ever insulted
her so she had to cry, that I would whip him if I had to
take a club. I told Pa about it, and I thought he would be
mad at me for taking the part of a girl that was tough, but,
by gosh, Pa hugged me, and the tears came in his eyes, and
he said I had got good blood in me, and I did just right; and
if I would show him the father of the boy that I whipped, Pa
said he could whip the old man, and Ma said for me to find
the poor girl and send her up to the house, and she would

give her a job making pillow cases and night shirts. Don't it
seem darn queer to you that everybody goes back on a poor
girl 'cause she makes a mistake, and the blasted whelp that is
to blame, gets a chromo? It makes me tired to think of it,"
and the boy got up and shook himself, and looked into the

O, HOW HER HAND TREMBLED WHEN SHE RAISED THE GLASS.

cracked mirror hanging upon a post, to see how his eye
was getting along.

"Say, young fellow, you are a thoroughbred," said the
grocery man, as he sprinkled some water on the asparagus
and lettuce, "and you can come in here and get all the herring you want, and never mind the black eye. I wish I had
it myself. Yes, it does seem tough to see people never allow
a girl to reform. Now, in Bible times, the Saviour forgave

Mary or somebody, I forget now what her name was, and she was a better girl than ever. What we need is more of the spirit of Christ, and the world would be better."

"What we want is about ten thousand Christs. We ought to have ten or fifteen right here in Milwaukee, and they would find plenty of business, too. But this climate seems to be too rough. Say, did I tell you about Pa and Ma having trouble?"

"No, what's the row?"

"Well, you see Ma wants to economize all she can, and Pa has been getting thinner since he quit drinking and reformed, and I have kept on growing until I am bigger than he is. Funny, ain't it, that a boy should be bigger than his Pa? Pa wanted a new suit of clothes, and Ma said she would fix him, and so she took one of my old suits and made it over for Pa; and he wore them a week before he knew it was an old suit made over, but one day he found a handful of dried up angle worms in the pistol pocket that I had forgot when I was fishing, and Pa laid the angle worms to Ma, and Ma had to explain that she made over one of my old suits for Pa. He was mad and took them off and threw them out the back window, and swore he would never humiliate himself by wearing his son's old clothes. Ma tried to reason with him, but he was awfully worked up, and said he was no charity hospital, and he stormed around to find his old suit of clothes, but Ma had sold them to a plaster of Paris image peddler, and Pa hadn't anything to wear, and he wanted Ma to go out in the alley and pick up the suit he threw out the window; but a rag man had picked them up and was going away, and Pa, he grabbed a linen duster and put it on and went out after the rag picker, and he run, and Pa after him; and the rag man told a policeman there was an escaped lunatic from the asylum, and he was chasing people all over the city, and the policeman took Pa by the linen ulster, and pulled it off, and he was a sight when they took him to the police station. Ma and me had to go down and bail him out, and the police lent us a tarpaulin to put over Pa, and we got him home, and he is wearing his summer pants while the tailor makes him a new suit of clothes. I think Pa is too excitable, and too particular. I never kicked on wearing Pa's old clothes, and I think he ought to wear mine now. Well, I must go down to the sweetened wind factory, and jerk soda," and the boy went out and hung up a sign in front of the store:

> *SPINAGE FOR GREENS, THAT*
> *THE CAT HAS MADE*
> *A NEST IN OVER SUNDAY.*

CHAPTER XIV

"Well, how's your eye?" said the grocery man to the
bad boy, as he blew in with the wind on the day of the
cyclone, and left the door open. "Shut that door. You want
to blow everything out of the store? Had any more fights,
protecting girls from dudes?"

"No, everything is quiet so far. I guess since I have got
a record as a fighter, the boys will be careful who they insult when I am around. But I have had the hardest week
I ever experienced, jerking soda for the Young Men's
Christian Association," said the boy, as he peeled a banana.

"What do you mean, boy? Don't cast any reflections on
such a noble Association. They don't drink, do they?"

"Drink! O, no! They don't drink anything intoxicating
but when it comes to soda they flood themselves. You know
there has been a National Convention of delegates from all
the Young Men's Christian Associations of the whole country, about three hundred, here, and our store is right on the
street where they pass four times a day, and I never saw
such appetites for soda. There has been one continual fizz
in our store since Wednesday. The boss wanted me to play
it on some of them by putting some brandy in with the
perfumery a few times, but I wouldn't do it. I guess a
few weeks ago, before I had led a different life, I wouldn't
had to be asked twice to play the game on anybody. But a

264

man can buy soda of me and be perfectly safe. Of course, if a man winks, when I ask him what flavor he wants, and says 'Never mind,' I know enough to put in brandy. That is different. But I wouldn't smuggle it into a man for nothing. This Christian Association Convention has caused a coldness between Pa and Ma, though."

"How's that? Your Pa isn't jealous, is he?" and the grocery man came around from behind the counter to get the latest gossip to retail to the hired girls who traded with him.

"Jealous nothin'," said the boy, as he took a few raisins out of a box. "You see, the delegates were shuffled out to all the church members to take care of, and they dealt two to Ma, and she never told Pa anything about it. They came to supper the first night, and Pa didn't get home, so when they went to the Convention in the evening, Ma gave them a night key, and Pa came home from the boxing match about eleven o'clock, and Ma was asleep. Just as Pa got most of his clothes off, he heard somebody fumbling at the front door, and he thought it was burglars. Pa has got nerve enough, when he is on the inside of the house and the burglars are on the outside. He opened a window and looked out and saw two suspicious looking characters trying to pick the lock with a skeleton key, and he picked up a new slop-jar that Ma bought when we moved, cover and all, and dropped it right down between the two delegates. Gosh, if it had hit one of them, there would have been the solemnest funeral you ever saw. Just as it struck, they got the door opened and came into the hall, and the wind was blowing pretty hard and they thought a cyclone had taken the cupola off the house. They were talking about being miraculously saved, and trying to strike a match on their wet pants, when Pa went to the head of the stairs and pushed over a wire stand filled with potted plants, which struck pretty near the delegates, and one of them said the house was coming down sure, and they better go into the cellar, and they went and got behind the furnace. Pa called me up and wanted me to go down cellar and tell the burglars we were onto them, and for them to get out, but I wasn't very well, so Pa locked his door and went to bed. I guess it must have been half-an-hour before Pa's cold feet woke Ma up, and then Pa told her not to move for her life, 'cause there were two of the savagest looking burglars that ever was, rummaging over the house. Ma smelled Pa's breath to see if he had got to drinking again, and then she got up and hid her oraide watch in her shoes, and her Onalaska diamond ear-rings in the Bible, where she said no burglar would ever find them, and Pa and Ma laid awake till daylight, and then Pa said he wasn't afraid, and he and Ma went down cellar. Pa stood on the bottom stair and looked around, and one of the delegates said, 'Mister, is the storm over, and is your family safe?' and Ma recognized the voice and said, 'Why, it's one of the delegates. What are you doing down there?' and Pa said, 'What's a delegate?' and then Ma explained it, and Pa apologized, and the delegate said it was no matter as they had enjoyed themselves real well in the cellar. Ma was mortified most to death, and the delegate told her it was all right. She was mad at Pa, first, but when she saw the broken slop-bowl on the front steps, and the potted plants in the hall, she wanted to kill Pa,, and I guess she would only for the society of the delegates. She couldn't help telling Pa that he was a bald headed old fool, but Pa didn't retaliate—he is too much of a gentleman to talk back in company. All he said was that a woman who is old enough to have delegates sawed off on her, ought to have sense enough to tell her husband, and then they all drifted off into conversation about the convention and the boxing match, and everything was all right on the surface; but after breakfast, when the delegates went to the convention, I noticed Pa went right down town and bought a new slop-jar and some more plants. Pa and Ma didn't speak all the forenoon, and I guess they wouldn't up to this time, only Ma's bonnet came home from the milliner's and she had to have some money to pay for it. Then she called Pa 'Pet,' and that settled it. When Ma calls Pa 'Pet,' that is twenty-five dollars. 'Dear, old darling,' means fifty dollars. But say, those christian young men do a heap of good, don't they? Their presence seems to make people better. Some boys down by the store were going to tie a

I COULD SEE MY GIRL'S BANGS RAISE RIGHT UP.

can on a dog's tail, yesterday, and somebody said, 'Here comes the Christian Association,' and those bad boys let the dog go. They tried to find the dog after the crowd had got by, but the dog knew his business. Well, I must go down and charge the soda fountain for a picnic that is expected from the country."

"Hold on a minute," said the grocery man as he wound a piece of brown paper around a cob and stuck it in a syrup

jug he had just filled for a customer, and then licked his
fingers. "I want to ask you a question. What has caused
you to change so from being bad? You were about as bad
as they make 'em, up to a few weeks ago, and now you seem
to have a soul, and get in your work doing good about as
well as any boy in town. What is it that ails you?"

"O, sugar, I don't want to tell," said the boy, as he
blushed and wiggled around on one foot, and looked silly;
"but if you won't laugh, I will tell you. It is my girl that
has made me good. It may be only temporary. If she goes
back on me I may be tough again; but if she continues
to hold out faithful I shall be a daisy all the time. Say, did
you ever love a girl? It would do you good, if you loved
anybody regular old fashioned the way I do, people could send
little children here to trade, and you wouldn't palm off any
wilted vegetables on to them, or give them short weight—if
you was in love, and felt that the one you loved saw every
act of yours, and you could see her eyes every minute, you
would throw away anything that was spoiled, and not try to
sell it, for fear you would offend her. I don't think any man
is fit to do business honestly unless he is in love, or has been
in love once. Now I couldn't do anything wrong if I tried,
because I should hear the still small voice of my girl saying
to me, 'Hennery, let up on that.' I slipped up on a banana peel
yesterday, and hurt myself, and I was just going to say
something offul, and I could see my girl's bangs raise right
up, and there was a pained look in her face, and a tear in her
eye, and, by gosh, I just smiled and looked tickled till her
hair went down and the smile came back again to her lips,
though it hurt me like blazes where I struck the sidewalk.
I was telling Pa about it, and asked him if he ever felt as
though his soul was going right out toward somebody, and he
said he did once on a steamboat excursion; but he ate a lemon
and got over it. Pa thinks it is my liver, and wants me to
take pills, but I tell you, boss, it has struck in me too deep
for pills, unless it is one that weighs about a hundred and
forty pounds, and wears a hat with a feather on. Say, if my

girl should walk right into a burning lake of red-hot lava, and beckon me to follow, I would take a hop, skip and jump, and—"

"O, give us a rest," said the grocery man, as he took a basin of water and sprinkled the floor, preparatory to sweeping out. "You have got the worst case I ever saw, and you better go out and walk around a block," and the boy went out and forgot to hang out any sign.

CHAPTER XV

The bad boy quits jerking soda—Enters the dramatic profession—
"What's a super"—The privileges of a supe's father—Behind the
scenes—The bad boy has played with McCullough—"I was the
populace"—Plays it on his Sunday school teacher—"I prithee, au
reservior, I go hence !"

"You look pretty sleepy," said the grocery man to the
bad boy, as he came in the store yawning, and stretched himself out on the counter with his head on a piece of brown
wrapping paper, in reach of a box of raisins, "What's the
matter? Been sitting up with your girl all night?"

"Naw! I wish I had. Wakefulness with my girl is
sweeter and more restful than sleep. No, this is the result of
being a dutiful son, and I am tired. You see Pa and Ma
have separated. That is, not for keeps, but Pa has got
frightened about burglars, and he gets up into the attic to
sleep. He says it is to get fresh air, but he knows better.
Ma has got so accustomed to Pa's snoring that she can't go
to sleep without it, and the first night Pa left she didn't
sleep a wink, and yesterday I was playing on an old accordion that I traded a dog collar for after our dog was poisoned, and when I touched the low notes I noticed Ma dozed
off to sleep, it sounded so much like Pa's snore, and last night
Ma made me set up and play for her to sleep. She rested
splendid, but I am all broke up, and I sold the accordion this
morning to the watchman who watches our block. It is
queer what a different effect music will have on different
people. While Ma was sleeping the sleep of innocence under
the influence of my counterfeit of Pa's snore, the night-
watchman was broke of his rest by it, and he bought it of

me to give to the son of an enemy of his. Well, I have quit
jerking soda."

"No, you don't tell me," said the grocery man, as he
moved the box of raisins out of reach. "You will never
amount to anything unless you stick to one trade or profession. A rolling hen never catches the early angleworm."

"O, but I am all right now. In the soda water business

MA MADE ME PLAY FOR HER TO SLEEP

there is no chance for genius to rise unless the soda fountain
explodes. It is all wind, and one gets tired of the constant
fizz. He feels that he is a fraud, and when he puts a little
syrup in a tumbler, and fires a little sweetened wind and
water in it until the soapsuds fills the tumbler, and charges ten
cents for that which only costs a cent a sensitive soda jerker,
who has reformed, feels that it is worse than three card
monte. I couldn't stand the wear on my conscience, so I

have got a permanent job as a super, and shall open the 1st
of September."

"Say, what's a super? It isn't one of these free lunch
places, that the mayor closes at midnight, is it?" and the grocery man looked sorry.

"O, thunder, you want salt on you. A super is an ad-
junct of the stage. A supe is a fellow that assists the stars
and things, carrying chairs and taking up carpets, and sweeping the sand off the stage after a dancer has danced a jig,
and he brings beer for the actors, and helps lace up corsets,
and anything he can do to add to the effect of the play.
Privately, now, I have been acting as a supe for a long time.
cn the sly, and my folks didn't know anything about it, but
since I reformed and decided to be good, I felt it my duty
to tell Ma and Pa about it. The news broke Ma all up, at
first, but Pa said some of the best actors in this country
were supes once, and some of them were now, and he thought
suping would be the making of me. Ma thought going on
the stage would be my ruination. She said the theater was
the hot-bed of sin, and brought more ruin than the church
could head off. But when I told her that they always gave
a supe two or three extra tickets for his family, she said the
theater had some redeeming features, and when I said my
entrance upon the stage would give me a splendid opportunity to get the recipe for face powder from the actresses,
for Ma, and I could find out how the actresses managed to
get number four feet into number one shoes, Ma said she
wished I could commence suping right off. Ma says there
are some things about the theater that are not so all-fired bad,
and she wants me to get seats for the first comic opera that
comes along. Pa wants it understood with the manager that
a supe's father has the right to go behind the scenes to see
that no harm befalls him, but I know what Pa wants. He
may seem pious, and all that, but he likes to look at ballet
girls better than any meek and lowly follower I ever see, and
some day you will hear music in the air. Pa thinks theaters
are very bad, when he has to pay a dollar for a reserved seat,

but when he can get it for nothing as a relative of one of the 'perfesh,' the theater has many redeeming qualities. Pa and Ma think I am going into the business fresh and green, but I know all about it. When I played with McCullough here once—"

"Oh, what are you giving us?" said the grocery man in disgust, "when you played with McCullough! What did you do?"

"What did I do? Why, you old seed cucumber, the whole play centered around me. Do you remember the scene in the Roman forum, where McCullough addressed the populace of Rome? I was the populace. Don't you remember a small fellow standing in front of the Roman orator taking it in; with a night shirt on, with bare legs and arms? That was me, and everything depended on me. Suppose I had gone off the stage at the critical moment, or laughed when I should have looked fierce at the inspired words of the Roman senator, it would have been a dead give away on Mc-Cullough. As the populace of Rome I consider myself a glittering success, and Mc took me by the hand when they carried Cæsar's dead body out, and he said, 'Us three did ourselves proud.' Such praise from McCullough is seldom accorded to a supe. But I don't consider the populace of the imperial city of Rome my master piece. Where I excel is in coming out before the curtain between the acts, and unhooking the carpet. Some supes go out and turn their backs to the audience, showing patches on their pants, and rip up the carpet with no style about them, and the dust flies, and the boys yell 'supe,' and the supe gets nervous and forgets his cue, and goes off tumbling over the carpet, and the orchestra leader is afraid the supe will fall on him. But I go out with a quiet dignity that is only gained by experience and I take hold of the carpet the way Hamlet takes up the skull of Yorick, and the audience is paralyzed. I kneel down on the carpet, to unhook it, in a devotional sort of a way that makes the audience bow their heads as though they were in church, and before they realize that I

18

am only a supe I have the carpet unhooked and march out the way a 'Piscopal minister does when he goes out between the acts at church to change his shirt. They never 'guy' me, 'cause I act well my part. But I kick on holding dogs for actresses. Some supes think they are made if they can hold a dog, but I have an ambition that a pug dog will not fill. I held Mary Anderson's cud of gum once, while she went on the stage, and when she came off and took her gum her fingers touched mine and I had to run my fingers in my hair to warm them. Gosh, but she'd freeze ice cream without salt. I'll be glad when the theatrical season opens, 'cause we actors get tired laying off."

"Well, I'd like to go behind the scenes with you some night," said the grocery man, offering the bad boy an orange to get solid with him, in view of future complimentary tickets. "No danger, is there?"

"No danger if you keep off the grass. But you'd a dide to see my Sunday school teacher one Saturday night last summer. He keeps books in a store, and is pretty soon week days, but he can tell you more about Daniel in the lion's den on Sunday than anybody. He knew I was solid at the theater, and wanted me to get him behind the scenes one night, and another supe wanted to go to the sparring match, and I thought it wouldn't be any harm to work my teacher in, so I got him a job that night to hold the dogs. for Uncle Tom's show. He was in one of the wings holding the chains, and the dogs were just anxious to go on, and it was all my teacher could do to hold them. I told him to wind the chains around his wrists, and he did so, and just then Eliza began to skip across the ice, and we sicked the blood hounds on before my teacher could unwind the chains from his wrists, and the dogs pulled him right out on the stage, on his stomach, and drawed him across, and he jerked one dog and kicked him in the stomach, and the dog turned on my teacher and took a mouthful of his coat tail and shook it, and I guess the dog got some meat, anyway the teacher climbed up a step-ladder, and the dogs treed him, and the step-ladder fell down, and we grabbed the dogs and put some court plaster on my teacher's nose, where the fire extinguisher peeled it, and he said he would go home, b'cause the theater was demoralizing in its tendencies. I s'pose it was not right, but when the teacher stood up to hear our Sunday

JUST THEN ELIZA BEGAN TO SKIP ACROSS THE ICE.

school lesson the next day, 'cause he was tired where the dog bit him, I said 'Sick-em,' in a whisper, when his back was turned, and he jumped clear over to the Bible class, and put his hands around to his coat tail as though he thought the Uncle Tom's Cabin party was giving a matinee in the church. The Sunday school lesson was about the dog's licking the sores of Lazarus, and the teacher said we must not confound the good dogs of Bible time with the savage beasts of the present day, that would shake the daylights out of Lazarus, and make him climb the cedars of Lebanon quicker than you could say Jack Robinson, and go off chewing a cud of bitter reflection on Lazarus' coat tail. I don't think a Sundayschool teacher ought to bring up personal reminiscences before a class of children, do you? Well, some time next fall you put on a clean shirt and a pair of sheet iron pants, with stove legs on the inside, and I will take you behind the scenes to see some good moral show. In the meantime, if you have an occasion to talk with Pa, tell him that Booth and Barrett, and Keene commenced on the stage as supes, and Salvini roasted peanuts in the lobby of some theater. I want our folks to feel that I am taking the right course to become a star. I prythee *au reservoir,* I go hence! but to return. Avaunt!" And the boy walked out on his toes *a la* Booth.

CHAPTER XVI

"I HEAR your Uncle Ezra is here on a visit," said the
grocery man to the bad boy. "I suppose you have been having a high old time. There is nothing that does a boy more
good than to have a nice visit with a good uncle, and hear
him tell about old times when he and the boy's father were
boys together."

"Well, I don't know about it," said the boy, as he took
a stick of mararoni, and began to blow paper wads through
it at a wood sawyer, who was filing a saw outside the door.
"When a boy who has been tough has got his pins all set to
reform, I don't think it does him any good to have a real
nice Uncle come to the house visiting. Anyway, that's my
experience. I have backslid the worst way, and it is going to
take me a month after Uncle Ezra goes away to climb up to
the grace that I have fallen from. It is darn discouraging,"
said the boy as he looked up to the ceiling in an innocent
sort of a way, and hid the macaroni under his coat when the
wood sawyer, who had been hit in the neck, dropped his
saw and got up mad.

"What's the trouble? Your uncle has the reputation
where he lives of being one of the pillars of society. But
you can't tell about these fellows when they get away from
home. Does he drink?"

"No, he don't drink; but as near as I can figure it, he and
Pa were about the worst pills in the box, when they were
young. I don't want you to repeat it, but when Pa and Ma

were married they eloped. Yes, sir—actually ran away and defied their parents—and they had to hide about a week, for fear Ma's father would fill Pa so full of cold lead that he would sink if he fell in the water. Pa has been kicked over the fence and chased down alleys dozens of times by Ma's grandfather, when he was sparking Ma, and Ma was a terror, too, 'cause her mother couldn't do anything with her, though she is awful precise now, and wants everybody to be too good. Why, Ma's mother used to warm her ears, and shake the daylights out of her, but it didn't do any good. She was mashed on Pa, and there was no cure for her except to have Pa prescribed for her as a husband, and they ran away. Uncle Ezra told me all about it. Ma hain't got any patience with girls now days that have minds of their own about fellows, and she thinks their parents ought to have all the say. Well, maybe she thinks she knows all about it. But when people get in love it is the same now as when Pa and Ma was trying to get out of the reach of my grandfather's shot gun. But Pa and Uncle Ezra and Ma are good friends, and they talk over old times and have a big laugh. I guess Uncle Ezra was too much for Pa in joking when they were boys 'cause Pa told me that all rules against joking were suspended while Uncle Ezra was here, and for me to play anything on him I could. I told Pa I was trying to lead a different life, but he said what I wanted to do was to make Uncle Ezra think of old times, and the only way was to kept him on the ragged edge. I thought if there was anything I could do to make it pleasant for my Uncle, it was my duty to do it, so I fixed the bed slats on the spare bed so they would fall down at 2 A. M. the first night, and then I retired. At two o'clock I heard the awfulest noise in the spare room, and a howling and screaming, and I went down to meet Uncle Ezra in the hall, and he asked me what was the matter in there, and I asked him if he didn't sleep in the spare room, and he said no, that Pa and Ma was in there, and he slept in their room. Then he went in the spare room and you'd a dide to see Pa. Ma had jumped out when the

slats first fell; and was putting her hair up in curl papers
when we got in, but Pa was all tangled up in the springs and
things.   His head had gone down first, and the mattress
and quilts rolled over him, and he was almost smothered

GRANDFATHER'S SHOT GUN.

and we had to take the bedstead down to get him out, **the**
way you have to unharness a horse when he runs away and
falls down before you can get him up.   Pa was mad, but
Uncle Ezra laughed at him, and told him he was only foundered, and all he wanted was a bran mash and some horse

liniment, and he would come out all right. Uncle Ezra went out into the hall to get a pail of water to throw on Pa, 'cause he said Pa was afire, when Pa asks me why in blazes I didn't fix the other bed slats, and I told him I didn't know they were going to change beds, and then Pa said 'Don't let it occur again. Pa lays everything to me. He is the most changeable man I ever saw. He told me to do everything Uncle Era wanted me to do, and then, when I helped Uncle Ezra to play a joke on Pa, he was mad. Say, I don't think this world is run right, do you? I haven't got much time to talk to you to-day, 'cause Uncle Ezra and me are going fishing, but don't it strike you that it is queer that parents trounce boys for doing just what they did themselves? Now, I have got a friend whose father is a lawyer. That lawyer would warm his boy if he should tell a lie or associate with anybody that was bad, and yet the lawyer will defend a man he knows is guilty of stealing, and get him clear and take the money he got from the thief, who stole it, to buy the same boy a new coat to wear to church, and he will defend a man who committed murder, and make an argument to the jury that will bring tears to their eyes, and they will clear the murderer. Queer, ain't it? And say, how is it that we send missionaries to Burmah, to convert them from heathenism, and the same vessel that takes the missionaries there carries from Boston a cargo of tin gods to sell to the heathen? Why wouldn't it be better to send the missionaries to Boston? I think the more a boy learns the more he gets mixed."

"Well, how's your theater? Have any of the great actors supported you lately?" said the grocery man, to change the subject.

"No, we are all off on vacations. Booth and Barrett, and lots of the stars, are gone to Europe, and the rest work down to less high-toned places. Some of the theater girls are waiters at summer resorts, and lots are visiting relatives on farms. I tell you, it makes a difference whether the relatives are visiting you or you are visiting them. Actors and actresses feel awfully when an old granger comes to town where they are playing, and wants to see them. They are ashamed of his homespun clothes, and cowhide boots, and they want to meet him in an alley somewhere, or in the

MY UNCLE EZRA IS PRETTY ROUGH.

basement of the theater, so other actors will not laugh at their rough relatives, but when the season is over an actor who can remember a relative out on a farm, is tickled to death, and the granger is all right enough there, and the actor does not think of the rough nutmeg grater hands, and the blistered nose, as long as the granger relative will put up fried pork and things, and 'support' the actor. My Uncle Ezra is pretty rough and it makes me tired sometimes when I am down town with him to have him go into a store where there are girl clerks and ask what things are for, that I know he don't want, and make the girls blush, but he is a good hearted old. man, and he and me are going to make a mint of money during vacation. He lives near a summer resort hotel, and has a stream that is full of minnows, and we are going to catch minnows and sell them to the dudes for fish bait. He says some of the fools will pay ten cents apiece for minnows, so if we sell a million minnows, we make a fortune. I am coming back in September and will buy out your grocery. Say, let me have a pound of raisins, and I'll pay you when I sell my uncle's minnows."

CHAPTER XVII

HE DISCUSSES THEOLOGY

Meditations on Noah's ark—The garden of Eden—The ancient dude
—Adam with a plug hat on—"I'm a thinker from Thinkersville"
—The apostles in a patrol wagon—Elijah and Elisha—The prodi-
gal son—A veal pot pie for dinner.

"WHAT are you sitting there for a half-an-hour for,
staring at vacancy?" said the grocery man to the bad boy,
as he sat on the stool by the stove one of these foggy
mornings, when everybody feels like quarreling, with his
fingers clasped around his knee, looking as though he did
not know enough to last him to bed. "What you thinking
about, anyway?"

"I was wondering where you would have been to-day if
Noah had run his ark into such a fog as this, and there had
been no fog-horn on Mount Ararat, and he had passed by
with his excursion and not made a landing, and had floated
around on the freshet until all the animals starved, and
the ark had struck a snag and burst a hole in its bottom.
I tell you, we can all congratulate ourselves that Noah
happened to blunder on that high ground. If that ark had
been lost, either by being foundered, or being blowed up
by Fenians because Noah was an Englishman, it would
have been cold work trying to populate this world. In
that case another Adam and Eve would have to be made
out of dirt and water, and they might have gone wrong
again and failed to raise a family, and where would we
have been? I tell you, when I think of the narrow escapes
we have had, it is a wonder to me that we have got along
as well as we have."

"Well, when did you get out of the asylum?" said the
grocery man, who had been standing back with his mouth

open looking at the boy as though he was crazy. "What you want is to have your head soaked. You are getting so you reach out too far with that small mind of yours. In about another year you will want to run this world yourself. I don't think you are reforming very much. It is wicked for a boy of your size to argue about such things. Your folks better send you to college."

"What do I want to go to college for, and be a heartless hazer, and a poor baseball player? I can be bad enough at home. The more I read, the more I think. I don't believe I can ever be good enough to go to heaven, anyway, and I guess I will go into the newspaper business, where they don't have to be good, and where they have passes everywhere. Do you know, I think when I was built they left out a cog wheel or something in my head. I can't think like some boys. I get to thinking about Adam and Eve in the garden of Eden, and of the Dude with the cloven hoof that flirted with Eve, and treated her and Adam to the dried apples, and I can't think of them as some boys do, with a fig leaf polonaise, and fig leaf vests. I imagine them dressed up in the latest style. I know it is wrong, but that is what a poor boy has to suffer who has an imagination, and where did I get the imagination? This confounded imagination of mine shows me Adam with a plug hat on, just like our minister wears, and a stand-up collar, and tight pants, and peaked-toed shoes, and Eve is pictured to me with a crushed-angle-worm colored dress and brown striped stockings, and newspapers in her dress to make it stick out, and a hat with dandelions on, and a red parasol, and a lace handkerchief, which she puts to her lips, and winks with her left eye to the masher who is standing by the corner of the house, in an attitude, while the tail with the dart on the end is wound around the rain-water barrel, so Eve won't see it and get scared. Say, don't you think it is better for a boy to think of our first parents with clothes on, than to think of them almost naked, exposed to the inclemency of the weather, with nothing but fig leaves pinned on? I want to do right, as near as I can, but I had rather think of them dressed like our folks are to-day, than to think of them in a cyclone with leaves for wearing apparel. Say, it is wrong to fight, but don't you think if Adam had put on a pair of boxing gloves, when he found the devil was getting too fresh about the place, and knocked

I KNOW IT'S WRONG TO THINK SO, BUT HOW CAN I HELP IT?

him out in a couple of rounds, and pasted him in the nose, and fired him out of the summer garden, that it would have been a big thing for this world? Now, honest?"

"Look-a-here," said the grocery man, who had been looking at the boy in dismay, "you better go right home, and let your Ma fix up some warm drink for you, and put you to bed. You are all wrong in the head, and if you are not attended to you will have brain fever. I tell you, boy, you are in danger. Come, I will go home with you."

"O, danger, nothin'. I am just telling how things look to a boy who has not got the facilities for being too good in his youth. Some boys can take things as they read them, and not think any for themselves, but I am a Thinker from Thinkersville, and my imagination plays the dickens with me. There is nothing I read about old times, but what I compare it with the same line of business at the present day. Now, when I think of the fishermen of Gallilee, drawing their seines, I wonder what they would have done if there had been a law against hauling seines, as there is in Wisconsin to-day, and I can see a constable with a warrant for the arrest of the Gallilee fishermen, snatching the old apostles and taking them to the police station in a patrol wagon. I know it is wrong to think like that, but how can I help it? Say, suppose those fishermen had been out hauling their seines, and our minister should come along with his good clothes on, his jointed rod, his nickel plated reel, and his silk fish line, and his patent fish hook, and put a frog on the hook and cast his line near the Gallilee fisherman and go to trolling for bass? What do you suppose the lone fisherman of the Bible times would have thought about the gall of the jointed-rod fisherman? Do you suppose they would have thrown stones in the water where he was trolling, or would they have told him there was good trolling around a point about half a mile up the shore, where they knew he wouldn't get a bite in a week, the way a fellow at Muskego lake lied to our minister a spell ago? I tell you, boss, it is a sad thing for a boy to have an imagination," and the boy put his other knee in the sling made by the clenched fingers of both hands, and waited for the grocery man to argue with him.

"I wish you would go away from here. I am afraid of you," said the grocery man. "I would give anything if your Pa or the minister would come in and have a talk with you. Your mind is wandering," and the grocery man went to the door and looked up and down the street to see if somebody wouldn't come in and watch the crazy boy, while he went to breakfast.

"O, Pa and the minister can't make a first payment on me. Pa gets mad when I ask questions, and the minister thinks I am past redemption. Pa said yesterday that baldness was caused, in every case, by men's wearing plug hats,

FINALLY HE GOT TO BE A COWBOY, HERDING HOGS.

and when 1 asked him where the good Elisha (whom the boys called 'Go up old bald head,' and the bears had a free lunch on them), got his plug hat, Pa said school was dismissed and I could go. When the minister was telling me about the good Elijah going up through the clouds in a chariot of fire, and I asked the minister what he thought Elijah would have thought if he had met our Sunday school superintendent coming down through the clouds on a bicycle, he put his hand on my head and said my liver was all wrong. Now, I will leave it to you if there was anything wrong about that. Say, do you know what I think is the most beautiful thing in the Bible?"

"No," said the grocery man, "and if you want to tell it I will listen five minutes, and then I am going to shut up the store and go to breakfast. You make me tired."

"Well, I think the finest thing is that story about the prodigal son, where the boy took all the money he could scrape up and went out West to paint the town red. He spent his money in riotous living, and saw everything that was going on, and got full of benzine, and struck all the gangs of toughs, both male and female, and his stomach went back on him, and he had malaria, and finally he got to be a cowboy, herding hogs, and had to eat husks that the pigs didn't want, and got pretty low down. Then he thought it was a pretty good scheme to be getting around home, where they had three meals a day, and spring mattresses; and he started home, beating his way on trains, and he didn't know whether the old man would receive him with open arms or pointed boots; but the old man came down to the depot to meet him, and right there before the passengers and the conductor and brakemen, he wasn't ashamed of his boy, though he was ragged, and looked as though he had been on the war path; and the old man fell on his neck and wept, and took him home in a hack, and had veal pot pie for dinner. That's what I call sense. A good many men now days would have put the police on the tramp and had him ordered out of town. What, are you going to close up the store? Well, I will see you later: I want to talk with you about something that is weighing on my mind," and the boy got out just in time to save his coat tail from being caught in the door, and when the grocery man came back from breakfast he found a sign in front:

THIS STORE IS CLOSED TILL FURTHER NOTICE.

SHERIFF.

CHAPTER XVIII

THE DEPARTED ROOSTER

The grocery man discourses on death—The dead rooster—A biograph-
ical sketch—The tenderness between the rooster and his faithful
hen—The hen retires to set—The chickens!—The proud rooster
dies—The fickle hen flirting in indecent haste.

"Why don't you take an ice pick and clean the dirt out
from under your finger nails?" said the grocery man to the
bad boy, as he came into the store and stroked the cat the
wrong way as she lay in the sun on the counter, on a quire
of manilla paper.

"Can't remove the dirt for thirty days—it is an emblem
of mourning. Had a funeral at our house, yesterday," and
the boy took a pickle out of a tub and put it in the cat's
mouth, and shut her teeth together on it, and then went to
the showcase, while the grocery man, whose back had been
turned during the pickle exercise, thought by the way the
cat jumped into the dried apple barrel and began to paw and
scratch with all four of her feet, and yowl, that she was going to have a fit.

"I haven't heard about it," said the grocery man, as he
took the cat by the neck and tossed her out in the back shed
into an old oyster box full of sawdust, with a parting in-
junction that if she was going to have fits she had better go
out where there was plenty of fresh air. "Death is always
a sad thing to contemplate. One day we are full of health
and joy and cold victuals, and the next we are screwed down
in a box, a few words are said over our remains, a few tears
are shed and there is a race to see ho wshall get back from the
cemetery first; and though we may think we are an important factor in the world's progress and sometimes feel
as though it would be unable to put up margins and have

19   289

to stop the deal, the world goes right along, and it must annoy people who die to realize that they don't count for game. The greatest man in the world is only a nine spot when he is dead because somebody else takes the tricks the dead man ought to have taken. But, say, who is dead at your house?"

"Our rooster! Take care, don't you hit me with that canvassed ham!" said the boy as the grocery man looked mad to learn that there was nobody dead but a rooster, when he had preached such a sermon on the subject. "Yes, how soon we are forgotten when we are gone. Now, you would have thought that rooster's hen would have remained faithful to him for a week at least. I have watched them all the spring and I never saw a more perfect picture of devotion than that between the bantam rooster and his hen. They were constantly together and there was nothing too good for her. He would dig up angle worms and call her, and when she came up on a gallop and saw the great big worm on the ground, she would look so proud of her rooster, and he would straighten up and look as though he was saying to her, 'I'm a daisy,' and then she would look at him as if she would like to bite him, and just as she was going to pick up the worm he would snatch it and swallow it himself and chuckle and walk around and be full of business, as though wondering why she didn't take the worm after he had dug it for her, and then the hen would look disappointed at first, and then she would look resigned, as much as to say, 'Worms are too rich for my blood anyway, and the poor dear rooster needs them more than I do, because he has to do all the crowing;' and she would go off and find a grasshopper and eat it on the sly for fear he would see her and complain because she didn't divide. O, I have never seen anything that seemed to me so human as the relations between that rooster and hen. He seemed to try to do everything for her. He would make her stop cackling when she laid an egg, and he would try to cackle, and crow over it as though he had laid it, and she would get off in a corner and cluck in a modest, retiring manner, as though she wished to convey the idea to the servant girls in the kitchen that the rooster had to do all the hard work, and she was only a useless appendage, fit only for society and company for him. But I was disgusted with h i m when the poor hen was setting. The first week that she sat on the eggs he seemed to be glad to have his hen retire to her boudoir to set, but after he had been shooed out of the gardens and flower b e d s h e seemed to be nervous, and evidently wanted to be petted, and he would go near the hen and she would seem to tell him to go and take a walk around t h e block, because she hadn't time to leave her business, and if she didn't attend to it they would have

I NEVER SAW A MORE PERFECT PICTURE
OF DEVOTION.

a lot of spoiled eggs on their hands, and no fam-

ily to bring up. He would scold and seem to tell
her that it was all foolishness, that for his part he didn't
want to hear a lot of chickens squawking around. He would
seem to argue with her that a brood of chickens would be a
dead give-away on them both, and they would be at once
classed as old folks, while if they were alone in the world
they would be spring chickens, and could go in young society, but the hen would scold back, and tell him he ought to
be ashamed of himself to talk that way, and he would go off
mad, and sulk around a spell, and then go to a neighbor's
hen house and sometimes he wouldn't come back till the
next day. The hen would be sorry she had spoken so cross,
and would seem pained at his going away and would look
anxiously for his return, and when he came back after being
out in the rain all night, she would be solicitous after his
health, and tell him he ought to wrap something around
him, but he acted as though he didn't care for his health,
and he would go out again and get chilled through. Finally
the hen come off the nest with ten chickens, and the rooster
seemed very proud, and when anybody came out to have a
look at them he would crow, and seemed to say they were
all his chickens, though the hen was a long time hatching
them, and if it had been him that was setting on them he
could have hatched them out in a week, or died a trying.
But the exposure told on him, and he went into a decline,
and one morning we found him dead. Do you know, I
never see a hen that seemed to realize a calamity as she did.
She looked pale, and her eyes looked red, and she seemed
to be utterly crushed. If the chickens, which were so young
they could not realize that they were little orphans, became
noisy, and got to pulling and hauling over a worm, and conducted themselves in an unseemly manner she would talk
to them in hen language, with tears in her eyes, and it was a
picture of woe. But the next day a neighboring rooster got
to looking through the fence from the alley, and trying to
flirt with her. At first she was indignant, and seemed to tell
him he ought to go about his business, and leave her alone,

but the dude kept clucking, and pretty soon the widowed hen edged up toward the fence, and asked him to come in, but the hole in the fence was too small for him, and then the chickens went out in the alley, and the hen followed them out. I shall always think she told the chickens to go out, so she would have an excuse to go after them, and flirt with the rooster and I think it is a perfect shame. She is out in the alley half the time, and I could cuff her. It seems to me wrong to so soon forget a deceased rooster, but I suppose a hen can't be any m o r e than h u m a n. Say, you don't want to buy a dead rooster do you? You could pick it and sell it to somebody that owes you, for a s p r i n g chicken."

WITH A PAPER PINNED ON ITS BREAST.

"No, I don't want any deceased poultry, that died of grief, and you better go home and watch your hen, or you will be bereaved some more," and the grocery man went out in the shed to see if the cat was over its fit, and when he came back the boy was gone, and after a while the grocery man saw a crowd in front of the store and he went out and found the dead rooster lying on the vegetable stand, with a paper pinned on its breast on which was a sign:

> *THIS RUSTER DIED OF COLIX*
> *FOR SALE CHEAP*
> *TO BOARDING HOUSE ONLY.*

He took the dead rooster and threw it out in the street, and looked up and down the street for the bad boy, and went in and hid a raw hide where he could reach it handy.

CHAPTER XIX

ONE MORE JOKE ON THE OLD MAN

Uncle Ezra returns—The basket on the steps—The anonymous letter—
"O, brother that I should live to see this day!" An ugly Dutch
baby—The old man wheels the baby now—A frog in the old man's
bed.

"I SEE your Pa wheeling the baby around a good deal
lately," said the grocery man to the bad boy, as he came in
the store one evening to buy a stick of striped peppermint
candy for the baby, while his Pa stopped the baby wagon
out on the sidewalk and waited for the boy, with an expression of resignation on his face.

"What's got into your Pa to be nurse girl this hot
weather?"

"O, we have had a circus at our house," said the boy, as
he came in after putting the candy in the baby's hand.
"You see, Uncle Ezra came back from Chicago, where he
had been to sell some cheese, and he stopped over a couple
of days with us, and he said we must play one more joke
on Pa before he went home. We played it, and it is a
wonder I am alive because I never saw Pa so mad in my
life. Now this is the last time I go into any joke on shares.
If I play any more jokes I don't want any old uncle to give
me away."

"What is it?" said the grocery man, as he took a stool
and sat out by the front door beside the boy who was trying
to eat a box of red raspberries on the sly.

"Well, uncle Ezra and me bribed the nurse girl to dress
up the baby one evening in some old, dirty baby clothes,
belonging to our wash woman's baby, and we put it in a
basket and placed the basket on the front door step, and put
a note in the basket and addressed it to Pa. We had the

nurse girl stay out in front, by the basement stairs, so the baby couldn't get away and she rung the bell and got behind something. Ma and Pa, and Uncle Ezra and me were in the back parlor when the bell rung, and Ma told me to go to the door, and I brought in the basket, and set it down, and told Pa there was a note in it for him. Ma, she came up and looked at the note as Pa tore it open, and Uncle Ezra looked in the basket and sighed. Pa read a part of the note and stopped and turned pale, and sat down, then Ma read some of it, and she didn't feel very well, and she leaned against the piano and grated her teeth. The note was in a girl's handwriting, and was like this:

'OLD BALD HEADED PET :—
You will have to take care of your child, because I cannot. Bring it up tenderly, and don't, for heaven's sake, send it to the Foundling Asylum. I shall go drown myself.
Your loving,
ALMIRA.' "

"What did your Ma say?" said the grocery man, becoming interested.

"O, Ma played her part well. Uncle Ezra had told her the joke, and she said, "Retch,' to Pa, just as the actresses do on the stage, and put her handkerchief to her eyes. Pa said it was 'false,' and Uncle Ezra said, 'O, brother, that I should live to see this day,' and I said, as I looked in the basket, 'Pa, it looks just like you, and I'll leave it to Ma.' That was too much, and Pa got mad in a minute. He always gets mad at me. But he went up and looked in the basket, and he said it was some Dutch baby, and was evidently from the lower strata of society, and the unnatural mother wanted to get rid of it, and he said he didn't know any 'Almira' at all. When he called it a Dutch baby, and called attention to its irregular features, that made Ma mad, and she took it up out of the basket and told Pa it was a perfect picture of him, and tried to put it in Pa's arms, but he wouldn't have it, and said he would call the police and have it taken to the poor house. Uncle Ezra took Pa in a corner and told him the best thing he could do would be to see 'Almira and compromise with her, and that made Pa mad, and he was going to hit Uncle Ezra with a chair. Pa was perfectly wild, and if he had a gun I guess he would have shot all of us. Ma took the baby up stairs and had the girl put it to bed, and

O, BROTHER, THAT I SHOULD LIVE TO SEE THIS DAY.

after Pa got mad enough Uncle Ezra told him it was all a joke, and it was his own baby, that we had put in the basket, and then he was madder than ever, and he told Uncle Ezra never to darken his door again. I don't know how he made up with Ma for calling it a Dutch baby from the Polack settlement, but anyway, he wheels it around every day, and Ma and Pa have got so they speak again."

"That is a mighty mean trick, and you ought to be ashamed of yourself. Where do you expect to fetch up when you die?" said the grocery man.

"I told Uncle Ezra it was a mean trick," said the boy, "but he said that wasn't a priming to some of the tricks Pa had played on him years ago. He says Pa used to play tricks on everybody. I may be mean, but I never played wicked jokes on blind people as Pa did when he was a boy. Uncle Ezra says once there was a party of four blind vocalists, all girls, gave an entertainment at the town where Pa lived, and they stayed at the hotel where Pa tended bar. Another thing I never sold rum, either, as Pa did. Well, before the blind vocalists went to bed Pa caught a lot of frogs and put them in the beds where the girls were to sleep, and when the poor blind girls got into bed the frogs hopped over them, and the way they got out was a caution. It is bad enough to have frogs hopping all over girls that can see, but for girls that are deprived of their sight, and don't know what anything is, except by the feeling of it, it looks to me like a pretty tough joke. I guess Pa is sorry now for what he did, 'cause when Uncle Ezra told the frog story, I brought home a frog and put it in Pa's bed. Pa has been afraid of paralysis for years, and when his leg, or anything gets asleep, he thinks that is the end of him. Before bedtime I turned the conversation onto paralysis, and told about a man about Pa's age having it on the West Side, and Pa was nervous, and soon after he retired I guess the frog wanted to get acquainted with Pa, 'cause he yelled six kinds of murder, and we went into his room. You know how cold a frog is? Well, you'd dide to see Pa. He laid still, and said his end had come, and Uncle Ezra asked him if it was the end with the head on or the feet, and Pa told him paralysis had marked him for a victim, and he could feel that his left leg was becoming dead. He said he could feel the cold, clammy hand of death walking up him, and he wanted Ma

to put a bottle of hot water to his feet. Ma got the bottle
of hot water and put it to Pa's feet, and the cork came out
and Pa said he was dead, sure enough, now, because he
was hot in the extremities and that a cold wave was going
up his leg. Ma asked him where the cold wave was, and
he told her, and she thought she would rub it, but she

WELL, HERE COMES OUR BABY WAGON.

began to yell the same kind of murder Pa did, and she said
a snake had gone up her sleeve. Then I thought it was
time to stop the circus, and I reached up Ma's lace sleeve
and caught the frog by the leg and pulled it out, and told
Pa I guessed he had taken my frog to bed with him, and I
showed it to him, and then he said I did it, and he would
maul me so I could not get up alone, and he said that a boy
that would do such a thing would go to hell as sure as

preachin' and I asked him if he thought a man who put frogs in the beds with blind girls, when he was a boy, would get to heaven, and then he told me to lite out, and I lit. I guess Pa will feel better when Uncle Ezra goes away, 'cause he thinks Uncle Ezra talks too much about old times. Well, here comes our baby wagon, and I guess Pa has done penance long enough, and I will go and wheel the kid a while. Say, you call Pa in, after I take the baby wagon, and tell him you don't know how he would get along without such a nice boy as me, and you can charge it in our next month's bill."

CHAPTER XX

"HERE, condemn you, you will pay for that cat," said the
grocery man to the bad boy, as he came in the store all
broke up, the morning after the 4th of July.

"What cat?" said the boy, as he leaned against the
zinc ice box to cool his back, which had been having trouble
with a bunch of fire crackers in his pistol pocket. We haven't
ordered any cat from here. Who ordered any cat sent to our
house? We get our sausage at the market," and the boy
rubbed some cold cream on his nose and eyebrows where the
skin was off.

"Yes, that is all right enough," said the grocery man,
"but somebody who knew where that cat slept, in the box
of sawdust, back of the store, filled it full of fire crackers,
Wednesday forenoon, when I was out to see the procession,
and never notified the cat, and touched them off, and the
cat went through the roof of the shed, and she hasn't got
hair enough left on her to put in tea. Now, you didn't show
up all the forenoon, and I went and asked your Ma where
you was, and she said you had been sitting up four nights
straight along with a sick boy in the Third Ward, and you
was sleeping all the forenoon the 4th of July. If that is so,
that lets you out on the cat, but it don't stand to reason.
Own up, now, was you asleep all the forenoon, the 4th while
other boys were celebrating, or did you scorch my cat?"
and the grocery man looked at the boy as though he would
believe every word he said, if he *was* bad.

301

"Well," said the bad boy as he yawned as though he had been up all night, "I am innocent of setting up with your cat, but I plead guilty to sitting up with Duffy. You see, I am bad, and it don't make any difference where I am, and Duffy thumped me once when we were playing marbles, and I said I would get even with him some time. His Ma washes for us, and when she told me that her boy was sick with fever, and had nobody to stay with him while she was away, I thought it would be a good way to get even with Duffy when he was weak, and I went down there to his shanty and gave him his medicine, and read to him all day, and he cried 'cause he knew I ought to have mauled him, and that night I sat up with him while his Ma did the ironing, and Duffy was so glad that I went down every day and stayed there every night, and fired medicine down him, and let his Ma sleep, and Duffy has got mashed on me, and he says I will be an angel when I die. Last night makes five nights I have sat up with him, and he has got so he can eat beef tea and crackers. My girl went back on me 'cause she said I was sitting up with some other girl. She said that Duffy story was too thin, but Duffy's Ma was washing at my girl's house and she proved what I said, and I was all right again. I slept all the forenoon the 4th, and then stayed with Duffy till four o'clock, and got a furlough and took my girl to the Soldiers' Home. I had rather set up with Duffy, though."

"O, get out. You can't make me believe you had rather stay in a sick room and set up with a boy, than to take a girl to the 4th of July," said the grocery man as he took a brush and wiped the saw dust off some bottles of pepper-sauce that he was taking out of a box. "You didn't have any trouble with the girl, did you?"

"No,—not with her," said the boy, as he looked into the little round zinc mirror to see if his eyebrows were beginning to grow. "But her Pa is so unreasonable. I think a man ought to know better than to kick a boy right where he has had a pack of fire crackers explode in his pocket. You see,

when I brought the girl back home, she was a wreck. Don't
you ever take a girl to the 4th of July. Take the advice of
a boy who has had experience. We hadn't more than got to
the Soldiers' Home grounds before some boys who were
playing tag grabbed hold of my girl's crushed-strawberry
polonaise and ripped it off. That made her mad, and she
wanted me to take offense at it, and I tried to reason with

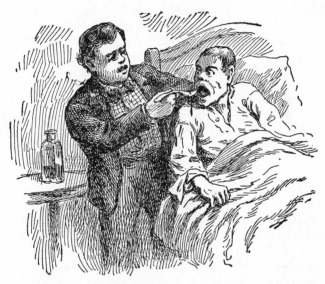

I THOUGHT IT WOULD BE A GOOD WAY TO GET EVEN WITH DUFFY.

the boys and they both jumped on me, and I see the only
way to get out of it honorably, was to get out real spry, and
I got out. Then we sat down under a tree, to eat lunch, and
my girl swallowed a pickle the wrong way, and I pounded
her on the back, the way Ma does when I choke, and she
yelled, and a policeman grabbed me and shook me, and
asked me what I was hurting that poor girl for, and told me
if I did it again he would arrest me! Everything went
wrong. After dark somebody fired a Roman candle into my
girl's hat, and set it on fire, and I grabbed the hat and

stamped on it, and spoiled the hair her Ma bought her. By gosh, I thought her hair was curly, but when the wig was off, her hair was as straight as could be. But she was purty, all the same. We got under another tree, to get away from the smell of burned hair, and a boy set off a nigger chaser, and it ran right at my girl's feet, and burned her stockings, and a woman put the fire out for her, while I looked for the boy that fired the nigger chaser, but I didn't want to find him. She was pretty near a wreck by that time, though she had all her dress left except the polonaise, and we went and sat under a tree in a quiet place, and I put my arm around her and told her never to mind the accidents, 'cause it would be dark when we got home, and just then a spark dropped down through the trees and fell in my pistol pocket, right next to her, where my bunch of fire crackers was, and they began to go off. Well, I never saw such a sight as she was. Her dress was one of these mosquito bar, cheese cloth dresses and it burned just like punk. I had presence of mind enough to roll her on the grass and put out the fire, but in doing that I neglected my own conflagration, and when I got her put out, my coat tail and trousers were a total loss. *My*, but she looked like a goose that had been picked, and I looked like a fireman that fell through a hatchway. My girl wanted to go home, and I took her home, and her Pa was setting on the front steps, and he wouldn't accept her, looking that way. He said he placed in my possession a whole girl, clothed in her right mind, and I had brought back a burnt offering. He teaches in our Sunday school, and knows how to talk pious, but his boots are offul thick. I tried to explain that I was not responsible for the fireworks, and that he could bring in a bill against the government and I showed him how I was bereaved of a coat tail and some pants, but he wouldn't reason at all, and when his foot hit me I thought it was the resurrection, sure, and when I got over the fence, and had picked myself up I never stopped till I got to Duffy's and I sat up with him, 'cause I thought her Pa was after me, and I thought he wouldn't enter a sick room and maul a watcher at the bedside of an invalid. But that settles it with me about celebrating. I don't care if we *did* whip the British, after declaring inde-

PA WENT TO DIG POTATOES FOR DINNER.

pendence, I don't want my pants burnt off. What is the declaration of independence good for to a girl who loses her polonaise, and has her hair burnt off, and a nigger chaser burning her stockings? No, sir, they may talk about the glorious 4th of July, but will it bring back that blonde

20

wig, or re-tail my coat? Hereafter I am a rebel, and I will
go out in the woods the way Pa does, and come home with
a black eye, got in a rational way."

"What, did your Pa get a black eye, too? I hadn't heard
about that," said the grocery man, giving the boy a handful
of unbaked peanuts to draw him out. "Didn't get to fighting, did he?"

"No, Pa don't fight. It is wrong, he says, to fight, unless
you are sure you can whip the fellow, and Pa always gets
whipped, so he quit fighting. You see, one of the deacons
in our church lives out on a farm, and his folks were going
away to spend the 4th, and he had to do all the chores, so
he invited Pa and Ma to come out to the farm and have a
nice quiet time, and they went. There is nothing Pa likes
better than to go out on a farm and pretend he knows
everything. When the farmer got Pa and Ma out there he
set them to work, and Ma shelled peas while Pa went to dig
potatoes for dinner. I think it was mean for the deacon to
send Pa out in the corn field to dig potatoes, and set the
dog on Pa, and tree him in an apple tree near the bee hives,
and then go and visit with Ma and leave Pa in the tree with
the dog barking at him. Pa said he never knew how mean
a deacon could be, until he had set on a limb of that apple
tree all the afternoon. About time to do chores the farmer
came and found Pa, and called the dog off, and Pa came
down, and then the farmer played the meanest trick of all.
He said city people didn't know how to milk cows, and Pa
said he wished he had as many dollars as he knew how to
milk cows. He said his spechulty was milking kicking
cows, and the farmer gave Pa a tin pail and a milking stool
and let down the bars, and pointed out to Pa 'The worst cow
on the place.' Pa knew his reputation was at stake, and he
went up to the cow and punched it in the flank and said,
'Hist, confound you.' Well, the cow wasn't a histing cow,
but a histing bull, and Pa knew it was a bull as quick as
he see it put down its head and beller, and Pa dropped the
pail and stool, and started for the bars, and the bull after

Pa. I don't think it was right in Ma to bet two shillings with the farmer that Pa would get to the bars before the bull did, though she won the bet. Pa said he knew it was a bull just as soon as the horns got tangled up in his coat tail, and when he struck on the other side of the bars, and his nose hit the ash barrel where they made lye for soap, Pa said he saw more fireworks than he did at the Soldiers' Home. Pa wouldn't celebrate any more, and he came home after thanking the farmer for his courtesies, but he wants me to borrow a gun and go out with him hunting. We are going to shoot a bull and a dog and some bees, maybe, we will shoot the farmer, if Pa keeps on as mad as he is now. Well, we won't have another 4th of July for a year, and may be by that time my girl's polonaise and hair will grow out, and that bull may become gentle so Pa can milk it. Ta-ta."

CHAPTER XXI

WORKING ON SUNDAY

Turning a grindstone is healthy—"Not any grindstone for Hennery!"—
This hypocrisy is played out—Another job on the old man—How
the days of the week got mixed—The numerous funerals—The
minister appears—The bad boy goes over the back fence.

"Hello," said the grocery man to the bad boy as he
came in looking sick at heart, and all broke up. "How is
your muscle this morning?"

"All right enough," said the boy with a look of inquiry,
as though wondering what was coming next. "Why?"

"O, nothing, only I was going to grind the hatchet, and
some knives and things, this morning, and I thought maybe
you would like to go out in the shed and turn the grindstone
for me to develop your muscles. Turning the grindstone
is the healthiest thing a boy can do."

"That is all right enough," said the bad boy, as he took
up a sweet cracker, "but please take a good look at me. Do
I look like a grindstone boy? Do I resemble a good little
boy that can't say 'No,' and goes off and turns a grindstone
half a day for some old duffer, who pays him by giving him
a handful of green currents or telling him he will be a man
some day, and the boys goes off one way, with a lame back,
while the good man goes the other way with a sharp scythe,
and a chuckle at the softness of the boy? You are mistaken
in me. I have passed the grindstone period, and you will
have to pick up another sardine who has never done circular
work. Not any grindstone for Hennery, if you please."

"You are getting too smart," said the grocery man as
he charged a pound of sweet crackers to the boy's father.
"You don't have to turn the grindstone if you don't
want to."

"That's what I thought," says the boy as he takes a
handful of blueberries. "You grindstone sharps, who are
always laying for a fool boy to give taffy to, and get him to
break his neck, don't play it fine enough. You bear too
hard on the grindstone. I have seen the time when a man
could get me to turn the grindstone for him till the cows
come home, by making me believe it was fun, and by telling

THEY MAKE A BOY BELIEVE HE IS BIGGER THAN GRANT.

me he never saw a boy that seemed to throw so much soul
into turning a grindstone as I did, but I have found that
such men are hypocrites. They inveigle a boy into their
nest, like the spider does the fly, and at first they don't bear
on hard, but just let the blade of the axe or scythe touch the
grindstone, and they make a boy believe he is a bigger man
than old Grant. They bet him he will get tired, and he bets
that he can turn a grindstone as long as anybody, and when

the boy has got his reputation at stake, then they begin to bear on hard, and the boy gets tired but he holds out, and when the tools are ground he says he is as fresh as a daisy, when he is tired enough to die. Such men do more to teach boys the hollowness of the world, and its tricky features, than anything, and they teach boys to know who are friends and who are foes. No, sir, the best way is to hire a grown person to turn your grindstone. I remember I turned a grindstone four hours for a farmer once, and when I got through he said I could go to the spring and drink all the water I wanted for nothing. He was the tightest man I ever saw. Why, tight! That man was tight enough to hold kerosene."

"That's all right. Who wanted you to turn the grindstone, anyway? But what is it about your Pa and Ma being turned out of church? I hear they scandalized themselves horribly last Sunday."

"Well, you see, me and my chum put up a job on Pa to make him think Sunday was only Saturday and Ma she fell into it, and I guess we are all going to get fired from the church for working on Sunday. You see they didn't go to meetin' last Sunday because Ma's new bonnet hadn't come, and Monday and Tuesday it rained and the rest of the week was so muddy no one called, or they could not get anywhere, so Monday I slid out early and got the daily paper, and on Tuesday my chum he got the paper off the steps and put Monday's paper in its place. I watched when they were reading it, but they did not notice the date. Then Wednesday we put Tuesday's paper on the steps and Pa said it seemed more than Tuesday, but Ma she got the paper of the day before and looked at the date and said it seemed so to her but she guessed they had lost a day somehow. Thursday we got Wednesday's paper on the steps, and Friday we rung in Thursday's paper, and Saturday my chum he got Friday's paper on the steps, and Ma said she guessed she would wash to-morrow, and Pa said he believed he would hoe in the garden and get the weeds out so it would look better to folks when they went by Sunday to church. Well, Sunday morning came, and with it Saturday's daily paper, and Pa barely glanced it over as he got on his overalls and went out in his shirt sleeves a hoeing in the front garden, and I and my chum helped Ma carry water to wash. She said it seemed the longest week she ever saw, but when we brought the water, and took a plate of pickles

IT WASN'T LONG BEFORE FOLKS BEGAN GOING TO CHURCH.

to the hired girl that was down with the mumps, we got in the lilac bushes and waited for the curtain to rise. It wasn't long before folks began going to church and you'd a dide laughing to see them all stop in front of where Ma was washing and look at her, and then go on to where Pa was hoeing weeds and stop and look at him and then drive on. After about a dozen teams had passed I heard Ma ask Pa if he knew who was dead, as there must be a funeral some-where. Pa had just hoed into a bumble-bee's nest and said he did not know of any that was dead, but knew some that ought to be, and Ma she did not ask any foolish questions any more. After about twenty teams had stopped, Ma she got nervous and asked Deacon Smith if he saw anything green; he said something about desecration, and drove away. Deacon Brown asked Pa if he did not think he was setting a bad example before his boy; but Pa, he said he thought it would be a good one if the boy could only be hired to do it. Finally Ma got mad and took the tub behind the house where they could not see her. About four o'clock that afternoon we saw a dozen of our congregation headed by the minister, file into our yard, and my chum and I knew it was time to fly, so we got on the back steps where we could hear. Pa met them at the door, expecting some bad news; and when they were seated, Ma she came in and remarked that it was a very unhealthy year, and it stood people in hand to meet their latter end. None of them said a word until the elder put on his specs, and said it was a solemn occasion, and Ma she turned pale, and wondered who it could be, and Pa says, 'Don't keep us in suspense, who is dead?' and the elder said no one was dead; but they called as a duty they owed the cause to take action on them for working on Sunday. Ma, she fainted away, and they threw a pitcher of water down her back, and Pa said he guessed they were a pack of lunatics, but they all swore it was Sunday, and they saw Ma washing and Pa out hoeing, as they went to church, and they had called to take action on them. Then there was a few minutes low conversation I could not catch, and then we heard Pa kick his chair over and say it was more tricks of that darned boy. Then we knew it was time to adjourn, and I was just getting through the back fence as Pa reached me with a barrel stave, and that's what makes me limp some!"

"That was real mean in you boys," said the grocery man. "It will be hard for your Pa and Ma to explain that matter. Just think how bad they must feel."

"O, I don't know. I remember hearing Pa and Uncle Ezra tell how they fooled their father once, and got him to go to mill with a grist, on Sunday, and Pa said he would defy anybody to fool him on the day of the week. I don't think a man ought to tempt his little boy by defying him to fool his father. Well, I'll take a glass of your fifty cent cider and go," and soon the grocery man looked out of the window and found somebody had added a cipher to the 'Sweet cider, only five cents a glass,' making it an expensive drink, considering it was made of sour apples.

CHAPTER XXII

The old man begins drinking again—Thinks betting is harmless—Had to walk home from Chicago—The spectacles changed—A small suit of clothes—The old man awfully bloated—"Hennery your Pa is a mighty sick man"—The swelling suddenly goes down.

"COME in," said the grocery man to the bad boy, as the youth stood on the steps in an uncertain sort of a way, as though he did not know whether he would be welcome or not. "I tell you, boy, I pity you. I understand your Pa has got to drinking again. It is too bad. I can't think of anything that humiliates a boy, and makes him so ashamed, as to have a father that is in the habit of hoisting in too much benzine. A boy feels as though everybody was down on him, and I don't wonder that such boys often turn out bad. What started your Pa to drinking again?"

"O, Ma thinks it was losing money on the Chicago races. You see, Pa is great on pointers. He don't usually bet unless he has got a sure thing, but when he gets what they call a pointer, that is, somebody tells him a certain horse is sure to win, because the other horses are to be pulled back, he thinks a job has been put up, and if he thinks he is on the inside of the ring he will bet. He says it does not do any hurt to bet, if you win, and he argues that a man who wins lots of money can do a great deal of good with it. But he had to walk home from the Chicago races all the same, and he has been steaming ever since. Pa can't stand adversity. But I guess we have got him all right now. He is the scartest man you ever saw," and the boy took a can opener and began to cut the zinc under the stove, just to see if it would work as well on zinc as on tin.

"What, you haven't been dissecting him again, have

you?" said the grocery man, as he pulled a stool up beside the boy to hear the news. "How did you bring him to his senses?"

"Well, Ma tried having the minister talk to Pa, but Pa talked Bible, about taking a little wine for the stomach's sake, and gave illustrations about Noah getting full, so the minister couldn't brace him up, and then Ma had some of

HIS HAND LOOKED LIKE A HAM.

the sisters come and talk to him, but he broke them all up by talking about what an appetite they had for champagne punch when they were out in camp last summer, and they couldn't have any effect on him, and so Ma said she guessed I would have to exercise my ingenuity on Pa again. Ma has an idea that I have got some sense yet, so I told her that if she would do just as I said, me and my chum would scare Pa so he would swear off. She said she would, and we went to work. First, I took Pa's spectacles down to an optician, Saturday night, and had the glasses taken out and a pair put in their place that would magnify, and I took them home and put them in Pa's spectacle case. Then I got a suit of clothes from my chum's uncle's trunk, about half the size of Pa's clothes. My chum's uncle is a very small man, and Pa is corpulent. I got a plug hat three sizes smaller than Pa's hat, and the name out of Pa's hat and put it in the small hat. I got a shirt about half big enough for Pa, and put his initials on the thing under the bosom, and got a number fourteen collar. Pa wears seventeen. Pa had promised to brace up and go to church Sunday morning, and Ma put these small clothes where Pa could put them on. I told Ma, when Pa woke up, to tell him he looked awfully bloated, and excite his curiosity, and then send for me."

" You didn't play such a trick as that on a poor old man, did you?" said the grocery man as a smile came over his face.

"You bet. Desperate diseases require desperate remedies. Well, Ma told Pa he looked awfully bloated, and that his dissipation was killing him, as well as all the rest of the family. Pa said he guessed he wasn't bloated very much, but he got up and put on his spectacles and looked at himself in the glass. You'd a dide to see him look at himself. His face looked as big as two faces, through the glass, and his nose was a sight. Pa looked scared, and then he held up his hand and looked at that. His hand looked like a ham. Just then I came in, and I turned pale, with some chalk on my face, and I begun to cry, and I said, 'O, Pa, what ails you? You are so swelled up I hardly knew you.' Pa looked sick to his stomach, and then he tried to get on his pants. O, my, it was all I could do to keep from laughing to see him pull them pants on. He could just get his legs in, and when I got a shoe horn and gave it to him, he was mad. He said it was a mean boy that would give his Pa a shoe horn to put on his pants with. The pants wouldn't come around Pa into ten inches, and Pa said he must have eat something that disagreed with him, and he laid it to a watermelon. Ma stuffed her handkerchief in her mouth to keep from laffing, when she see Pa look at hisself. The legs of the pants were so tight Pa could hardly breathe, and he turned pale, and said: 'Hennery, your Pa is a mighty sick man,' and then Ma and me both laughed, and he said we wanted him to die so we could spend his life insurance in riotous living. But when Pa put on the condensed shirt, Ma she laid down on the lounge and fairly yelled, and I laughed till my side ached. Pa got it

TAKE IT AWAY! MY HEAD IS ALL WRONG TOO.

over his head, and got his hands in the sleeves, and couldn't get it either way, and he couldn't see us laugh, but he could hear us, and he said, 'It's darned funny, ain't it, to have a parent swelled up this way? If I bust you will both be sorry.' Well, Ma took hold of one side of the shirt, and I took hold of the other, and we pulled it on, and when Pa's head came up through the collar, his face was blue. Ma told him she was afraid he would have a stroke of apoplexy before he got his clothes on, and I guess Pa thought so too He tried to get the collar on, but it wouldn't go half way around his neck, and he looked in the glass and cried, he

looked so. He sat down in a chair and panted, he was so
out of breath, and the shirt and pants ripped, and Pa said
there was no use living if he was going to be a rival to a fat
woman in the side show. Just then I put the plug hat on
Pa's head, and it was so small it was going to roll off, when
Pa tried to fit it on his head, and then he took it off and
looked inside of it to see if it was his hat, and when he found
his name in it, he said, 'Take it away. My head is all wrong
too.' Then he told me to go for the doctor, mighty quick.
I got the doctor and told him what we were trying to do
with Pa, and he said he would finish the job. So the doc.
came in, and Pa was on the lounge, and when the doc. saw
him, he said it was lucky he was called just as he was or we
would have required an undertaker. He put some pounded
ice on Pa's head the first thing, ordered the shirt cut open,
and we got the pants off. Then he gave Pa an emetic, and
had his feet soaked, and Pa said, 'Doc., if you will bring me
out of this I will never drink another drop.' The doc. told
Pa that his life was not worth a button if he ever drank
again, and left about half a pint of sugar pills to be fired into
Pa every five minutes. Ma and me sat up with Pa all day
Sunday, and Monday morning I changed the spectacles,
and took the clothes home and along about noon Pa said
he felt as though he could get up. Well, you never see a
tickleder man than he was when he found the swelling had
gone down so he could get his pants and shirt on, and he
says that doctor is the best in this town. Ma says I am a
smart boy, and Pa has taken the pledge, and we are all
right. Say, you don't think there is anything wrong in a
boy playing it on his Pa once in a while, do you?"

"Not much. You have very likely saved your Pa's life.
No, sir, joking is all right when by so doing you can break
a person of a bad habit," and the grocery man cut a chew of
tobacco off a piece of plug that was on the counter, which
the boy had soaked in kerosene, and before he had fairly got
it rolled in his cheek, he spit it out and began to gag, and
as the boy started leisurely out the door, the grocery man

said, "Look-a-here, condemn you, don't you ever tamper
with my tobacco again, or, by thunder, I'll maul you," and
he followed the boy to the door, spitting cotton all the way;
and, as the boy went around the corner, the grocery man
thought how different a joke seemed when it was on somebody else. And then he turned to go in and rinse the kerosene out of his mouth, and found a sign on a box of new
green apples, as follows:

> *COLIC OR CHOLERA INFANTUM*
> *YOU PAYS YOUR MONEY*
> *AND TAKES YOUR CHOICE.*

CHAPTER XXIII

Ghosts don't steal wormy figs—A grand rehearsal—The minister murders Hamlet—The watermelon knife—The old man wanted to rehearse the drunken scene in Rip Van Winkle—No hugging allowed —Hamlet wouldn't have two ghosts—"How would you like to be an idiot?"

"I AM thy father's ghost," said a sheeted form in the doorway of the grocery, one evening, and the grocery man got behind the cheese box, while the ghost continued in a sepulchral voice "doomed for a certain time to walk the night," and, waving a chair round, the ghost strode up to the grocery man, and with the other ghostly hand reached into a box of figs.

"I AM THY FATHER'S GHOST."

"No, you ain't no ghost," said the grocery man, recognizing the bad boy. "Ghosts do not go prowling around groceries stealing wormy figs. What do you mean by this sinful masquerade business? My father never had no ghost!"

"O, we have struck it now," said the bad boy as he pulled off his mask and rolled up the sheet he had worn around him. "We are going to have amateur theatricals, to raise money to have the church carpeted, and I am going to boss the job."

320

"You don't say," answered the grocery man, as he thought how much he could sell to the church people for a strawberry and ice cream festival, and how little he could sell for amateur theatricals. "Who is going into it, and what are you going to play?"

"Pa and Ma, and me, and the minister, and three choir singers, and my chum, and the minister's wife, and two deacon's, and an old maid are rehearsing, but we have not decided what to play yet. They all want to play a different play, and I am fixing it so they can all be satisfied. The minister wants to play Hamlet, Pa wants to play Rip Van Winkle, Ma wants to play Mary Anderson, the old maid wants to play a boarding school play, and the choir singers want an opera, and the minister's wife wants to play Lady Macbeth, and my chum and me want to play a double song and dance, and I am going to give them all a show. We had a rehearsal last night, and I am the only one able to be around to-day. You see they have all been studying different plays, and they all wanted to talk at once. We let the minister sail in first. He had on a pair of his wife's black stockings, and a mantle made of a linen buggy-lap blanket, and he wore a mason's cheese knife such as these fellows with poke bonnets and white feathers wear when they get an invitation to a funeral or an excursion. Well, you never saw Hamlet murdered the way he did it. His interpretation of the character was that Hamlet was a dude that talked through his nose and while he was repeating Hamlet's soliloquy, Pa, who had come in with an old hunting suit on, as Rip Van Winkle, went to sleep, and he didn't wake up till Lady Macbeth came in, in the sleep-walking scene. She couldn't find a knife, so I took a slice of watermelon and sharpened it for her, and she made a mistake in the one she was to stab, and she stabbed Hamlet in the neck with a slice of watermelon, and the core of the melon fell on Pa's face, as he lay asleep as Rip and when Lady Macbeth said, 'Out damned spot,' Pa woke up and felt the gob of watermelon on his face, and he

21

thought he had been murdered, and Ma came in on a hop,
skip and jump as 'Parthenia,' and threw her arms around
a deacon who was going to play the grave digger, and began to call him pet names, and Pa was mad, and the choir
singers they began to sing, 'In the North Sea lived a whale,'
and then they quit acting.   You'd a dide to see Hamlet.
The piece of watermelon went down his neck, and Lady
Macbeth went off and left it in the wound under his collar,
and Ma had to pull it out, and Hamlet said the seeds and
the juice was running down inside his shirt, and he said he
wouldn't play if he was going to be stabbed with a slice of
melon, so while his wife was getting the melon seeds out of
his neck, and drying the juice on his shirt, I sharpened a
cucumber for Lady Macbeth to use as a dagger, but Hamlet kicked on cucumbers, too, and I had more trouble than
any stage manager ever had.   Then Pa wanted to rehearse
the drunken scene in Rip Van Winkle, where he hugs
Gretchen and drinks out of a flask behind her back, and he
got one of the choir singers to act as Gretchen, and I guess
he would have been hugging till this time, and have swallowed the flask, if Ma had not taken him by the ear and said
a little of that would go a good ways in an entertainment
for the church.   Pa said he didn't know as it was any worse
than her prancing up to a grave digger and hugging him
till the filling came out of his teeth, and then the minister
decided that we wouldn't have any hugging at all in the
play, and the choir girls said they wouldn't play, and the
old maids struck, and the play came to a stand-still."

"Well, that beats anything I ever heard tell of.   It's a
shame for people outside the profession to do play acting,
and I won't go to the entertainment unless I get a pass,"
said the grocery man.   "Did you rehearse any more?"

"Yes, the minister wanted to try the ghost scene,"
said the boy, "and he wanted me to be the ghost. Well, they
have two 'Markses' and two 'Topsies' in Uncle Tom's
Cabin, and I thought two ghosts in Hamlet would about
fill the bill for amateurs, so I got my chum to act as one

ghost. I wanted to have something new in ghosts, so my chum and me got two pairs of Ma's long stockings, one pair red and one pair blue, and I put on a red one and a blue one, and my chum did the same. Then we got some ruffled clothes belonging to Ma, and put them on, and we put

MA SAID A LITTLE OF THAT WOULD GO A GOOD WAYS.

sheets over us, clear to our feet, and when Hamlet got to yearning for his father's ghost, I came in out of the bath room with the sheet over me, and said I was the huckle-berry he was looking for, and my chum followed me out and said he was a twin ghost, also, and then Hamlet got on his ear and said he wouldn't play with two ghosts, and he went off pouting, and then my chum and me pulled off the sheets and danced a clog dance. Well, when the rest of the troop saw our make up, it nearly killed them. Most of them had seen ballet dancers, but they never saw them with different colored socks. The minister said the benefit was rapidly becoming a farce, and before we had danced half a minute Ma recognized her socks, and she came for me with a hot box, and made me take them off, and Pa was mad and said the dancing was the only thing that was worth the price of admission, and he scolded Ma, and the choir girls sided with Pa, and just then my chum caught his toe in the carpet and fell down, and that loosened the plaster overhead and about a bushel fell on the crowd. Pa thought lightning had struck the house, the minister thought it was a judgment on them all for play acting, and he began to shed his Hamlet costume with one hand and pick the plaster out of his hair with the other. The women screamed and tried to get the plaster out of their necks, and while Pa was brushing off the choir singers Ma said the rehearsal was adjourned, and they all went home, but we are going to rehearse again on Friday night. The play cannot be considered a success, but we will bring it out all right by the time the entertainment is to come off."

"By gum," said the grocery man, "I would like to have seen that minister as Hamlet. Didn't he look funny?"

"Funny! Well, I should remark. He seemed to predominate. That is, he was too fresh, too numerous, as it were. But at the next rehearsal I am going to work in an act from Richard the Third, and my chum is going to play the Chinaman of the Danites, and I guess we will take the cake. Say, I want to work in an idiot somewhere. How would you like to play the idiot? You wouldn't have to rehearse or anything—"

At this point the bad boy was seen to go out of the grocery store real spry, followed by a box of wooden clothes pins, that the grocery man had thrown after him.

CHAPTER XXIV

THE CRUEL WOMAN AND THE LUCKLESS DOG

The bad boy with a dog and a black eye—Where did you steal him?
Angels don't break dog's legs—A woman who breaks dog's legs has
no show with St. Peter—Another burglar scare—The grocery
delivery man scared.

"HELLO!" said the grocery man to the bad boy, as he
came in with a black eye, leading a hungry looking dog that
was walking on three legs, and had one leg tied up with a
red silk handkerchief. "What is this—a part of your amateur theater? Now you get out of here with that dog
mighty quick. A boy that hurts dogs so they have to have
their legs tied up, is no friend of mine," and the grocery
man took up a broom to drive the dog out of doors."

"There, you calm yourself," says the boy to the grocery
man, as the dog got behind the boy and looked up at the
grocery man as though he was not afraid as long as the bad
boy was around. "Set up the crackers and cheese, sausage,
and pickles, and everything this dog wants to eat—he is a
friend of mine—that dog is my guest, and those are my
splints on his broken leg, and that is my handkerchief that
my girl gave me, wound around it, and you touch that dog
except in the way of kindness, and down comes your
house." And the boy doubled up his fists as though he
meant business.

"Poor doggie," said the grocery man, as he cut off a
piece of sausage and offered it to the dog, which was de-
clined with thanks, expressed by the wagging tail. "Where
did you steal him?"

"I didn't steal him, and he is no cannibal. He won't eat
your sausage!" and the boy put up his elbow as though to
ward off an imaginary blow. "You see, this dog was fol-

lowing a pet dog that belonged to a woman, and she tried
to shoo him away, but he wouldn't shoo. This dog did not
know that he was a low born, miserable dog, and had no
right to move in the society of an aristocratic pet dog, and
he followed right along. He thought this was a free country, and one dog was as good as another, and he followed
that woman and her pet dog right into her door yard. The
pet dog encouraged this dog, and he went in the yard, and
when the woman got up on the steps she threw a velocipede
at this dog and broke his leg, and then she took up her pet
and went in the house so she wouldn't hear this dog howl.
She is a nice woman, and I see her go to meeting every
Sunday with a lot of morocco books in her hands, and once
I pumped the organ in the church where she goes, and she
was so pious I thought she was an angel—but angels don't
break dogs' legs. I bet when she goes up to the gate and
sees St. Peter open the book and look for the charges
against her she will tremble as though she had fits. And
when St. Peter runs his finger down the ledger, and stops
at the dog column, and turns and looks at her over his spectacles, and says, 'Madam, how about your stabbing a poor
dog with a velocipede, and breaking its leg?' she will claim
it was an accident; but she can't fool Pete. He is on to
everybody's racket, and if they get in there, they have got
to have a clean record."

"Say, look-a-here," said the grocery man, as he looked
at the boy in astonishment as he unwound the handkerchief
to dress the dog's broken leg, while the dog looked up in
the boy's face with an expression of thankfulness and con-
fidence that he was an able practitioner in dog bone-setting,
"what kind of talk is that? You talk of heaven as though
the books were kept like the books of a grocery, and you
speak too familiarly of St. Peter."

"Well, I didn't mean any disrespect," said the boy, as
he fixed the splint on the dog's leg, and tied it with a string,
while the dog licked his hand, "but I learned in Sunday
school that up there they watch even the sparrow's fall, and

they wouldn't be apt to get left on a dog bigger than a
whole flock of sparrows, 'specially when the dog's fall was
accompanied with such noise as a velocipede makes when it
falls down stairs.   No, sir, a woman who throws a velocipede at a poor, homeless dog, and breaks its leg, may carry
a car load of prayer books, and she may attend to all the

"SAY, LOOK-A-HERE," SAID THE GROCERY MAN.

sociables, but according to what I have been told, if she
goes sailing up to the gate of New Jerusalem, as though she
owned the whole place and expects to be ushered into a
private box, she will get left.   The man in the box office
will tell her she is not on the list, and that there is a variety
show below, where the devil is a star, and fallen angels are
dancing the cancan with sheet iron tights, on brimstone

lakes and she can probably crawl under the canvas but she can't get in among the angelic hosts until she can satisfactorily explain that dog story that is told of her. Possibly I have got a raw way of expressing myself, but I had rather take my chances if I should apply for admission up there, with this lame dog under my arm than to take hers with a pug dog that hain't got any legs broke. A lame dog and a clear conscience beats a pet dog, when your conscience feels nervous. Now I am going to lay this dog in a barrel of dried apples, where your cat sleeps, and give him a little rest, and I will give you four minutes to tell me all you know, and you will have three minutes on your hands with nothing to say. Unbutton your lip and give your teeth a vacation."

"Well, you *have* got gall. However, I don't know but you are right about that woman that hurt the dog. Still, it may have been her way of petting a strange dog. We should try to look upon the charitable side of people's eccentricities. But say, I want to ask you if you have seen anything of my man that delivers groceries. Saturday night I sent him over to your house to deliver some things, about ten o'clock, and he has not showed up since. What do you think has become of him?"

"Well, by gum, that accounts for it. Saturday night, about ten o'clock, we heard somebody in the back yard, around the kitchen door, just as we were going to bed, and Pa was afraid it was a burglar after the church money he had collected last Sunday. He had got to turn it over the next day, to pay the minister's expenses on his vacation, and it made him nervous to have it around. I peeked out of the window and saw the man, and I told Pa, and Pa got a revolver and began shooting through the wire screen to the kitchen window, and I saw the man drop the basket and begin to climb over the fence real sudden, and I went out and began to groan, as though somebody was dying in the alley, and I brought in the basket with the mackerel and green corn, and told Pa that from the groaning out

there I guess he had killed the grocery delivery man, and
I wanted Pa to go out and help me hunt for the body, but
he said he was going to take the midnight train and go

THE MAN BEGAN TO CLIMB.

out West on some business, and Pa lit out. I guess your
man was scared and went one way and Pa was scared and
went the other. Won't they be astonished when they meet
each other on the other side of the world? Pa will shoot

him again when they meet if he gives Pa any sass. Pa says when he gets mad he had just as soon eat as to kill a man."

"Well, I guess my man has gone off to a Sunday pic-nic or something, and will come back when he gets sober, but how are your theatricals getting along?" asked the grocery man.

"O, that scheme is all busted," said the boy. "At least until the minister gets back from his vacation. The congregation has noticed a red spot on his hand for some time, and the ladies said what he needed was rest. They said if that spot was allowed to go on it might develop into a pimple, and the minister might die of blood poison, superinduced by overwork, and they took up a collection, and he has gone. The night they bid him good-bye, the spot on his hand was the subject of much comment. The women sighed and said it was lucky they noticed the spot on his hand before it had sapped his young life away. Pa said Job had more than four hundred boils worse than that, and he never took a vacation, and then Ma dried Pa up. She told Pa he had never suffered from blood poison, and Pa said he could raise cat boils for the market and never squeal. Ma see the only way to shut Pa up was to let him go home with the choir singer. So she bounced him off with her, and he didn't get home till most 'leven o'clock, but Ma she set up for him. Maybe what she said to Pa made him go West after peppering your burglar. Well, I must go home now, 'cause I run the family since Pa lit out. Say, send some of your most expensive canned fruits and things over to the house. Darn the expense." And the bad boy took the lame dog under his arm and walked out.

CHAPTER XXV

THE BAD BOY GROWS THOUGHTFUL

Why is lettuce like a girl?—King Solomon a fool—Think of any sane
man having a thousand wives—He would have to have two hotels
during vacation—300 blondes—600 brunettes, etc.—A thousand
wives taking ice cream—I don't envy Solomon his thousand.

"WHAT are you sitting there like a bump on a log for?"
asked the grocery man of the bad boy, as the youth had sat
on a box for half-an-hour, with his hands in his pockets,
looking at a hole in the floor, until his eyes were set like a
dying horse. "What you thinking of, anyway? It seems
to me boys set around and think more than they used to
when I was a boy," and the grocery man brushed the
wilted lettuce and shook it, and tried to make it stand up
stiff and crisp, before he put it out doors; but the contrary
lettuce which had been picked the day before, looked so
tired that the boy noticed it.

"That lettuce reminds me of a girl. Yesterday I was
in here when it was new, like the girl going to the picnic,
and it was as fresh and proud, and starched up, and kitteny,
and full of life, and sassy as a girl starting out for a picnic.
To-day it has got back from the picnic, and, like the girl,
the starch is all taken out, and it is limber, and languid, and
tired, and can't stand up alone, and it looks as though it
wanted to be laid at rest beside the rotten apples in the
alley, rather than be set out in front of a store to be sold
to honest people, and give them the gangrene of the liver,"
and the boy put on a health commissioner air that frightened the grocery man, and he threw the lettuce out the
back door.

"You never mind about my lettuce," said the grocery

331

man, "I can attend to my affairs. But now tell me what you were thinking about here all the morning?"

"I was thinking what a fool King Solomon was," said the boy, with the air of one who has made a statement that has got to be argued pretty strong to make it hold water.

"Now, look-a-here," said the grocery man in anger, "I have stood it to have you play tricks on me, and have listened to your condemned foolishness without a murmur as long as you have confined yourself to people now living, but when you attack Solomon—the wisest man, the great king—and call him a fool, friendship ceases, and you must get out of this store. Solomon in all his glory, is a friend of mine, and no fool boy is going to abuse him in my presence. Now, you dry up!"

"Sit down on the ice box," said the boy to the grocery man, "what you need is rest. You are overworked. Your alleged brain is equal to wilted lettuce, and it can devise ways and means to hide rotten peaches under good ones, so as to sell them to blind orphans; but when it comes to grasping great questions, your small brain cannot comprehend them. Your brain may go up sideways to a great question and rub against it, but it cannot surround it, and grasp it. That's where you are deformed. Now, it is different with me. I can raise brain to sell to you grocery men. Listen. This Solomon is credited with being the wisest man, and yet history says he had a thousand wives. Just think of it. You have got one wife, and Pa has got one, and all the neighbors have one, if they have had any kind of luck. Does not one wife make you pay attention? Wouldn't two wives break you up? Wouldn't three cause you to see stars? How would ten strike you? Why, man alive, you do not grasp the magnitude of the statement that Solomon had a thousand wives. A thousand wives, standing side by side, would reach about four blocks. Marching by fours it would take them twenty minutes to pass a given point. The largest summer resort hotel only holds about five hundred people, so Sol would have had to hire two hotels if he took his wives out for a day in the country. If you would stop and think once in a while you would know more."

The grocery man's eyes had begun to stick out as the bad boy continued, as though the statistics had never b e e n brought to his attention before, but he was bound to stand by his old friend Solomon, and he said, "Well, Solomon's wives must have been different from our wives of the present day."

"Not much," said the boy, as he saw he was paralyzing the grocery man. "Women have been about the same ever since Eve. She got mashed on the old original dude, and it stands to reason that Solomon's wives were no better than the mother of the human race. Statistics show that one woman out of every ten is red headed. That would give Solomon an even hundred red headed wives. Just that hundred red headed wives would be enough to make an ordinary man think that there is a land that is fairer than this. Then there would be, out of the other nine hundred,

"THAT LETTUCE REMINDS
ME OF A GIRL."

about three hundred blondes, and the other six hundred
would be brunettes, and maybe he had a few albinos, and
bearded women, and fat women, and dwarfs. Now, those
thousand women had appetites, desires for dress and style,
the same as all women. Imagine Solomon saying to them:
'Girls, let's all go down to the ice cream saloon and have a
dish of ice cream.' Can you, with your brain muddled with
codfish and new potatoes, realize the scene that would follow? Suppose after Solomon's broom brigade had got
seated in the ice creamery, one of the red headed wives
should catch Solomon winking at a strange girl at another
table. You may think Solomon did not know enough to
wink, or that he was not that kind of a flirt, but he *must*
have been or he could never have succeeded in marrying a
thousand wives in a sparsely settled country. No, sir, it
looks to me as though Solomon, in all his glory, was an old
masher, and from what I have seen of men being bossed
around with one wife, I don't envy Solomon his thousand.
Why, just imagine that gang of wives going and ordering
fall bonnets. Solomon would have to be a king or a Van-
derbilt to stand it. Ma wears five dollar silk stockings,
and Pa kicks awfully when the bill comes in. Imagine
Solomon putting up for a few thousand pair of silk stockings. I am glad you will sit down and reason with me in a
rational way about some of these Bible stories that take
my breath away. The minister stands me off when I try
to talk with him about such things, and tells me to study the
parable of the Prodigal Son, and the deacons tell me to go
and soak my head. There is darn little encouragement for a
boy to try and figure out things. How would you like to
have a thousand red headed wives come into the store this
minute and tell you they wanted you to send carriages
around to the house at three o'clock so they could go for a
drive? Or how would you like to have a hired girl come
rushing in and tell you to send up six hundred doctors, because six hundred of your wives had been taken with
cholera morbus? Or—"

"O, don't mention it," said the grocery man, with a shudder.   "I wouldn't take Solomon's place, and be the natural protector of a thousand wives if anybody would give me the earth.   Think of getting up in a cold winter morning and building a thousand fires.   Think of two thousand pair of hands in a fellow's hair!   Boy, you have shown me that Solomon needed a guardian over him.   He didn't have sense."

THE BABY IS TEETHING.

"Yes," says the boy, "and think of two thousand feet, each one as cold as a brick of chocolate ice cream.   A man would want a back as big as the fence of a fair ground.   But I don't want to harrow up your feelings.   I must go and put some arnica on Pa.   He has got home and says he has been to a summer resort on a vacation, and he is all covered with blotches.   He says it is mosquito bites, but Ma thinks he has been shot full of bird shot by some watermelon farmer. Ma hasn't got any sympathy for Pa because he didn't take her along, but if she had been there she would have been filled with bird shot, too.   But you musn't detain me.   Between Pa and the baby I have got all that I can attend to.

The baby is teething, and Ma makes me put my fingers in the baby's mouth to help it cut teeth. That is a humiliating position for a boy as big as I am. Say, how many babies do you figure that Solomon had to buy rubber toothing rings for in all his glory?"

And the boy went out, leaving the grocery man reflecting on what a family Solomon must have had, and how he needed to be the wisest man to get along without a circus afternoon and evening.

CHAPTER XXVI

The bad boy works on a farm for a deacon—He knows when he has got enough—How the deacon made him flax around—And how he made it warm for the deacon.

"Want to buy any cabbages?" said the bad boy to the grocery man, as he stopped at the door of the grocery, dressed in blue wamus, his breeches tucked in his boots, and an old hat on his head, with a hole that let out his hair through the top. He had got out of a democrat wagon, and was holding the lines hitched to a horse about forty years old, that leaned against the hitching post to rest. "Only a shilling apiece."

"O, go 'way," said the grocery man. "I only pay three cents apiece." And then he looked at the boy and said, "Hello, Hennery, is that you? I have missed you all the week, and now you come to me sudden, disguised as a granger. What does all this mean?

"It means that I have been the victim of as vile a conspiracy as ever was known since Cæsar was stabbed, and Marc Antony orated over his prostrate corpse in the Roman forum, to an audience of supes and scene shifters," and the boy dropped the lines on the sidewalk, said, "Whoa, gol darn you," to the horse that was asleep, wiped his boots on the grass in front of the store and came in, and seated himself on the old half bushel. "There, this seems like home again."

"What's the row?—who has been playing it on you?" And the grocery man smelled a sharp trade in cabbages, as well as other smells peculiar to the farm.

"Well, I'll tell you. Lately our folks have been constantly talking of the independent life of the farmer, and how easy it is, and how they would like it if I would learn to be a farmer. They said there was nothing like it, and several of the neighbors joined in and said I had the natural ability to be one of the most successful farmers in the state. They all drew pictures of the fun it was to work on a farm where you could get your work done and take your fish-pole and go off and catch fish, or a gun, and go out and kill game, and how you could ride horses, and pitch hay, and smell the sweet perfume, and go to husking bees, and dances, and everything, and they got me all worked up so I wanted to go to work on a farm. Then an old deacon that belongs to our church, who runs a farm about eight miles out of town, he came on the scene, and said he wanted a boy, and if I would go out and work for him he would be easy on me because he knew my folks, and we belonged to the same church. I can see it now. It was all a put up job on me, just like they play three card monte on a fresh stranger. I was took in. By gosh, I have been out there a week, and here's what there is left of me. The only way I got a chance to come to town was to tell the farmer I could sell cabbages to you for a shilling a piece. I knew you sold them for fifteen cents and I thought that would give me a shilling. So the farmer said he would pay me my wages in cabbages at a shilling apiece and only charge me a dollar for the horse and wagon to bring them in. So you only pay three cents. Here are thirty cabbages, which will come to ninety cents. I pay a dollar for the horse, and when I get back to the farm I owe the farmer ten cents, besides working a week for nothing. O, it is all right. I don't kick, but this ends farming for Hennery. I know when I have got enough of an easy life on a farm. I prefer a hard life, breaking stones on the streets, to an easy, dreamy life on a farm "

"They *did* play it on you, didn't they?" said the grocery man. "But wasn't the old deacon a good man to work for?"

"Good man nothing," said the boy, as he took up a piece of horseradish and began to grate it on the inside of his

rough hand. "I tell you there's a heap of difference in a
deacon in Sunday school, telling about sowing wheat and
tares, and a deacon out on a farm in a hurry season, when
there is hay to get in and wheat to harvest all at the same
time. I went out to the farm Sunday evening with the
deacon and his wife, and they couldn't talk too much about
the nice time we would have, and the fun; but the deacon
changed more than forty degrees in five minutes after we
got to the farm. He jumped out of the wagon and pulled
off his coat and let his wife climb out over the wheel, and
yelled to the hired girl to bring out the milk pail, and told
me to fly around and unharness the horse, and throw down a
lot of hay for the work animals, and then told me to run
down to the pasture and drive up a lot of cows. The pasture was half a mile away, and the cows were scattered
around in the woods, and the mosquitoes were thick, and I
got all covered with mud and burrs, and stung with thistles,
and when I got the cattle near to the house, the old deacon
yelled to me that I was slower than molasses in the winter,
and then I took a club and tried to hurry the cows, and he
yelled at me to stop hurrying, 'cause I would retard the
flow of milk. By gosh I *was* mad. I asked for a mosquito
bar to put over me the next time I went after the cows, and
the people all laughed at me, and when I sat down on the
fence to scrape the mud off my Sunday pants the deacon
yelled like he does in the revival, only he said, 'Come, come,
procrastination is the thief of time. You get up and hump
yourself and go and feed the pigs.' He was so darn mean
that I could not help throwing a burdock burr against the
side of the cow he was milking, and it struck her right in the
flank on the other side from where the deacon was. Well,
you'd a dide to see the cow jump up and blat. All four of
her feet were off the ground at a time, and I guess most of
them hit the deacon on his Sunday vest, and the rest hit the
milk pail, and the cow backed against the fence and bellered,
and the deacon was all covered with milk and cow hair,
and he got up and throwed the three legged stool at the

cow and hit her on the horn and it glanced off and hit me
on the pants just as I went over the fence to feed the pigs.
I didn't know a deacon could talk so sassy at a cow, and
come so near swearing without actually saying cuss words.
Well, I lugged swill until I was homesick to my stomach,
and then I had to clean off horses, and go to the neighbors
about a mile away to borrow a lot of rakes to use the next
day. I was so tired I almost cried, and then I had to draw
two barrels of water with a well bucket, to cleanse for washing the next day, and by that time I wanted to die. It was
most nine o'clock, and I began to think about supper, when
the deacon said all they had was bread and milk for supper
Sunday night, and I rasseled with a tin basin of skim milk,
and some old back number bread, and wanted to go to bed,
but the deacon wanted to know if I was heathen enough to
want to go to bed without evening prayers. There was no
one thing I was less mashed on than evening prayers about
that minute, but I had to take a prayer half an hour long on
top of that skim milk, and I guess it curdled the milk, for I
hadn't been in bed more than half an hour before I had the
worst colic a boy ever had, and I thought I should die all
alone up in that garret, on the floor, with nothing to make
my last hours pleasant but some rats playing with ears of
seed corn on the floor, and mice running through some dry
pea pods. But how different the deacon talked in the evening devotions from what he did when the cow was gallop-
ing on him in the barn yard. Well, I got through the colic
and was just getting to sleep when the deacon yelled for me
to get up and hustle down-stairs. I thought maybe the
house was on fire, 'cause I smelled smoke, and I got into my
trousers and came down stairs on a jump yelling 'Fire,' when
the deacon grabbed me and told me to get down on my
knees, and before I knew it he was into the morning devotions, and when he said 'Amen' and jumped and said for us
to fire breakfast into us quick and get to work doing chores;
I looked at the clock and it was just three o'clock in the
morning, just the time Pa comes home and goes to bed in

town, when he is running a political campaign. Well, sir, I had to jump from one thing to another from three o'clock in the morning till nine at night, pitching hay, driving reaper, raking and binding, shocking wheat, hoeing corn, and everything, and I never got a kind word. I spoiled my clothes, and I think another week would make a pirate

MUD, BURRS AND MOSQUITOES WERE THICK.

of me. But during it all I had the advantage of a pious example. I tell you, you think more of such a man as the deacon if you don't work for him, but only see him when he comes to town, and you hear him sing, 'Heaven is my Home,' through his nose. He even is farther from home than any place I ever heard of. He would be a good mate on a Mississippi river steamboat if he could swear, and I guess he could soon learn. Now you take these cabbages and give me ninety cents, and I will go home and borrow ten cents to make up the dollar, and send my chum back with the horse and wagon and my resignation. I was not cut out for a farmer. Talk about fishing, the only fish I saw was a salt white fish we had for breakfast one morning, which was salted by Noah, in the ark," and while the grocery man was unloading the cabbages the boy went off to look for his chum, and later the two boys were seen driving off to the farm with two fishing poles sticking out of the hind end of the wagon.

CHAPTER XXVII

DRINKING CIDER IN THE CELLAR

The deacon will not accept Hennery's resignation—He wants butter on
his pancakes—His chum joins him—The skunk in the cellar—The
poor boy gets the "ager."

"WELL, I swow, here comes a walking hospital," said
the grocery man as the bad boy's shadow came in the store,
followed by the boy, who looked sick and yellow, and tired,
and he had lost half his flesh. "What's the matter with
you? Haven't got the yellow fever, have you?" and the
grocery man placed a chair where the invalid could fall
into it.

"No, got the ager," said the boy as he wiped the perspiration off his upper lip, and looked around the store to see
if there was anything in sight that would take the taste of
quinine out of his mouth. "Had too much dreamy life of
ease on the farm, and been shaking ever since. Darn
farm anyway."

"What, you haven't been to work for the deacon any
more, have you? I thought you sent in your resignation,"
and the grocery man offered the boy some limberger cheese
to strengthen him.

"O, take that cheese away," said the boy, as he turned
pale and gagged. "You don't know what a sick person
needs any more than a professional nurse. What I want is
to be petted. You see I went out to the farm with my chum,
and I took the fish poles and remained in the woods while
he drove the horse to the deacon's; and he gave the deacon
my resignation, and the deacon wouldn't accept it. He said
he would hold my resignation until after harvest, and then
act on it. He said he could put me in jail for breach of
promise, if I quit work and left him without giving proper

343

notice; and my chum came and told me, and so I concluded
to go to work rather than have any trouble, and the deacon
said my chum could work a few days for his board if he
wanted to. It was pretty darn poor board for a boy to work
for, but my chum wanted to be with me, so he stayed. Pa
and Ma came out to the farm to stay a day or two to help.
Pa was going to help harvest, and Ma was going to help the
deacon's wife, but Pa wanted to carry the jug to the field,
and lay under a tree while the rest of us worked, and Ma
just talked the arm off the deacon's wife. The deacon and
Pa laid in the shade and see my chum and me work, and Ma
and the deacon's wife gossiped so they forgot to get dinner,
and my chum and me organized a strike, but we were beaten
by monopoly. Pa took me by the neck and thrashed out
a shock of wheat with my heels, and the deacon took my
chum and sat down on him, and we begged and they gave
us our old situations back. But we got even with them
that night. I tell you, when a boy tries to be good, and quit
playing jokes on people, and then has everybody down on
him, and has his Pa hire him out on a farm to work for a
deacon that hasn't got any soul except when he is in church,
and a boy has to get up in the night to get breakfast and go
to work, and has to work until late at night, and they kick
because he wants to put butter on his pancakes, and feed
him skim milk and rusty fat pork, it makes him tough, and
he would play a joke on his aged grandmother. After my
chum and me got all the chores done that night, we sat out
on a fence back of the house in the orchard, eating green apples in the moonlight, and trying to think of a plan of revenge. Just then I saw a skunk back of the house, right by
the outside cellar door, and I told my chum that it would
serve them right to drive the skunk down cellar and shut
the door, but my chum said that would be too mean. I
asked him if it would be any meaner than for the deacon to
snatch us bald headed because we couldn't mow hay away
fast enough for two men to pitch it, and he said it
wouldn't, and so we got on each side of the skunk and sort

of scared it down cellar, and then we crept up softly and
closed the cellar doors. Then we went in the house and I
whispered to Ma and asked her if she didn't think the deacon had some cider, and Ma she began to hint that she
hadn't had a good drink of cider since last winter, and the
deacon's wife said us boys could take a pitcher and go down
cellar and draw some. That was too much. I didn't want

"WHOOSH."

any cider, anyway, so I told them that I belonged to a temperance society, and I should break my pledge if I drawed
cider, and she said I was a good boy, for me never to touch a
drop of cider. Then she told my chum where the cider barrel was, down cellar; but he ain't no slouch. He said he
was afraid to go down cellar in the dark, and so Pa said he
and the deacon would go down and draw the cider, and the
deacon's wife asked Ma to go down, too, and look at the

fruit and berries she had canned for winter, and they all went down cellar. Pa carried an old tin lantern with holes in it, to light the deacon to the cider barrel; and the deacon's **wife** had a taller candle to show Ma the canned fruit. I tried to get Ma not to go, 'cause Ma is a friend of mine, and I didn't want her to have anything to do with the circus; but she said she guessed she knew her business. When anybody says they guess they know their own business, that settles it with me, and I don't try to argue with them. Well, my chum and me sat there in the kitchen, and I stuffed a piece of red table cloth in my mouth to keep from laughing, and my chum held his nose with his finger and thumb, so he wouldn't snort right out. We could hear the cider run in the pitcher, and then it stopped, and the deacon drank out of the pitcher, and then Pa did, and then they drawed some more cider, and Ma and the deacon's wife were talking about how much sugar it took to can fruit, and the deacon told Pa to help himself out of a crock of fried cakes, and I heard the cover on the crock rattle, and just then I heard the old tin lantern rattle on the brick floor of the cellar, the deacon said 'Merciful goodness;' Pa said 'Helen and damnation, I am stabbed,' and Ma yelled 'Goodness sakes alive,' and then there was a lot of dishpans on the stairs begun to fall, and they all tried to get up cellar at once, and they fell over each other; and O my, what a frowy smell came up to the kitchen from the cellar. It was enough to kill anybody. Pa was the first to get to the head of the stairs and he stuck his head in the kitchen, and drew in a long breath, and said '*Whoosh!* Hennery, your Pa is a mighty sick man.' The deacon came up next, and he had run his head into a hanging shelf and broken a glass jar of huckleberries, and they were all over him, and he said, 'Give me air. Earth's but a desert drear.' Then Ma and the deacon's wife came up on a gallop, and they looked tired. Pa began to peel off his coat and vest and said he was going out to bury them, and Ma said he could bury her, too, and I asked the deacon if he didn't notice a faint odor of sewer gas coming from the cellar, and my chum said it smelled more to him as though something had crawled in the cellar and died. Well, you never saw a sicker crowd, and I felt sorry for Ma and the deacon, 'cause their false teeth fell out, and I knew Ma couldn't gossip and the deacon couldn't talk sassy without teeth. But you'd dide to see Pa. He was mad, and thought the deacon had put up the job on him, and he was going to knock the deacon out in two rounds, when Ma said there was no use of getting mad about a dispensation of providence, and Pa said one more such dispensation of providence would just kill him on the spot. They finally got the house aired, and my chum and me slept on the hay in the barn, after we had opened the outside cellar door so the animal could get out, and the next morning I had the fever and ague, and Pa and Ma brought me home, and I have been firing quinine down my neck ever since. Pa says it is malaria, but it is getting up before daylight in the morning and prowling around a farm doing chores before it is time to do chores, and I don't want any more farm. I thought at Sunday school last Sunday, when the superintendent talked about the odor of sanctity that pervaded the house on that beautiful morning, and looked at the deacon, that the deacon thought the superintendent was referring to him and Pa, but maybe it was an accident. Well, I must go home and shoot another charge of quinine into me," and the boy went out as if he was on his last legs, though he acted as if he was going to have a little fun while he did last.

A CATALOGUE OF SELECTED DOVER BOOKS
IN ALL FIELDS OF INTEREST

A CATALOGUE OF SELECTED DOVER BOOKS
IN ALL FIELDS OF INTEREST

WHAT IS SCIENCE?, *N. Campbell*
The role of experiment and measurement, the function of mathematics, the nature of scientific laws, the difference between laws and theories, the limitations of science, and many similarly provocative topics are treated clearly and without technicalities by an eminent scientist. "Still an excellent introduction to scientific philosophy," H. Margenau in *Physics Today.* "A first-rate primer . . . deserves a wide audience," *Scientific American.* 192pp. 5⅜ x 8.

S43   Paperbound $1.25

THE NATURE OF LIGHT AND COLOUR IN THE OPEN AIR, *M. Minnaert*
Why are shadows sometimes blue, sometimes green, or other colors depending on the light and surroundings? What causes mirages? Why do multiple suns and moons appear in the sky? Professor Minnaert explains these unusual phenomena and hundreds of others in simple, easy-to-understand terms based on optical laws and the properties of light and color. No mathematics is required but artists, scientists, students, and everyone fascinated by these "tricks" of nature will find thousands of useful and amazing pieces of information. Hundreds of observational experiments are suggested which require no special equipment. 200 illustrations; 42 photos. xvi + 362pp. 5⅜ x 8.

T196   Paperbound $2.00

THE STRANGE STORY OF THE QUANTUM, AN ACCOUNT FOR THE GENERAL READER OF THE GROWTH OF IDEAS UNDERLYING OUR PRESENT ATOMIC KNOWLEDGE, *B. Hoffmann*
Presents lucidly and expertly, with barest amount of mathematics, the problems and theories which led to modern quantum physics. Dr. Hoffmann begins with the closing years of the 19th century, when certain trifling discrepancies were noticed, and with illuminating analogies and examples takes you through the brilliant concepts of Planck, Einstein, Pauli, Broglie, Bohr, Schroedinger, Heisenberg, Dirac, Sommerfeld, Feynman, etc. This edition includes a new, long postscript carrying the story through 1958. "Of the books attempting an account of the history and contents of our modern atomic physics which have come to my attention, this is the best," H. Margenau, Yale University, in *American Journal of Physics.* 32 tables and line illustrations. Index. 275pp. 5⅜ x 8.

T518   Paperbound $2.00

GREAT IDEAS OF MODERN MATHEMATICS: THEIR NATURE AND USE, *Jagjit Singh*
Reader with only high school math will understand main mathematical ideas of modern physics, astronomy, genetics, psychology, evolution, etc. better than many who use them as tools, but comprehend little of their basic structure. Author uses his wide knowledge of non-mathematical fields in brilliant exposition of differential equations, matrices, group theory, logic, statistics, problems of mathematical foundations, imaginary numbers, vectors, etc. Original publication. 2 appendixes. 2 indexes. 65 ills. 322pp. 5⅜ x 8.

T587   Paperbound $2.25

THE MUSIC OF THE SPHERES: THE MATERIAL UNIVERSE — FROM ATOM TO QUASAR, SIMPLY EXPLAINED, *Guy Murchie*
Vast compendium of fact, modern concept and theory, observed and calculated data, historical background guides intelligent layman through the material universe. Brilliant exposition of earth's construction, explanations for moon's craters, atmospheric components of Venus and Mars (with data from recent fly-by's), sun spots, sequences of star birth and death, neighboring galaxies, contributions of Galileo, Tycho Brahe, Kepler, etc.; and (Vol. 2) construction of the atom (describing newly discovered sigma and xi subatomic particles), theories of sound, color and light, space and time, including relativity theory, quantum theory, wave theory, probability theory, work of Newton, Maxwell, Faraday, Einstein, de Broglie, etc. "Best presentation yet offered to the intelligent general reader," *Saturday Review*. Revised (1967). Index. 319 illustrations by the author. Total of xx + 644pp. 5⅜ x 8½.
T1809, T1810 Two volume set, paperbound $4.00

FOUR LECTURES ON RELATIVITY AND SPACE, *Charles Proteus Steinmetz*
Lecture series, given by great mathematician and electrical engineer, generally considered one of the best popular-level expositions of special and general relativity theories and related questions. Steinmetz translates complex mathematical reasoning into language accessible to laymen through analogy, example and comparison. Among topics covered are relativity of motion, location, time; of mass; acceleration; 4-dimensional time-space; geometry of the gravitational field; curvature and bending of space; non-Euclidean geometry. Index. 40 illustrations. x + 142pp. 5⅜ x 8½. S1771 Paperbound $1.35

HOW TO KNOW THE WILD FLOWERS, *Mrs. William Starr Dana*
Classic nature book that has introduced thousands to wonders of American wild flowers. Color-season principle of organization is easy to use, even by those with no botanical training, and the genial, refreshing discussions of history, folklore, uses of over 1,000 native and escape flowers, foliage plants are informative as well as fun to read. Over 170 full-page plates, collected from several editions, may be colored in to make permanent records of finds. Revised to conform with 1950 edition of Gray's Manual of Botany. xlii + 438pp. 5⅜ x 8½. T332 Paperbound $2.25

MANUAL OF THE TREES OF NORTH AMERICA, *Charles Sprague Sargent*
Still unsurpassed as most comprehensive, reliable study of North American tree characteristics, precise locations and distribution. By dean of American dendrologists. Every tree native to U.S., Canada, Alaska; 185 genera, 717 species, described in detail—leaves, flowers, fruit, winterbuds, bark, wood, growth habits, etc. plus discussion of varieties and local variants, immaturity variations. Over 100 keys, including unusual 11-page analytical key to genera, aid in identification. 783 clear illustrations of flowers, fruit, leaves. An unmatched permanent reference work for all nature lovers. Second enlarged (1926) edition. Synopsis of families. Analytical key to genera. Glossary of technical terms. Index. 783 illustrations, 1 map. Total of 982pp. 5⅜ x 8. T277, T278 Two volume set, paperbound $6.00

IT'S FUN TO MAKE THINGS FROM SCRAP MATERIALS,
Evelyn Glantz Hershoff
What use are empty spools, tin cans, bottle tops? What can be made from rubber bands, clothes pins, paper clips, and buttons? This book provides simply worded instructions and large diagrams showing you how to make cookie cutters, toy trucks, paper turkeys, Halloween masks, telephone sets, aprons, linoleum block- and spatter prints — in all 399 projects! Many are easy enough for young children to figure out for themselves; some challenging enough to entertain adults; all are remarkably ingenious ways to make things from materials that cost pennies or less! Formerly "Scrap Fun for Everyone." Index. 214 illustrations. 373pp. 5⅜ x 8½. T1251 Paperbound $1.75

SYMBOLIC LOGIC and THE GAME OF LOGIC, *Lewis Carroll*
"Symbolic Logic" is not concerned with modern symbolic logic, but is instead a collection of over 380 problems posed with charm and imagination, using the syllogism and a fascinating diagrammatic method of drawing conclusions. In "The Game of Logic" Carroll's whimsical imagination devises a logical game played with 2 diagrams and counters (included) to manipulate hundreds of tricky syllogisms. The final section, "Hit or Miss" is a lagniappe of 101 additional puzzles in the delightful Carroll manner. Until this reprint edition, both of these books were rarities costing up to $15 each. Symbolic Logic: Index. xxxi + 199pp. The Game of Logic: 96pp. 2 vols. bound as one. 5⅜ x 8.
T492 Paperbound $2.00

MATHEMATICAL PUZZLES OF SAM LOYD, PART I
selected and edited by M. Gardner
Choice puzzles by the greatest American puzzle creator and innovator. Selected from his famous collection, "Cyclopedia of Puzzles," they retain the unique style and historical flavor of the originals. There are posers based on arithmetic, algebra, probability, game theory, route tracing, topology, counter and sliding block, operations research, geometrical dissection. Includes the famous "14-15" puzzle which was a national craze, and his "Horse of a Different Color" which sold millions of copies. 117 of his most ingenious puzzles in all. 120 line drawings and diagrams. Solutions. Selected references. xx + 167pp. 5⅜ x 8.
T498 Paperbound $1.25

STRING FIGURES AND HOW TO MAKE THEM, *Caroline Furness Jayne*
107 string figures plus variations selected from the best primitive and modern examples developed by Navajo, Apache, pygmies of Africa, Eskimo, in Europe, Australia, China, etc. The most readily understandable, easy-to-follow book in English on perennially popular recreation. Crystal-clear exposition; step-by-step diagrams. Everyone from kindergarten children to adults looking for unusual diversion will be endlessly amused. Index. Bibliography. Introduction by A. C. Haddon. 17 full-page plates, 960 illustrations. xxiii + 401pp. 5⅜ x 8½.
T152 Paperbound $2.25

PAPER FOLDING FOR BEGINNERS, *W. D. Murray and F. J. Rigney*
A delightful introduction to the varied and entertaining Japanese art of origami (paper folding), with a full, crystal-clear text that anticipates every difficulty; over 275 clearly labeled diagrams of all important stages in creation. You get results at each stage, since complex figures are logically developed from simpler ones. 43 different pieces are explained: sailboats, frogs, roosters, etc. 6 photographic plates. 279 diagrams. 95pp. 5⅝ x 8⅜.
T713 Paperbound $1.00

PRINCIPLES OF ART HISTORY,
H. Wölfflin
Analyzing such terms as "baroque," "classic," "neoclassic," "primitive," "picturesque," and 164 different works by artists like Botticelli, van Cleve, Dürer, Hobbema, Holbein, Hals, Rembrandt, Titian, Brueghel, Vermeer, and many others, the author establishes the classifications of art history and style on a firm, concrete basis. This classic of art criticism shows what really occurred between the 14th-century primitives and the sophistication of the 18th century in terms of basic attitudes and philosophies. "A remarkable lesson in the art of seeing," *Sat. Rev. of Literature.* Translated from the 7th German edition. 150 illustrations. 254pp. 6⅛ x 9¼. T276 Paperbound $2.00

PRIMITIVE ART,
Franz Boas
This authoritative and exhaustive work by a great American anthropologist covers the entire gamut of primitive art. Pottery, leatherwork, metal work, stone work, wood, basketry, are treated in detail. Theories of primitive art, historical depth in art history, technical virtuosity, unconscious levels of patterning, symbolism, styles, literature, music, dance, etc. A must book for the interested layman, the anthropologist, artist, handicrafter (hundreds of unusual motifs), and the historian. Over 900 illustrations (50 ceramic vessels, 12 totem poles, etc.). 376pp. 5⅜ x 8.   T25   Paperbound $2.50

THE GENTLEMAN AND CABINET MAKER'S DIRECTOR,
Thomas Chippendale
A reprint of the 1762 catalogue of furniture designs that went on to influence generations of English and Colonial and Early Republic American furniture makers. The 200 plates, most of them full-page sized, show Chippendale's designs for French (Louis XV), Gothic, and Chinese-manner chairs, sofas, canopy and dome beds, cornices, chamber organs, cabinets, shaving tables, commodes, picture frames, frets, candle stands, chimney pieces, decorations, etc. The drawings are all elegant and highly detailed; many include construction diagrams and elevations. A supplement of 24 photographs shows surviving pieces of original and Chippendale-style pieces of furniture. Brief biography of Chippendale by N. I. Bienenstock, editor of *Furniture World.* Reproduced from the 1762 edition. 200 plates, plus 19 photographic plates. vi + 249pp. 9⅛ x 12¼.   T1601   Paperbound $3.50

AMERICAN ANTIQUE FURNITURE: A BOOK FOR AMATEURS,
Edgar G. Miller, Jr.
Standard introduction and practical guide to identification of valuable American antique furniture. 2115 illustrations, mostly photographs taken by the author in 148 private homes, are arranged in chronological order in extensive chapters on chairs, sofas, chests, desks, bedsteads, mirrors, tables, clocks, and other articles. Focus is on furniture accessible to the collector, including simpler pieces and a larger than usual coverage of Empire style. Introductory chapters identify structural elements, characteristics of various styles, how to avoid fakes, etc. "We are frequently asked to name some book on American furniture that will meet the requirements of the novice collector, the beginning dealer, and . . . the general public. . . . We believe Mr. Miller's two volumes more completely satisfy this specification than any other work," *Antiques.* Appendix. Index. Total of vi + 1106pp. 7⅞ x 10¾.
T1599, T1600   Two volume set, paperbound $7.50

THE BAD CHILD'S BOOK OF BEASTS, MORE BEASTS FOR WORSE CHILDREN, and A MORAL ALPHABET, *H. Belloc*
Hardly and anthology of humorous verse has appeared in the last 50 years without at least a couple of these famous nonsense verses. But one must see the entire volumes — with all the delightful original illustrations by Sir Basil Blackwood — to appreciate fully Belloc's charming and witty verses that play so subacidly on the platitudes of life and morals that beset his day — and ours. A great humor classic. Three books in one. Total of 157pp. 5⅜ x 8.
T749   Paperbound $1.00

THE DEVIL'S DICTIONARY, *Ambrose Bierce*
Sardonic and irreverent barbs puncturing the pomposities and absurdities of American politics, business, religion, literature, and arts, by the country's greatest satirist in the classic tradition. Epigrammatic as Shaw, piercing as Swift, American as Mark Twain, Will Rogers, and Fred Allen, Bierce will always remain the favorite of a small coterie of enthusiasts, and of writers and speakers whom he supplies with "some of the most gorgeous witticisms of the English language" (H. L. Mencken). Over 1000 entries in alphabetical order. 144pp. 5⅜ x 8.   T487   Paperbound $1.00

THE COMPLETE NONSENSE OF EDWARD LEAR.
This is the only complete edition of this master of gentle madness available at a popular price. *A Book of Nonsense, Nonsense Songs, More Nonsense Songs and Stories* in their entirety with all the old favorites that have delighted children and adults for years. The Dong With A Luminous Nose, The Jumblies, The Owl and the Pussycat, and hundreds of other bits of wonderful nonsense: 214 limericks, 3 sets of Nonsense Botany, 5 Nonsense Alphabets, 546 drawings by Lear himself, and much more. 320pp. 5⅜ x 8.   T167   Paperbound $1.75

THE WIT AND HUMOR OF OSCAR WILDE, *ed. by Alvin Redman*
Wilde at his most brilliant, in 1000 epigrams exposing weaknesses and hypocrisies of "civilized" society. Divided into 49 categories—sin, wealth, women, America, etc.—to aid writers, speakers. Includes excerpts from his trials, books, plays, criticism. Formerly "The Epigrams of Oscar Wilde." Introduction by Vyvyan Holland, Wilde's only living son. Introductory essay by editor. 260pp. 5⅜ x 8.   T602   Paperbound $1.50

A CHILD'S PRIMER OF NATURAL HISTORY, *Oliver Herford*
Scarcely an anthology of whimsy and humor has appeared in the last 50 years without a contribution from Oliver Herford. Yet the works from which these examples are drawn have been almost impossible to obtain! Here at last are Herford's improbable definitions of a menagerie of familiar and weird animals, each verse illustrated by the author's own drawings. 24 drawings in 2 colors; 24 additional drawings. vii + 95pp. 6½ x 6.   T1647   Paperbound $1.00

THE BROWNIES: THEIR BOOK, *Palmer Cox*
The book that made the Brownies a household word. Generations of readers have enjoyed the antics, predicaments and adventures of these jovial sprites, who emerge from the forest at night to play or to come to the aid of a deserving human. Delightful illustrations by the author decorate nearly every page. 24 short verse tales with 266 illustrations. 155pp. 6⅝ x 9¼.
T1265   Paperbound $1.50

THE PRINCIPLES OF PSYCHOLOGY,
William James
The full long-course, unabridged, of one of the great classics of Western
literature and science. Wonderfully lucid descriptions of human mental
activity, the stream of thought, consciousness, time perception, memory, imagination, emotions, reason, abnormal phenomena, and similar topics. Original
contributions are integrated with the work of such men as Berkeley, Binet,
Mills, Darwin, Hume, Kant, Royce, Schopenhauer, Spinoza, Locke, Descartes,
Galton, Wundt, Lotze, Herbart, Fechner, and scores of others. All contrasting
interpretations of mental phenomena are examined in detail—introspective
analysis, philosophical interpretation, and experimental research. "A classic,"
Journal of Consulting Psychology. "The main lines are as valid as ever,"
Psychoanalytical Quarterly. "Standard reading...a classic of interpretation,"
Psychiatric Quarterly. 94 illustrations. 1408pp. 5⅜ x 8.

T381, T382   Two volume set, paperbound $6.00

VISUAL ILLUSIONS: THEIR CAUSES, CHARACTERISTICS AND APPLICATIONS,
M. Luckiesh
"Seeing is deceiving," asserts the author of this introduction to virtually every
type of optical illusion known. The text both describes and explains the
principles involved in color illusions, figure-ground, distance illusions, etc.
100 photographs, drawings and diagrams prove how easy it is to fool the sense:
circle⁓ that aren't round, parallel lines that seem to bend, stationary figures that
seem to move as you stare at them — illustration after illustration strains our
credulity at what we see. Fascinating book from many points of view, from
applications for artists, in camouflage, etc. to the psychology of vision. New
introduction by William Ittleson, Dept. of Psychology, Queens College. Index.
Bibliography. xxi + 252pp. 5⅜ x 8½.   T1530   Paperbound $1.50

FADS AND FALLACIES IN THE NAME OF SCIENCE,
Martin Gardner
This is the standard account of various cults, quack systems, and delusions
which have masqueraded as science: hollow earth fanatics. Reich and orgone
sex energy, dianetics, Atlantis, multiple moons, Forteanism, flying saucers,
medical fallacies like iridiagnosis, zone therapy, etc. A new chapter has been
added on Bridey Murphy, psionics, and other recent manifestations in this
field. This is a fair, reasoned appraisal of eccentric theory which provides
excellent inoculation against cleverly masked nonsense. "Should be read by
everyone, scientist and non-scientist alike," R. T. Birge, Prof. Emeritus of
Physics, Univ. of California; Former President, American Physical Society.
Index. x + 365pp. 5⅜ x 8.   T394   Paperbound $2.00

ILLUSIONS AND DELUSIONS OF THE SUPERNATURAL AND THE OCCULT,
D. H. Rawcliffe
Holds up to rational examination hundreds of persistent delusions including
crystal gazing, automatic writing, table turning, mediumistic trances, mental
healing, stigmata, lycanthropy, live burial, the Indian Rope Trick, spiritualism,
dowsing, telepathy, clairvoyance, ghosts, ESP, etc. The author explains and
exposes the mental and physical deceptions involved, making this not only
an exposé of supernatural phenomena, but a valuable exposition of characteristic types of abnormal psychology. Originally titled "The Psychology of
the Occult." 14 illustrations. Index. 551pp. 5⅜ x 8. T503 Paperbound $2.75

FAIRY TALE COLLECTIONS, *edited by Andrew Lang*
Andrew Lang's fairy tale collections make up the richest shelf-full of traditional children's stories anywhere available. Lang supervised the translation of stories from all over the world—familiar European tales collected by Grimm, animal stories from Negro Africa, myths of primitive Australia, stories from Russia, Hungary, Iceland, Japan, and many other countries. Lang's selection of translations are unusually high; many authorities consider that the most familiar tales find their best versions in these volumes. All collections are richly decorated and illustrated by H. J. Ford and other artists.

THE BLUE FAIRY BOOK. 37 stories. 138 illustrations. ix + 390pp. 5⅜ x 8½.
T1437   Paperbound $1.95

THE GREEN FAIRY BOOK. 42 stories. 100 illustrations. xiii + 366pp. 5⅜ x 8½.
T1439   Paperbound $1.75

THE BROWN FAIRY BOOK. 32 stories. 50 illustrations, 8 in color. xii + 350pp. 5⅜ x 8½.
T1438   Paperbound $1.95

THE BEST TALES OF HOFFMANN, *edited by E. F. Bleiler*
10 stories by E. T. A. Hoffmann, one of the greatest of all writers of fantasy. The tales include "The Golden Flower Pot," "Automata," "A New Year's Eve Adventure," "Nutcracker and the King of Mice," "Sand-Man," and others. Vigorous characterizations of highly eccentric personalities, remarkably imaginative situations, and intensely fast pacing has made these tales popular all over the world for 150 years. Editor's introduction. 7 drawings by Hoffmann. xxxiii + 419pp. 5⅜ x 8½.
T1793   Paperbound $2.25

GHOST AND HORROR STORIES OF AMBROSE BIERCE,
edited by E. F. Bleiler
Morbid, eerie, horrifying tales of possessed poets, shabby aristocrats, revived corpses, and haunted malefactors. Widely acknowledged as the best of their kind between Poe and the moderns, reflecting their author's inner torment and bitter view of life. Includes "Damned Thing," "The Middle Toe of the Right Foot," "The Eyes of the Panther," "Visions of the Night," "Moxon's Master," and over a dozen others. Editor's introduction. xxii + 199pp. 5⅜ x 8½.
T767   Paperbound $1.50

THREE GOTHIC NOVELS, *edited by E. F. Bleiler*
Originators of the still popular Gothic novel form, influential in ushering in early 19th-century Romanticism. Horace Walpole's *Castle of Otranto*, William Beckford's *Vathek*, John Polidori's *The Vampyre*, and a *Fragment* by Lord Byron are enjoyable as exciting reading or as documents in the history of English literature. Editor's introduction. xi + 291pp. 5⅜ x 8½.
T1232   Paperbound $2.00

BEST GHOST STORIES OF LEFANU, *edited by E. F. Bleiler*
Though admired by such critics as V. S. Pritchett, Charles Dickens and Henry James, ghost stories by the Irish novelist Joseph Sheridan LeFanu have never become as widely known as his detective fiction. About half of the 16 stories in this collection have never before been available in America. Collection includes "Carmilla" (perhaps the best vampire story ever written), "The Haunted Baronet," "The Fortunes of Sir Robert Ardagh," and the classic "Green Tea." Editor's introduction. 7 contemporary illustrations. Portrait of LeFanu. xii + 467pp. 5⅜ x 8.
T415   Paperbound $2.50

EASY-TO-DO ENTERTAINMENTS AND DIVERSIONS WITH COINS, CARDS, STRING, PAPER AND MATCHES, *R. M. Abraham*
Over 300 tricks, games and puzzles will provide young readers with absorbing fun. Sections on card games; paper-folding; tricks with coins, matches and pieces of string; games for the agile; toy-making from common household objects; mathematical recreations; and 50 miscellaneous pastimes. Anyone in charge of groups of youngsters, including hard-pressed parents, and in need of suggestions on how to keep children sensibly amused and quietly content will find this book indispensable. Clear, simple text, copious number of delightful line drawings and illustrative diagrams. Originally titled "Winter Nights' Entertainments." Introduction by Lord Baden Powell. 329 illustrations. v + 186pp. 5⅜ x 8½.   T921 Paperbound $1.00

AN INTRODUCTION TO CHESS MOVES AND TACTICS SIMPLY EXPLAINED, *Leonard Barden*
Beginner's introduction to the royal game. Names, possible moves of the pieces, definitions of essential terms, how games are won, etc. explained in 30-odd pages. With this background you'll be able to sit right down and play. Balance of book teaches strategy — openings, middle game, typical endgame play, and suggestions for improving your game. A sample game is fully analyzed. True middle-level introduction, teaching you all the essentials without oversimplifying or losing you in a maze of detail. 58 figures. 102pp. 5⅜ x 8½.   T1210   Paperbound $1.25

LASKER'S MANUAL OF CHESS, *Dr. Emanuel Lasker*
Probably the greatest chess player of modern times, Dr. Emanuel Lasker held the world championship 28 years, independent of passing schools or fashions. This unmatched study of the game, chiefly for intermediate to skilled players, analyzes basic methods, combinations, position play, the aesthetics of chess, dozens of different openings, etc., with constant reference to great modern games. Contains a brilliant exposition of Steinitz's important theories. Introduction by Fred Reinfeld. Tables of Lasker's tournament record. 3 indices. 308 diagrams. 1 photograph. xxx + 349pp. 5⅜ x 8. T640 Paperbound $2.50

COMBINATIONS: THE HEART OF CHESS, *Irving Chernev*
Step-by-step from simple combinations to complex, this book, by a well-known chess writer, shows you the intricacies of pins, counter-pins, knight forks, and smothered mates. Other chapters show alternate lines of play to those taken in actual championship games; boomerang combinations; classic examples of brilliant combination play by Nimzovich, Rubinstein, Tarrasch, Botvinnik, Alekhine and Capablanca. Index. 356 diagrams. ix + 245pp. 5⅜ x 8½.   T1744   Paperbound $2.00

HOW TO SOLVE CHESS PROBLEMS, *K. S. Howard*
Full of practical suggestions for the fan or the beginner — who knows only the moves of the chessmen. Contains preliminary section and 58 two-move, 46 three-move, and 8 four-move problems composed by 27 outstanding American problem creators in the last 30 years. Explanation of all terms and exhaustive index. "Just what is wanted for the student," Brian Harley. 112 problems, solutions. vi + 171pp. 5⅜ x 8.   T748   Paperbound $1.35

SOCIAL THOUGHT FROM LORE TO SCIENCE,
H. E. Barnes and H. Becker
An immense survey of sociological thought and ways of viewing, studying, planning, and reforming society from earliest times to the present. Includes thought on society of preliterate peoples, ancient non-Western cultures, and every great movement in Europe, America, and modern Japan. Analyzes hundreds of great thinkers: Plato, Augustine, Bodin, Vico, Montesquieu, Herder, Comte, Marx, etc. Weighs the contributions of utopians, sophists, fascists and communists; economists, jurists, philosophers, ecclesiastics, and every 19th and 20th century school of scientific sociology, anthropology, and social psychology throughout the world. Combines topical, chronological, and regional approaches, treating the evolution of social thought as a process rather than as a series of mere topics. "Impressive accuracy, competence, and discrimination . . . easily the best single survey," *Nation.* Thoroughly revised, with new material up to 1960. 2 indexes. Over 2200 bibliographical notes. Three volume set. Total of 1586pp. 5⅜ x 8.

T901, T902, T903   Three volume set, paperbound $9.00

A HISTORY OF HISTORICAL WRITING, *Harry Elmer Barnes*
Virtually the only adequate survey of the whole course of historical writing in a single volume. Surveys developments from the beginnings of historiography in the ancient Near East and the Classical World, up through the Cold War. Covers major historians in detail, shows interrelationship with cultural background, makes clear individual contributions, evaluates and estimates importance; also enormously rich upon minor authors and thinkers who are usually passed over. Packed with scholarship and learning, clear, easily written. Indispensable to every student of history. Revised and enlarged up to 1961. Index and bibliography. xv + 442pp. 5⅜ x 8½.

T104   Paperbound $2.50

JOHANN SEBASTIAN BACH, *Philipp Spitta*
The complete and unabridged text of the definitive study of Bach. Written some 70 years ago, it is still unsurpassed for its coverage of nearly all aspects of Bach's life and work. There could hardly be a finer non-technical introduction to Bach's music than the detailed, lucid analyses which Spitta provides for hundreds of individual pieces. 26 solid pages are devoted to the B minor mass, for example, and 30 pages to the glorious St. Matthew Passion. This monumental set also includes a major analysis of the music of the 18th century: Buxtehude, Pachelbel, etc. "Unchallenged as the last word on one of the supreme geniuses of music," John Barkham, *Saturday Review Syndicate.* Total of 1819pp. Heavy cloth binding. 5⅜ x 8.

T252   Two volume set, clothbound $15.00

BEETHOVEN AND HIS NINE SYMPHONIES, *George Grove*
In this modern middle-level classic of musicology Grove not only analyzes all nine of Beethoven's symphonies very thoroughly in terms of their musical structure, but also discusses the circumstances under which they were written, Beethoven's stylistic development, and much other background material. This is an extremely rich book, yet very easily followed; it is highly recommended to anyone seriously interested in music. Over 250 musical passages. Index. viii + 407pp. 5⅜ x 8.

T334   Paperbound $2.25

THREE SCIENCE FICTION NOVELS,
John Taine
Acknowledged by many as the best SF writer of the 1920's, Taine (under the name Eric Temple Bell) was also a Professor of Mathematics of considerable renown. Reprinted here are *The Time Stream*, generally considered Taine's best, *The Greatest Game*, a biological-fiction novel, and *The Purple Sapphire*, involving a supercivilization of the past. Taine's stories tie fantastic narratives to frameworks of original and logical scientific concepts. Speculation is often profound on such questions as the nature of time, concept of entropy, cyclical universes, etc. 4 contemporary illustrations. v + 532pp. 5⅜ x 8⅜.

T1180   Paperbound $2.00

SEVEN SCIENCE FICTION NOVELS,
H. G. Wells
Full unabridged texts of 7 science-fiction novels of the master. Ranging from biology, physics, chemistry, astronomy, to sociology and other studies, Mr. Wells extrapolates whole worlds of strange and intriguing character. "One will have to go far to match this for entertainment, excitement, and sheer pleasure . . ."*New York Times.* Contents: The Time Machine, The Island of Dr. Moreau, The First Men in the Moon, The Invisible Man, The War of the Worlds, The Food of the Gods, In The Days of the Comet. 1015pp. 5⅜ x 8.

T264   Clothbound $5.00

28 SCIENCE FICTION STORIES OF H. G. WELLS.
Two full, unabridged novels, *Men Like Gods* and *Star Begotten*, plus 26 short stories by the master science-fiction writer of all time! Stories of space, time, invention, exploration, futuristic adventure. Partial contents: *The Country of the Blind, In the Abyss, The Crystal Egg, The Man Who Could Work Miracles, A Story of Days to Come, The Empire of the Ants, The Magic Shop, The Valley of the Spiders, A Story of the Stone Age, Under the Knife, Sea Raiders,* etc. An indispensable collection for the library of anyone interested in science fiction adventure. 928pp. 5⅜ x 8.   T265   Clothbound $5.00

THREE MARTIAN NOVELS,
Edgar Rice Burroughs
Complete, unabridged reprinting, in one volume, of Thuvia, Maid of Mars; Chessmen of Mars; The Master Mind of Mars. Hours of science-fiction adventure by a modern master storyteller. Reset in large clear type for easy reading. 16 illustrations by J. Allen St. John. vi + 490pp. 5⅜ x 8½.

T39   Paperbound $2.50

AN INTELLECTUAL AND CULTURAL HISTORY OF THE WESTERN WORLD,
Harry Elmer Barnes
Monumental 3-volume survey of intellectual development of Europe from primitive cultures to the present day. Every significant product of human intellect traced through history: art, literature, mathematics, physical sciences, medicine, music, technology, social sciences, religions, jurisprudence, education, etc. Presentation is lucid and specific, analyzing in detail specific discoveries, theories, literary works, and so on. Revised (1965) by recognized scholars in specialized fields under the direction of Prof. Barnes. Revised bibliography. Indexes. 24 illustrations. Total of xxix + 1318pp.

T1275, T1276, T1277   Three volume set, paperbound $7.50

HEAR ME TALKIN' TO YA, *edited by Nat Shapiro and Nat Hentoff*
In their own words, Louis Armstrong, King Oliver, Fletcher Henderson, Bunk Johnson, Bix Beiderbecke, Billy Holiday, Fats Waller, Jelly Roll Morton, Duke Ellington, and many others comment on the origins of jazz in New Orleans and its growth in Chicago's South Side, Kansas City's jam sessions, Depression Harlem, and the modernism of the West Coast schools. Taken from taped conversations, letters, magazine articles, other first-hand sources. Editors' introduction. xvi + 429pp. 5⅜ x 8½. T1726 Paperbound $2.00

THE JOURNAL OF HENRY D. THOREAU
A 25-year record by the great American observer and critic, as complete a record of a great man's inner life as is anywhere available. Thoreau's Journals served him as raw material for his formal pieces, as a place where he could develop his ideas, as an outlet for his interests in wild life and plants, in writing as an art, in classics of literature, Walt Whitman and other contemporaries, in politics, slavery, individual's relation to the State, etc. The Journals present a portrait of a remarkable man, and are an observant social history. Unabridged republication of 1906 edition, Bradford Torrey and Francis H. Allen, editors. Illustrations. Total of 1888pp. 8⅜ x 12¼.
T312, T313 Two volume set, clothbound $25.00

A SHAKESPEARIAN GRAMMAR, *E. A. Abbott*
Basic reference to Shakespeare and his contemporaries, explaining through thousands of quotations from Shakespeare, Jonson, Beaumont and Fletcher, North's *Plutarch* and other sources the grammatical usage differing from the modern. First published in 1870 and written by a scholar who spent much of his life isolating principles of Elizabethan language, the book is unlikely ever to be superseded. Indexes. xxiv + 511pp. 5⅜ x 8½. T1582 Paperbound $2.75

FOLK-LORE OF SHAKESPEARE, *T. F. Thistelton Dyer*
Classic study, drawing from Shakespeare a large body of references to supernatural beliefs, terminology of falconry and hunting, games and sports, good luck charms, marriage customs, folk medicines, superstitions about plants, animals, birds, argot of the underworld, sexual slang of London, proverbs, drinking customs, weather lore, and much else. From full compilation comes a mirror of the 17th-century popular mind. Index. ix + 526pp. 5⅜ x 8½.
T1614 Paperbound $2.75

THE NEW VARIORUM SHAKESPEARE, *edited by H. H. Furness*
By far the richest editions of the plays ever produced in any country or language. Each volume contains complete text (usually First Folio) of the play, all variants in Quarto and other Folio texts, editorial changes by every major editor to Furness's own time (1900), footnotes to obscure references or language, extensive quotes from literature of Shakespearian criticism, essays on plot sources (often reprinting sources in full), and much more.

HAMLET, *edited by H. H. Furness*
Total of xxvi + 905pp. 5⅜ x 8½.
T1004, T1005 Two volume set, paperbound $5.25

TWELFTH NIGHT, *edited by H. H. Furness*
Index. xxii + 434pp. 5⅜ x 8½. T1189 Paperbound $2.75

La Boheme by Giacomo Puccini,
translated and introduced by Ellen H. Bleiler
Complete handbook for the operagoer, with everything needed for full enjoyment except the musical score itself. Complete Italian libretto, with new, modern English line-by-line translation—the only libretto printing all repeats; biography of Puccini; the librettists; background to the opera, Murger's La Boheme, etc.; circumstances of composition and performances; plot summary; and pictorial section of 73 illustrations showing Puccini, famous singers and performances, etc. Large clear type for easy reading. 124pp. 5⅜ x 8½.

T404   Paperbound $1.25

Antonio Stradivari: His Life and Work (1644-1737),
W. Henry Hill, Arthur F. Hill, and Alfred E. Hill
Still the only book that really delves into life and art of the incomparable Italian craftsman, maker of the finest musical instruments in the world today. The authors, expert violin-makers themselves, discuss Stradivari's ancestry, his construction and finishing techniques, distinguished characteristics of many of his instruments and their locations. Included, too, is story of introduction of his instruments into France, England, first revelation of their supreme merit, and information on his labels, number of instruments made, prices, mystery of ingredients of his varnish, tone of pre-1684 Stradivari violin and changes between 1684 and 1690. An extremely interesting, informative account for all music lovers, from craftsman to concert-goer. Republication of original (1902) edition. New introduction by Sydney Beck, Head of Rare Book and Manuscript Collections, Music Division, New York Public Library. Analytical index by Rembert Wurlitzer. Appendixes. 68 illustrations. 30 full-page plates. 4 in color. xxvi + 315pp. 5⅜ x 8½.

T425   Paperbound $2.25

Musical Autographs from Monteverdi to Hindemith,
Emanuel Winternitz
For beauty, for intrinsic interest, for perspective on the composer's personality, for subtleties of phrasing, shading, emphasis indicated in the autograph but suppressed in the printed score, the mss. of musical composition are fascinating documents which repay close study in many different ways. This 2-volume work reprints facsimiles of mss. by virtually every major composer, and many minor figures—196 examples in all. A full text points out what can be learned from mss., analyzes each sample. Index. Bibliography. 18 figures. 196 plates. Total of 170pp. of text. 7⅞ x 10¾.

T1312, T1313   Two volume set, paperbound $5.00

J. S. Bach,
Albert Schweitzer
One of the few great full-length studies of Bach's life and work, and the study upon which Schweitzer's renown as a musicologist rests. On first appearance (1911), revolutionized Bach performance. The only writer on Bach to be musicologist, performing musician, and student of history, theology and philosophy, Schweitzer contributes particularly full sections on history of German Protestant church music, theories on motivic pictorial representations in vocal music, and practical suggestions for performance. Translated by Ernest Newman. Indexes. 5 illustrations. 650 musical examples. Total of xix + 928pp. 5⅜ x 8½.

T1631, T1632   Two volume set, paperbound $4.50

THE METHODS OF ETHICS, *Henry Sidgwick*
Propounding no organized system of its own, study subjects every major methodological approach to ethics to rigorous, objective analysis. Study discusses and relates ethical thought of Plato, Aristotle, Bentham, Clarke, Butler, Hobbes, Hume, Mill, Spencer, Kant, and dozens of others. Sidgwick retains conclusions from each system which follow from ethical premises, rejecting the faulty. Considered by many in the field to be among the most important treatises on ethical philosophy. Appendix. Index. xlvii + 528pp. 5⅜ x 8½.
T1608 Paperbound $2.50

TEUTONIC MYTHOLOGY, *Jakob Grimm*
A milestone in Western culture; the work which established on a modern basis the study of history of religions and comparative religions. 4-volume work assembles and interprets everything available on religious and folkloristic beliefs of Germanic people (including Scandinavians, Anglo-Saxons, etc.). Assembling material from such sources as Tacitus, surviving Old Norse and Icelandic texts, archeological remains, folktales, surviving superstitions, comparative traditions, linguistic analysis, etc. Grimm explores pagan deities, heroes, folklore of nature, religious practices, and every other area of pagan German belief. To this day, the unrivaled, definitive, exhaustive study. Translated by J. S. Stallybrass from 4th (1883) German edition. Indexes. Total of lxxvii + 1887pp. 5⅜ x 8½.
T1602, T1603, T1604, T1605 Four volume set, paperbound $11.00

THE I CHING, *translated by James Legge*
Called "The Book of Changes" in English, this is one of the Five Classics edited by Confucius, basic and central to Chinese thought. Explains perhaps the most complex system of divination known, founded on the theory that all things happening at any one time have characteristic features which can be isolated and related. Significant in Oriental studies, in history of religions and philosophy, and also to Jungian psychoanalysis and other areas of modern European thought. Index. Appendixes. 6 plates. xxi + 448pp. 5⅜ x 8½.
T1062 Paperbound $2.75

HISTORY OF ANCIENT PHILOSOPHY, *W. Windelband*
One of the clearest, most accurate comprehensive surveys of Greek and Roman philosophy. Discusses ancient philosophy in general, intellectual life in Greece in the 7th and 6th centuries B.C., Thales, Anaximander, Anaximenes, Heraclitus, the Eleatics, Empedocles, Anaxagoras, Leucippus, the Pythagoreans, the Sophists, Socrates, Democritus (20 pages), Plato (50 pages), Aristotle (70 pages), the Peripatetics, Stoics, Epicureans, Sceptics, Neo-platonists, Christian Apologists, etc. 2nd German edition translated by H. E. Cushman. xv + 393pp. 5⅜ x 8.
T357 Paperbound $2.25

THE PALACE OF PLEASURE, *William Painter*
Elizabethan versions of Italian and French novels from *The Decameron,* Cinthio, Straparola, Queen Margaret of Navarre, and other continental sources — the very work that provided Shakespeare and dozens of his contemporaries with many of their plots and sub-plots and, therefore, justly considered one of the most influential books in all English literature. It is also a book that any reader will still enjoy. Total of cviii + 1,224pp.
T1691, T1692, T1693 Three volume set, paperbound $6.75

THE WONDERFUL WIZARD OF OZ, *L. F. Baum*
All the original W. W. Denslow illustrations in full color—as much a part of "The Wizard" as Tenniel's drawings are of "Alice in Wonderland." "The Wizard" is still America's best-loved fairy tale, in which, as the author expresses it, "The wonderment and joy are retained and the heartaches and nightmares left out." Now today's young readers can enjoy every word and wonderful picture of the original book. New introduction by Martin Gardner. A Baum bibliography. 23 full-page color plates. viii + 268pp. 5⅜ x 8.
T691 Paperbound $1.75

THE MARVELOUS LAND OF OZ, *L. F. Baum*
This is the equally enchanting sequel to the "Wizard," continuing the adventures of the Scarecrow and the Tin Woodman. The hero this time is a little boy named Tip, and all the delightful Oz magic is still present. This is the Oz book with the Animated Saw-Horse, the Woggle-Bug, and Jack Pumpkinhead. All the original John R. Neill illustrations, 10 in full color. 287pp. 5⅜ x 8. T692 Paperbound $1.75

ALICE'S ADVENTURES UNDER GROUND, *Lewis Carroll*
The original *Alice in Wonderland*, hand-lettered and illustrated by Carroll himself, and originally presented as a Christmas gift to a child-friend. Adults as well as children will enjoy this charming volume, reproduced faithfully in this Dover edition. While the story is essentially the same, there are slight changes, and Carroll's spritely drawings present an intriguing alternative to the famous Tenniel illustrations. One of the most popular books in Dover's catalogue. Introduction by Martin Gardner. 38 illustrations. 128pp. 5⅜ x 8½.
T1482 Paperbound $1.00

THE NURSERY "ALICE," *Lewis Carroll*
While most of us consider *Alice in Wonderland* a story for children of all ages, Carroll himself felt it was beyond younger children. He therefore provided this simplified version, illustrated with the famous Tenniel drawings enlarged and colored in delicate tints, for children aged "from Nought to Five." Dover's edition of this now rare classic is a faithful copy of the 1889 printing, including 20 illustrations by Tenniel, and front and back covers reproduced in full color. Introduction by Martin Gardner. xxiii + 67pp. 6⅛ x 9¼.
T1610 Paperbound $1.75

THE STORY OF KING ARTHUR AND HIS KNIGHTS, *Howard Pyle*
A fast-paced, exciting retelling of the best known Arthurian legends for young readers by one of America's best story tellers and illustrators. The sword Excalibur, wooing of Guinevere, Merlin and his downfall, adventures of Sir Pellias and Gawaine, and others. The pen and ink illustrations are vividly imagined and wonderfully drawn. 41 illustrations. xviii + 313pp. 6⅛ x 9¼.
T1445 Paperbound $1.75

Prices subject to change without notice.

Available at your book dealer or write for free catalogue to Dept. Adsci, Dover Publications, Inc., 180 Varick St., N.Y., N.Y. 10014. Dover publishes more than 150 books each year on science, elementary and advanced mathematics, biology, music, art, literary history, social sciences and other areas.